100
MATHS
LESSONS

YEAR 2

Published by Scholastic Ltd,
Villiers House,
Clarendon Avenue,
Leamington Spa,
Warwickshire CV32 5PR

© 1999 Scholastic Ltd
Text © Suzanne Edwards 1999
1 2 3 4 5 6 7 8 9 9 0 1 2 3 4 5 6 7 8

SERIES CONSULTANT
Ann Montague-Smith

AUTHOR
Suzanne Edwards

EDITOR
Steven Carruthers

ASSISTANT EDITOR
Irene Goodacre

SERIES DESIGNER
Joy White

DESIGNERS
Paul Cheshire, Mickey Pledge
and Rachel Warner

COVER PHOTOGRAPH
Kim Oliver

ILLUSTRATIONS
Gill Richardson
(page 180 – Paul Cheshire)

British Library Cataloguing-in-Publication Data
A catalogue record for this book is available from the British Library.

ISBN 0-439-01694-0

ACKNOWLEDGEMENTS

The publishers wish to thank:
The Controller of HMSO and the DfEE for the use of extracts from *The National Numeracy Strategy: Framework for Teaching Mathematics* © March 1999, Crown Copyright (1999, DfEE, Her Majesty's Stationery Office).
Galt Educational and NES Arnold Educational Supplies for kindly loaning the equipment used on the front cover.

CONTENTS

INTRODUCTION

100 Maths Lessons is a series of year-specific teachers' resource books, for Reception to Year 6, that provide a core of support material for the teaching of mathematics within the National Numeracy Strategy *Framework for Teaching Mathematics* (March 1999) and within the structure of the 'dedicated mathematics lesson'. Each book offers three terms of medium-term planning grids, teaching objectives and lesson plans. At least 100 maths lessons are given in detail, with outlines for all the others needed to provide support for teachers for a whole year of maths teaching. Photocopiable activity pages and resources are included to support the learning. Regular assessment is built into the structure of the book, with assessment activity pages which can be kept as evidence of attainment.

The activities in this book are designed to encourage pupils to develop mental strategies, to use paper and pencil methods appropriately, and to use and apply their mathematics in realistic tasks. There is a strong emphasis upon encouraging pupils to explain to each other the mathematics that they have used, the strategies that they employed and to compare these with each other to determine efficiency of method.

Each **100 Maths Lessons** book provides support across all the mathematics topics and learning objectives specified for a particular year group. However, the pages of the books have been hole-punched and perforated, so that they can be removed and placed in teachers' own resource files, where they can be interleaved with complementary materials from the school's existing schemes. This makes the integration of favourite material into this series very easy.

These books are intended as a support for the dedicated mathematics lesson for the school mathematics coordinator, teachers and trainee teachers. The series of books can be used as the basis of planning, teaching and assessment for the whole school, from Reception to Year 6. These resources can be adapted for use by the whole school for single-aged classes, mixed-age classes, single- and mixed-ability groups, and for team planning across a year or a key stage. There is sufficient detail in the differentiated group activities within the 100 lesson plans to offer guidance to classroom assistants working with a group. The content of these activities is appropriate for, and adaptable to, the requirements of Primary 2–3 in Scottish schools. Teachers in schools which decide not to adopt the National Numeracy Strategy should choose activities to match their planning.

USING THIS BOOK

THE MATERIALS

This book provides at least 100 maths lesson plans for Year 2, and further activity ideas to support all other dedicated maths lessons required during the year. Each maths lesson plan contains ideas for developing pupils' oral and mental maths, a detailed explanation of the main part of the lesson, ideas for differentiated activities, and suggestions for the plenary session. The book follows the Year 2 planning grid given in the National Numeracy Strategy *Framework for Teaching Mathematics* and so for each teaching section, whether one, two or three units of work, there are some detailed lessons plans and objectives and outline content for the other lessons. These materials should be regarded as a core for developing your own personalised folder for the year. More detail on planning and managing all aspects of the National Numeracy Strategy can be found in the *Framework for Teaching Mathematics*.

ADAPTING AND PERSONALISING THE MATERIALS

The materials are based upon the 'Teaching programme and planning grid' for Year 2 from the National Numeracy Strategy *Framework for Teaching Mathematics*. What follows is a suggested method of using this book to its full potential, but bear in mind that you may need to make adjustments to these materials in order to meet the learning needs of the pupils in your class.
● Separate the pages of the book and place them in an A4 ring binder.
● Check that the activities are of a suitable level for your pupils and agree with colleagues who teach higher and lower years that the entry level is a good match. If not, you can use materials from the **100 Maths Lessons** books for the previous or subsequent year, as appropriate.

● Add your own favourite materials in the relevant places.
● If your school uses a published scheme, insert suitable teacher and pupil resources into your file to supplement these materials.

PREPARING A SCHEME OF WORK

All schools are required to write detailed schemes of work, and this series has been designed to facilitate this process. The termly 'Planning grids' given in these books (see page 22 for example) are provided at the beginning of the work for each term and list all the learning objectives.

ORGANISATION

The Organisation chart outlines the key activities for each part of each maths lesson and can be used as a weekly plan.

LESSON PLANS

After the Organisation chart comes a short section detailing which lessons are shown as full lesson plans and which are extensions of what has already been taught in a previous lesson. Some of these will be shown in grid form.

	LEARNING OUTCOMES	ORAL AND MENTAL STARTER	MAIN TEACHING ACTIVITY	PLENARY
LESSON 1	● Say the number names in order to at least 100, from and back to zero. ● Count reliably up to 100 objects by grouping them in tens. ● **Know what each digit in a two-digit number represents, including 0 as a place holder.**	ADDITION AND SUBTRACTION FACTS ABOUT 10: Hold up numeral cards to show addition or subtraction pairs to 10.	COUNTING IN ONES AND TENS TO 100: Recite counts, then count objects by grouping.	Review work from Main teaching activity.
LESSON 2	● **Describe and extend simple number sequences: count on or back in ones or tens, starting from any two-digit number.**	COUNTING IN ONES AND TENS TO 100: Repeat from Lesson 1.	COUNTING ON/BACK IN ONES: Starting from a given number, with a number square.	Counting on/ back in ones from a given number.
LESSON 3	● Say the number names in order to at least 100, from and back to zero. ● **Describe and extend simple number sequences: count on or back in ones or tens, starting from any two-digit number.**	COUNTING ROUND: Counting in ones and tens to 100, then playing a circle game, counting on/back in ones from a given number.	COUNTING ON/BACK IN ONES: Counting with a number square.	COUNTING ROUND: Reprise Oral and mental starter.

ORAL AND MENTAL SKILLS   **Know by heart:** all pairs of numbers with a total of 10 (Year 1 revision). Say the number names in order to at least 100, from and back to zero. **Describe and extend simple number sequences: count on or back in ones or tens starting from any two-digit number.**

DETAILED LESSON PLANS

Each detailed lesson plan is written to the following headings:

Resources
Provides a list of what you need for that lesson.

Preparation
Outlines any advance preparation needed before the lesson begins, such as making resources or photocopying worksheets.

Learning outcomes
These are based upon the objectives in the 'Teaching programme: Year 2' from the *Framework for Teaching Mathematics*. All the objectives are covered at least once in this book. Key objectives for Year 2 are highlighted in bold as they are in the *Framework for Teaching Mathematics*. If a lesson does not cover an objective in its entirety, then only the portion which is intended to be covered is listed in the 'Learning outcomes' (or any of the grids provided).

The specific objectives for the **Oral and mental starter** and **Main teaching activity** are listed separately.

Vocabulary

The National Numeracy Strategy *Mathematical Vocabulary* booklet has been used to provide the vocabulary lists. New or specific vocabulary to be used during the lesson is listed. Use this vocabulary with the whole class so that all the children have a chance to hear it and begin to understand it. Encourage pupils to use the vocabulary orally, when asking or answering questions, so that they develop an understanding of its mathematical meaning. Flashcards can be made by printing out onto card the appropriate sections from the CD-ROM which should have accompanied your school's copy of the *Framework for Teaching Mathematics*.

Oral and mental starter

This is designed to occupy the first 5–10 minutes of the lesson, but the duration of the work is not critical. This section contains activity suggestions to develop oral and mental work to be used with the whole class and is based on what has already been taught. Some suggestions for differentiated questioning are included to show how all the children can benefit. The detail in the lesson plan will help you to: provide a variety of sequentially-planned, short oral and mental activities throughout the week; use a good range of open and closed questions; encourage all the children to take part; target differentiated questions to individuals, pairs or small groups.

Main teaching activity

This sets out what to do in the whole-class teaching session and should last for about 30 minutes. In some lessons much of the time will be spent in whole-class, interactive teaching. In others, the whole-class session will be shorter, with differentiated activities for groups, pairs or individuals. The detailed lesson plan will help you to organise this part of the lesson appropriately.

Differentiation

This section suggests activities for differentiated group, paired or individual work, for the more able and less able children within the class. These activities will take the form of reinforcement, enrichment or extension, and many will provide challenges to encourage pupils to use and apply their mathematics.

Plenary

This session is a chance to bring the children together again for a 10-minute whole-class session. This offers opportunities to: assess pupils' progress; summarise the key facts learned; compare the strategies used; make links to other topics; plan for the next topic.

EXTENSION LESSON PLANS

These provide activities which extend those already covered. They are less detailed, as they are based on one of the previous lessons for that week.

OUTLINE LESSON PLANS

These contain brief descriptions, in grid form, of further lessons. These extend the scope of the book to give sufficient material for a year's work. Since they develop work already introduced, there are no vocabulary suggestions as the same range of words will be needed as in the previous, related lesson(s). For example:

RESOURCES	A set of shuffled cards 1–20 (one card for each child); a copy of photocopiable page 13 for each child; paper, pencils, crayons or felt-tipped pens; Cuisenaire rods or interlocking cubes.
LEARNING OUTCOMES	**ORAL AND MENTAL STARTER** ● **Know by heart: multiplication facts for the 2 times table.** ● Derive quickly: division facts corresponding to the 2 and 10 times tables. **MAIN TEACHING ACTIVITY** ● **Understand the operation of multiplication as repeated addition or as describing an array.** ● Use the × and = signs to record mental calculations in a number sentence.
ORAL & MENTAL STARTER	2 TIMES TABLE: As for Lesson 1, above, but with the 2 times table.
MAIN TEACHING ACTIVITY	BUILDING THE 2 TIMES TABLE: As for Lesson 1, above, but with the 2 times table.
DIFFERENTIATION	More able: encourage the children to extend the table as far as possible – to 50, to 100, above 100? Less able: provide Cuisenaire rods or interlocking cubes for children who require support.
PLENARY	As for Lesson 1, but with the 2 times table.

USING THE LESSON PLANS

The plans are designed so that you can work through them in order, if you wish. However, you may prefer to choose the lessons that are appropriate for your pupils, and combine these with your favourite activities from other sources. By placing the pages of this book into a ring binder you can easily incorporate your own supplementary materials.

WEEKLY PLANNING

If you wish to use the ready-prepared plans, follow the Organisation chart which appears at the beginning of each unit or block of units of work.

If you prefer to plan your week using some of the lesson plans in the book, and other activities you have chosen yourself, then make some photocopies of the blank 'Weekly planning chart' on page xx of this book. These can then be completed with details of all the activities which you intend to use, those chosen from this book and those which you have taken from other sources.

MIXED-AGE CLASSES

If you have a mixed-age class, you will probably need to use the materials from more than one book in this series. You will find the blank 'Weekly planning chart' on page 11 a useful planning tool, as you can combine planning from two books onto this chart.

BLANK WEEKLY PLANNING CHART

Make photocopies of this chart, complete a copy on a weekly basis and keep this in your planning file. You may prefer to enlarge the chart to A3.

Week beginning: 7 September

Learning objectives for oral and mental skills	• Know by heart: all pairs of numbers with a total of 10 (Year 1 revision). • Say the number names in order to at least 100, from and back to zero. • Describe and extend number sequences: count on or back in ones or tens starting from any two-digit number.				
	Oral and mental starter	Main teaching activity	Differentiation	Plenary	Resources
M o n d a y	Addition and subtraction facts about 10: numbers to make 10.	Counting in ones and tens to 100: Counting tubs of cubes by grouping T and U.	Less able: tubs of 11 and 21. More able: tub of 98.	How many in each tub? Record class results on flip chart.	Three sets of 1–10 cards; tubs A–F of cubes (each set different colour) : 22; 27; 31; 34; 45; 50,

CLASSROOM ORGANISATION

WHOLE-CLASS TEACHING

During a whole-class session it is important that all the children can see you, the board or flip chart and their table top. In many classrooms space is at a premium, so it is worth spending time considering how the furniture can best be arranged. If you have a carpeted area for whole-class work, think about whether the lesson you are planning to teach would work well with the children seated on the carpet, or whether they would be better placed at their tables, especially if you want them to manipulate apparatus, such as interlocking cubes, or they need to spread out numeral cards in front of them.

GROUP WORK

Again, it is important that the pupils sit so that they can see you, and the board or flip chart if necessary. While they are working in groups you may wish to ask whole-class questions, or remind pupils of how much time is left to complete their task, so eye contact will help to ensure that everyone is listening.

WORKING WITH OTHER ADULTS

If you have classroom helpers, brief them before the lesson starts on which group you would like them to work with; the purpose of the task; the vocabulary they should be helping to develop; and give some examples of the type of questions they should be asking. Check that all the resources needed are available or, if not, that the helper knows where to find them. You may want to ask a classroom helper to work with just one or two pupils; perhaps they are finding the work difficult, or have been absent and need an opportunity to catch up on missed work. Whatever the reason, always ensure that the helper is well briefed before the lesson starts, and allow a few minutes after the lesson has finished to discuss any specific observations which the helper would like to make.

CHILDREN WITH SPECIAL EDUCATIONAL NEEDS

Include children with special educational needs in the whole-class work. If you have a classroom helper or support assistant ask him or her to sit beside the pupils with special needs to provide support. This could include repeating the questions quietly or encouraging them to use individual resources (such as counting apparatus) to find the answer. During differentiated questioning, ensure that some questions are specifically focused for these pupils and encourage them to answer appropriately.

To assist all pupils in reading new vocabulary, and particularly to help those with reading difficulties, make flash cards for the specific mathematics vocabulary which will be used in a series of lessons and encourage the children to read these.

Pupils who are partially-sighted or deaf will need to sit close to you, so take this into account when considering the layout of the classroom for maths lessons. Those with emotional or behaviour difficulties will benefit from the structure and routines of the daily maths lesson and, where possible, from the support of a helper who can encourage on-task working. For children who are learning English as an additional language, speak more slowly, repeat instructions, and provide visual clues on worksheets or puzzle cards. For pupils who have an Individual Education Plan (IEP) which includes mathematics as an area of learning difficulty, use other books from this series to find activities of an appropriate level which can be linked to the work of the rest of the class.

HOMEWORK

For Year 2 pupils it is recommended that homework is given on a weekly basis. These activities should be designed to be shared with a parent or carer, or could include simple puzzles. A homework diary, which is completed by home and school, is useful for logging what the homework is and how the pupil responded. Use a range of types of tasks:
● Choose favourite shared homework activities and send these home regularly. Suitable material may be found in *IMPACT Maths Homework* (Key Stage One titles) and *Mental Maths Homework for 7 year olds*, all written by The IMPACT Project (Scholastic).
● Suggest a maths game to be played at home that will help the children to practise using mental strategies with addition, subtraction, simple multiplication and division.
● Suggest some practical activities that children can do at home which involve using money, measuring and telling the time, such as buying, preparing and cooking food.

RESOURCES

PHOTOCOPIABLE SHEETS

These support the work and can take the form of resource sheets or activity sheets. They are marked with the photocopiable symbol:

Some sheets have many applications and are used throughout the book: these 'resource sheets' appear at the end of this 'Introduction'. The other 'activity sheets' can be found at the end of the relevant unit(s).

Resource sheets

These include individual number lines, 0–99 number squares, clock faces and coin cards and can be found on pages 13–20. Make enough of these at the start of the year for each pupil to have at least one (set). You may wish to ask for help from parents and friends of the school to make these resources. Photocopy the pages onto card, then cut out and laminate as required. Store class sets of number lines and squares in marked boxes.

You will also need several sets of numeral cards 0–99 (specified under **Resources** in different lessons), consider making these with different-coloured card so that the children can put them away more easily, using the colour of their set as an aid. Store them in small polythene bags or tins, or with a rubber band around each set.

Activity sheets

These pages are located at the end of the relevant unit(s) and relate to specific activities. They may offer practical activities, more traditional worksheets or games. Photocopy them on to A4 paper for your pupils. Some activities suggest an extra A3 enlargement to be made to be used as a demonstration teaching chart or for whole-class use.

CLASSROOM EQUIPMENT

All the equipment used in this book will normally be found within any primary school. The following list shows what will be needed on a regular basis. Alternatives are suggested where they would be equally appropriate. It is important that you create a mathematically-stimulating environment for the children, where they regularly encounter numbers. It is therefore assumed that all classrooms will have a long class number line with big numerals and a large 100 square. Ideally the children should be able to read all the numbers easily from their seats. A chalk board and chalk, or flip chart and marker pens, are essential for interactive whole-class sessions. You will also need:

- Multiple sets of numeral cards 0–100.
- Multiple sets of playing cards Ace–10.
- Sets of cards numbered in ordinal numbers 1st to 100th.
- A 'washing line' strung across the room.
- Counting apparatus, such as counters, sorting toys, wooden cubes, beads and laces. Counting sticks: easily made by taking a metre length of wood and dividing it into ten alternately-coloured sections (some metre rulers are marked in this way).
- Cuisenaire rods.
- Base 10 apparatus: ones and tens.
- Lots of interlocking cubes, such as Multilink.
- Pan balances, metre and centimetre rulers, tape measures, standard units – kg and ½ kg masses; litre and ½ litre measures.
- Measuring apparatus including collections of plastic containers for capacity and 'junk' materials stored in labelled plastic tubs.
- A teaching clock, cardboard clocks, minute timers and stopwatches.
- Shape apparatus: for example, shape tiles, logic blocks, 3-D shapes, feely bags.
- Sorting hoops.
- Construction kits, Plasticine etc.
- Coins, preferably real.
- Multiple sets of dice: spotted and numbered 1–6, money, and blank.
- Multiple sets of dominoes.
- Roamer or PIP.
- Geoboards and elastic bands

USING INFORMATION COMMUNICATIONS TECHNOLOGY

Make use of your favourite mathematical games software as a paired or small group activity. Some of the activities in this book use a programmable toy, such as Roamer or PIP. Pupils can use data-handling software to prepare simple graphs as part of the activity.

PUBLICATIONS

Do use your favourite mathematical stories, poems and rhymes as well as the published material available in school. The following Scholastic publications contain some useful ideas:

Oral and mental starter
Developing Mental Maths with 5–7 year olds

Homework
IMPACT Maths Homework (Key Stage One)
Mental Maths Homework for 6/7 year olds
Quick Mental Maths for 6/7 year olds

Main teaching activity
Maths Focus Kit 2
Practising Mental Maths with 7 year olds
Quick Mental Maths for 7 year olds

Assessment
Maths Focus Kit 2
Scholastic Portfolio Assessment: Maths KS1

ASSESSMENT

During the week at the end of each half term, an assessment period of two lessons is built into the planning. This gives you the opportunity to make medium-term assessments of the key objectives for Year 2. The aim of these assessments is to:
● Find out what progress each pupil has made, what he or she knows, understands and can do, whether he or she can apply and use mathematics in context, and whether he or she has any weaknesses.
● Give you information on which to base feedback to pupils and their parents or carers. It will also help you to plan work for the next few weeks.

ASSESSMENT ADVICE

This is placed just before the assessment activity photocopiable sheets. Here you will find information on the aspects of mathematics which are to be assessed; some assessment activities for oral and mental starters which can be used with the whole class, others which can be used with groups, pairs and individuals; and advice on using the photocopiable assessment tasks provided.

ASSESSMENT ACTIVITIES

These activities have been designed so that you can observe pupils at work, and ask questions. Explain the purpose of the activity to them before they begin, as this will help them to demonstrate to you the things that you want to observe, such as clear recording, discussion of which strategy they used, why they used it, and so on. Target small groups for a specific activity and period of time, and work with them, observing how individuals respond to the activity. You may find it useful to have a notebook handy to make informal notes on observations and discussions.

If you have a classroom helper, he or she can also be involved in the assessment process. Explain the purpose of the assessment, what to do, and what to look for. After the lesson has finished make time to discuss observations and keep notes on individual pupils' achievements and weaknesses.

ASSESSMENT PHOTOCOPIABLE SHEETS

There are two photocopiable sheets for each half-term assessment period. Each sheet has specific assessment criteria printed at the bottom. Photocopy the pages for individual pupils to complete while you observe others undertaking the assessment activities.

Mark the completed sheets, then give pupils feedback on their strengths, and set targets for improvement in their areas of weakness. The sheets can be kept in a portfolio as part of the evidence of the children's achievement.

CLASS ASSESSMENT RECORDING SHEET

Found on page 12, this lists the key objectives for Year 2 from the National Numeracy Strategy *Framework for Teaching Mathematics*. Photo-enlarge this sheet to A3, and record individuals' progress on it. By the end of the year, after six assessment sessions, you will have a wealth of assessment evidence to pass on to the children's next teacher.

Each half-term assessment offers opportunities to assess all the relevant key objectives that have been taught. Some key objectives re-occur in later assessments. It is not necessary to assess every child each time. Use your assessment records to decide whether to re-assess a child or whether it is appropriate to leave a specific assessment objective which has already been learned.

STANDARD ASSESSMENT TESTS

The work in this book is designed to support teachers in planning their daily maths lessons for Year 2 in relation to the National Numeracy Strategy and its overall aim of raising standards. There is no specific planning or preparation guidance given for the Standard Assessment Tasks for mathematics (SATs) because arrangements and time-tabling for their administration are likely to vary between schools. Your preparation and administration of the SATs should be planned and organised in accordance with your school policy. Some schools may wish to use the two half-termly sessions allocated for assessment within the planning framework, while others may select to integrate the SATs within their dedicated maths lessons. However, your school may prefer for SATs to take place outside time allocated for these maths lessons. The *Framework* does not allocate lessons to every day of the school year. Therefore, abandoning the National Numeracy Strategy for a week and using some of the 'spare days' for the SATs is another option.

Weekly planning chart

(Photo-enlarge to A3.)

Week beginning:

Learning objectives
for oral and mental
skills

	Oral and mental starter	Main teaching activity	Differentiation	Plenary	Resources
Monday					
Tuesday					
Wednesday					
Thursday					
Friday					

Year 2: class assessment record sheet

Name													
Key Objectives: Year 2	Count, read, write and order whole numbers to at least 100; know what each digit represents (including 0 as a place holder).	Describe and extend simple number sequences (including odd/even numbers, counting on and back in ones or tens from any two-digit number, and so on).	Understand that subtraction is the inverse of addition; state the subtraction corresponding to a given addition and vice versa.	Know by heart all addition and subtraction facts for each number to at least 10.	Use knowledge that addition can be done in any order to do mental calculations more efficiently.	Understand the operation of multiplication as repeated addition or as describing an array.	Know and use halving as the inverse of doubling. Know by heart facts for the 2 and 10 multiplication tables.	Estimate, measure and compare lengths, masses and capacities, using standard units; suggest suitable units and equipment for such measurements.	Read a simple scale to the nearest labelled division, including using a ruler to draw and measure lines to the nearest centimetre.	Use the mathematical names for common 2-D and 3-D shapes; sort shapes and describe some of their features.	Use mathematical vocabulary to describe position, direction and movement.	Choose and use appropriate operations and efficient calculation strategies to solve problems, explaining how the problem was solved.	Other:

0–99 Number square

0	1	2	3	4	5	6	7	8	9
10	11	12	13	14	15	16	17	18	19
20	21	22	23	24	25	26	27	28	29
30	31	32	33	34	35	36	37	38	39
40	41	42	43	44	45	46	47	48	49
50	51	52	53	54	55	56	57	58	59
60	61	62	63	64	65	66	67	68	69
70	71	72	73	74	75	76	77	78	79
80	81	82	83	84	85	86	87	88	89
90	91	92	93	94	95	96	97	98	99

0–20 Number lines

| 0 | 1 | 2 | 3 | 4 | 5 | 6 | 7 | 8 | 9 | 10 | 11 | 12 | 13 | 14 | 15 | 16 | 17 | 18 | 19 | 20 |

| 0 | 1 | 2 | 3 | 4 | 5 | 6 | 7 | 8 | 9 | 10 | 11 | 12 | 13 | 14 | 15 | 16 | 17 | 18 | 19 | 20 |

| 0 | 1 | 2 | 3 | 4 | 5 | 6 | 7 | 8 | 9 | 10 | 11 | 12 | 13 | 14 | 15 | 16 | 17 | 18 | 19 | 20 |

Coin cards

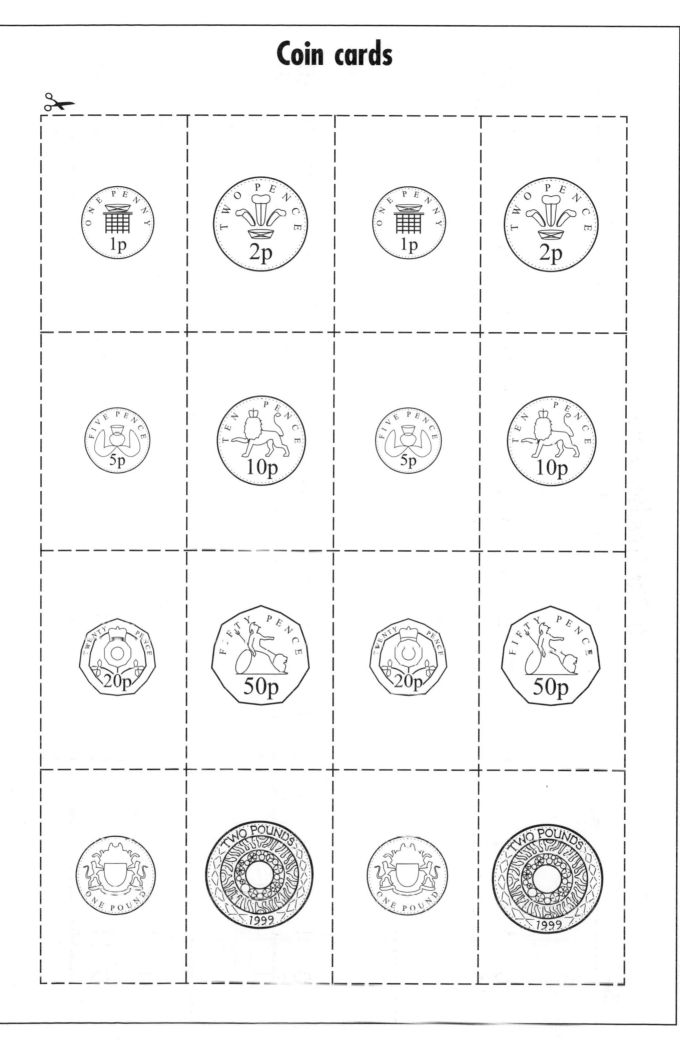

Clock faces

Faces

Blank number square

0									
									99

0–100 Tens number lines

Line 1: 0 10 20 30 40 50 60 70 80 90 100

Line 2: 0 10 20 30 40 50 60 70 80 90 100

Line 3: 0 10 20 30 40 50 60 70 80 90 100

Dotty paper

Term 1 develops children's
knowledge of numbers to 100 to
include ordinal numbers and place
value with tens and units, and
introduces odd and even numbers
and rounding to the nearest 10.
Understanding of addition and
subtraction is extended through
mental strategies, including using
known number facts and place
value, and solving problems,
including using money up to £1.00.
Finding halves of shapes and
small numbers is introduced. Then
multiplication facts for the 2 and
10 times tables, and doubling and
halving are taught and practised.
Children are taught to recognise,
name and know some properties of
2-D and 3-D shapes. They are
taught to estimate and measure
length and mass using standard
units, to read the time to the hour
and half hour and to carry out
simple data-handling activities.

ENLARGE THIS SHEET TO A3 AND USE IT AS YOUR MEDIUM-TERM PLANNING.

Oral and mental skills: Say the number names in order to at least 100, from and back to zero. **Know what each digit in a two-digit number represents, including 0 as a place holder, and partition two-digit numbers into a multiple of tens and ones (TU).** Count reliably up to 100 objects by grouping them in tens. **Describe and extend simple number sequences: count on or back in ones or tens, starting from any two-digit number.** Read and write whole numbers to at least 100 in figures and words. Say the number that is 10 more or less than any given two-digit number. Begin to add three single-digit numbers mentally (totals up to about 20). **Know by heart:** all pairs of numbers with a total of 10 (Year 1 revision); **all addition and subtraction facts for each number to at least 10;** all pairs of numbers with a total of 20 (e.g. 13 + 7, 6 + 14). Use and begin to read the vocabulary of estimation and approximation; give a sensible estimate of at least 50 objects. **Use knowledge that addition can be done in any order to do mental calculations more efficiently.** For example: put the larger number first and count on in ones, then tens or ones; add three small numbers by putting the largest number first and/or find a pair totalling 10; partition into '5 and a bit' when adding 6, 7, 8 and 9; partition additions into tens and units, then recombine. Derive quickly: doubles of all numbers to at least 15. Use mental addition and subtraction to solve simple word problems involving numbers and money, using one or two steps. Explain how the problem was solved.

Unit	Topic	Objectives: children will be taught to...
1	Counting and properties of numbers	● Say the number names in order to at least 100, from and back to zero. **Describe and extend simple number sequences: count on or back in ones or tens, starting from any two-digit number.** Count reliably up to 100 objects by grouping them in tens. **Know what each digit in a two-digit number represents, including 0 as a place holder.**
2–4	Place value, ordering, estimating, rounding Understanding + and – Mental calculation strategies (+ and –) Money and 'real life' problems Making decisions and checking results	● **Read and write whole numbers to at least 100** in figures and words. **Know what each digit in a two-digit number represents, including 0 as a place holder,** and partition two-digit numbers into a multiple of tens and ones (TU). Use and begin to read the vocabulary of comparing and ordering numbers, including ordinal numbers to 100. Say the number that is 1 or 10 more or less than any given two-digit number. Use and begin to read the vocabulary of estimation and approximation; give a sensible estimate of at least 50 objects. ● **Know by heart: all addition and subtraction facts for each number to at least 10.** Use the +, – and = signs to record mental additions and subtractions. ● **Use knowledge that addition can be done in any order to do mental calculations more efficiently.** For example: put the larger number first and count on in ones, then tens or ones; partition into '5 and a bit' when adding 6, 7, 8 or 9, then recombine; partition additions into tens and units, then recombine. **Know by heart:** all pairs of numbers with a total of 20. Begin to add three single-digit numbers mentally (totals up to about 20). Add three small numbers by putting the largest number first and/or find a pair totalling 10. Derive quickly: doubles of all numbers to at least 15. ● Use mental addition/subtraction to solve simple word problems involving numbers and money, using one or two steps. Explain how the problem was solved. Recognise all coins and begin to use £.p notation for money. Find totals, give change, and work out which coins to pay. ● Checking results of calculations: repeat addition in a different order.
5–6	Measures, including problems Shape and space Reasoning about shapes	● Use and begin to read the vocabulary related to length. **Estimate, measure and compare lengths using standard units** (m, cm); **suggest suitable units and equipment for such measurements. Read a simple scale to the nearest labelled division, including using a ruler to draw and measure lines to the nearest centimetre,** recording estimates and measurements as '3 and a bit metres long' or 'about 8 centimetres'. Use mental addition and subtraction to solve simple word problems involving measures, using one or two steps. Explain how the problem was solved. ● **Use the mathematical names for common 3-D and 2-D shapes. Sort shapes and describe some of their features.** Make and describe shapes, pictures and patterns. Relate solid shapes to pictures of them. ● Solve mathematical problems or puzzles, recognise simple patterns and relationships, generalise and predict. Suggest extensions by asking 'What if …?' or 'What could I try next?'
7	Assess and review	● **Describe and extend simple number sequences: count on or back in ones or tens starting from any two-digit number. Read and write whole numbers to at least 100. Know what each digit in a two-digit number represents, including 0 as a place holder. Know by heart: all addition and subtraction facts for each number to at least 10. Use knowledge that addition can be done in any order to do mental calculations more efficiently. Estimate, measure and compare lengths using standard units** (m, cm); **suggest suitable units and equipment for such measurements. Read a simple scale to the nearest labelled division, including using a ruler to draw and measure lines to the nearest centimetre. Use the mathematical names for common 3-D and 2-D shapes. Sort shapes and describe some of their features.**

Oral and mental skills: Describe and extend simple number sequences: count on or back in ones or tens, starting from any two-digit number; count on in twos from and back to zero or any small number. Say the number that is 10 more or less than any given two-digit number. **Know by heart:** all pairs of numbers with a total of 20; **multiplication facts for the 2 and 10 times tables,** doubles of all numbers to 10 and the corresponding halves. **Know and use halving as the inverse of doubling.** Derive quickly: division facts corresponding to the 2 and 10 times tables; doubles of all numbers to at least 15. **Use knowledge that addition can be done in any order to do mental calculations more efficiently.** For example: partition additions into tens and units, then recombine. Add three small numbers by putting the largest number first and/or find a pair totalling 10. Find a small difference by counting up from the smaller to the larger number. Use known number facts and place value to add/subtract mentally. Find totals, give change, and work out which coins to pay.

Unit	Topic	Objectives: children will be taught to...
8	Counting and properties of numbers Reasoning about numbers	● **Describe and extend simple number sequences: count on or back in ones or tens, starting from any two-digit number;** count on in twos from and back to zero or any small number and **recognise odd and even numbers** to at least 30. ● Solve mathematical problems or puzzles, recognise simple patterns or relationships, generalise and predict. Suggest extensions by asking 'What if …?' or ' What could I try next?' Investigate a general statement about familiar numbers by finding examples that satisfy it. **Explain how a problem was solved** orally and, where appropriate, in writing.
9	Place value, ordering, estimating, rounding Understanding + and – Mental calculation strategies (+ and –) Money and 'real life' problems Making decisions and checking results	● **Know what each digit in a two-digit number represents, including 0 as a place holder,** and partition two-digit numbers into a multiple of tens and ones (TU). Round numbers less than 100 to the nearest 10. Use and begin to read the vocabulary of comparing and ordering numbers, including ordinal numbers to 100. ● **Use knowledge that addition can be done in any order to do calculations more efficiently.** For example: add three small numbers by putting the largest number first and/or find a pair totalling 10; partition additions into tens and units, then recombine. ● Use mental addition and subtraction to solve simple word problems involving numbers in 'real life' or money, using one or two steps.
10–11	Understanding × and ÷ Mental calculation strategies (× and ÷) Money and 'real life' problems Making decisions and checking results Fractions	● **Understand the operation of multiplication as repeated addition or as describing an array,** and begin to understand division as grouping (repeated subtraction) or sharing. **Know and use halving as the inverse of doubling.** Use and begin to read the related vocabulary. Use the ×, ÷ and = signs to record mental calculations in a number sentence. ● Use simple multiplication and division to solve simple word problems involving numbers in 'real life'. Use mental addition and subtraction to solve simple word problems involving money. Recognise all coins and begin to use £.p notation for money. Find totals, give change, and work out which coins to pay. ● Begin to recognise and find one half and one quarter of shapes and small numbers of objects. Begin to recognise that two halves or four quarters make one whole and that two quarters and one half are equivalent.
12–13	Measures, and time, including problems Handling data	● **Estimate, measure and compare masses, using standard units** (kg); **suggest suitable units and equipment for such measurements. Read a simple scale to the nearest labelled division.** Use and begin to read the vocabulary related to time. Order the months of the year. Read the time to the hour and half hour on an analogue clock. Use mental addition and subtraction to solve simple word problems involving numbers in 'real life' or measures. Find a small difference by counting up from the smaller to the larger number. ● Solve a given problem by sorting, classifying and organising information in simple ways.
14	Assess and review	● **Describe and extend simple number sequences: count on or back in ones or tens, starting from any two-digit number. Recognise odd and even numbers. Know what each digit in a two-digit number represents, including 0 as a place holder. Use knowledge that addition can be done in any order to do mental calculations more efficiently. Understand the operation of multiplication as repeated addition or as describing an array. Know and use halving as the inverse of doubling. Know by heart: multiplication facts for the 2 and 10 times tables. Estimate, measure and compare masses using standard units; suggest suitable units and equipment for such measurements.**

UNIT 1

ORGANISATION (3 LESSONS)

	LEARNING OUTCOMES	ORAL AND MENTAL STARTER	MAIN TEACHING ACTIVITY	PLENARY
LESSON 1	• Say the number names in order to at least 100, from and back to zero. • Count reliably up to 100 objects by grouping them in tens. • **Know what each digit in a two-digit number represents, including 0 as a place holder.**	ADDITION AND SUBTRACTION FACTS ABOUT 10: Hold up numeral cards to show addition or subtraction pairs to 10.	COUNTING IN ONES AND TENS TO 100: Recite counts, then count objects by grouping.	Review work from Main teaching activity.
LESSON 2	• **Describe and extend simple number sequences: count on or back in ones or tens, starting from any two-digit number.**	COUNTING IN ONES AND TENS TO 100: Repeat from Lesson 1.	COUNTING ON/ BACK IN ONES: Starting from a given number, with a number square.	COUNTING ON/ BACK IN ONES: Counting from a given number.
LESSON 3	• Say the number names in order to at least 100, from and back to zero. • **Describe and extend simple number sequences: count on or back in ones or tens, starting from any two-digit number.**	COUNTING ROUND: Counting in ones and tens to 100, then playing a circle game, counting on/back in ones from a given number.	COUNTING ON/ BACK IN ONES: Counting with a number square.	COUNTING ROUND: Reprise oral and mental starter.

ORAL AND MENTAL SKILLS **Know by heart:** all pairs of numbers with a total of 10 (Year 1 revision). Say the number names in order to at least 100, from and back to zero. **Describe and extend simple number sequences: count on or back in ones or tens, starting from any two-digit number.**

Lessons 1–3 are given in full and concentrate on revising and building confidence with numbers and number facts at the beginning of a new term. Revision of mental skills learned in Year 1 will encourage a positive start.

RESOURCES

Flip chart and pen; paper and pencils; self-adhesive address labels; elastic bands; several sets of numeral cards 1–10 shuffled together (sufficient for one card for each child); a sorting hoop for each pair of children. For each group: six large plastic margarine tubs; different sets of objects for counting.

PREPARATION

Place a different number of objects (between 20 and 50) in each tub and label the tubs A–F. Shuffle the sets of 1–10 cards and secure each one with an elastic band. Place a set of tubs, sorting hoops, sheets of paper and pencils on each table.

LEARNING OUTCOMES

ORAL AND MENTAL STARTER
● **Know by heart:** all pairs of numbers with a total of 10 (Year 1 revision).

MAIN TEACHING ACTIVITY
● Say the number names in order to at least 100, from and back to zero.
● Count reliably up to 100 objects by grouping them in tens.
● **Know what each digit in a two-digit number represents, including 0 as a place holder.**

VOCABULARY

Counting in ones, tens, hundreds; larger; more than; smaller than; fewer than; number words; add; plus; and; altogether; total; equals; units; ones; tens; stands for; recite; represents; write in figures.

ORAL AND MENTAL STARTER

ADDITION AND SUBTRACTION FACTS ABOUT 10: Sit the children in a circle and give each child one of the cards from the shuffled 1–10 sets. Explain that you will say a number between 0 and 10 and the children should hold up their card if they are holding a number which, when added to your number, will make 10. Say: *Show me the number to add to 7.* (3) Repeat this with other numbers, moving quickly from one fact to another to encourage rapid recall. Change the rule to 'the number left when your number is subtracted from 10'. Say: *Show me the number left when 6 is taken away from 10.* (4)

MAIN TEACHING ACTIVITY

COUNTING IN ONES AND TENS TO 100: Sit the children in a circle and explain that they will be counting to 100. Count aloud together from 0 – 100 in ones forwards and backwards to zero, and then in tens forwards and backwards to zero. Now ask them to count in ones around the circle (the first child says 1, the second says 2, and so on). Practise the game slowly at first, prompting children who get stuck, then speed up the pace. Choose a different child to start the count each time.

Ask the children to make room in the circle for a flip chart. Explain that they will be counting objects in tubs. Place a sorting hoop on the floor in front of the flip chart. Tip the objects from one tub carefully into the hoop and ask one child to group them in tens. Ask: *How many tens? How many ones left over? How many altogether?* Together, count the objects in tens and count on any remaining objects in ones. Demonstrate the method of recording this on the chart, for example:

Tub E → 48
Tub B → 35

Discuss the recording, ask: *In the 48 what does the '4' mean? What does the '8' mean?* Talk about how tens and ones are recorded.

Tell the children to return to their tables to work with a partner. Each pair chooses a tub and counts the number of objects by grouping in tens, then replaces the objects in the tub. Each child records the total on a sheet as was shown on the chart. They then swap their tub for another until they have counted the objects in each tub.

DIFFERENTIATION

More able: provide an 'extension' tub with nearly (or more than) 100 objects.
Less able: prepare several 'special' tubs with less objects (11, 14, 21 and so on). Provide a recording sheet with tens and units columns to fill in (as shown opposite).

Tub	T	U
A B ↓ etc		

PLENARY

Review the work from the **Main teaching activity**. Ask different children to say how many objects were in each tub and record this on the flip chart. Discuss the recording and ask what each number means in relation to tens and units. Ask: *Which tub contained the most/least number of objects?*

RESOURCES

Copies of photocopiable page 13 (0–99 Number square) and photocopiable page 27 (Counting in ones); a teaching chart (a copy or enlargement of the 0–99 number square); individual number squares; small cubes; paper and pencils; A4 card; a small easel.

PREPARATION

Make a Number square teaching chart by copying photocopiable page 13 on to a large sheet of card. Make a copy of page 13 on A4 card for each child. Laminate the teaching chart and individual number squares for repeated use. Make a copy of photocopiable page 27 for each child. Place individual number squares, some cubes, copies of page 27 and pencils on each table.

LEARNING OUTCOMES
ORAL AND MENTAL STARTER
● Say the number names in order to at least 100, from and back to zero.

MAIN TEACHING ACTIVITY
● **Describe and extend simple number sequences: count on or back in ones or tens starting from any two-digit number.**

VOCABULARY

Numbers 0 – 100; count on; count back; ones; tens; more; less; count from, count to; number square; number line; write in figures.

ORAL AND MENTAL STARTER

COUNTING IN ONES AND TENS TO 100: Sit the children in a circle and tell them they will be counting to 100. Count aloud together from 0–100 in ones forwards and backwards to zero and then in tens forwards and backwards to zero. Move on to counting on and back from other numbers.

MAIN TEACHING ACTIVITY

COUNTING ON/BACK IN ONES: Sit the children facing the 0–99 Number square teaching chart. Explain that they are to count in ones from the numbers you will point to on the number square Point to a number on the chart, for example 45, and ask the children to say the number aloud. Say: *Count on in ones from 45 to 55*. Do this a few times with different numbers, then change the rule to 'Counting back in ones'. Say, for example: *Count back in ones from 39 to 29*. Then show the children a copy of page 27. Explain that they will be playing a game where they throw a cube on to a number square, write down the number it lands on and then count on in ones, writing the numbers in the boxes to the end of the line. Demonstrate by throwing a cube on to a number square and writing the numbers on the sheet. Tell the children to do this three times. On the second half of the sheet, they write down the number the cube lands on and count back in ones, writing the numbers in the boxes to the end of the line three times. Check that the children are clear on what they have to do before they return to their tables to carry out the activity.

DIFFERENTIATION

More able: repeat the activity on a fresh sheet with the rule 'Counting in twos'.
Less able: use 0–49 number rectangles cut from a 0–99 Number square. For those who are confident with numbers to 20 only, make a master copy inserting the numbers 5, 7 and 9 in the first squares in the Count on section and 18, 16 and 14 in the second. Give each child a number line to use if they require help.

PLENARY

Sit the children in a semicircle facing the teaching chart. Repeat 'Counting on/back in ones' from the beginning of the **Main teaching activity**.

RESOURCES

Number square teaching chart and individual number squares (see Lesson 2); flip chart and pen; small cubes; pencils and paper; A4 card; elastic bands; photocopiable pages 28 (Two-way counts) and 14 (Number lines); sets of numeral cards 0–20.

PREPARATION

Make at least one copy of photocopiable page 28 for each child. For less able children: make two (or more) copies of photocopiable page 14 on A4 card. Cut into individual number lines and laminate for repeated use. Prepare a shuffled set of 0–20 cards for each child. Secure each set with an elastic band.

LEARNING OUTCOMES

ORAL AND MENTAL STARTER and MAIN TEACHING ACTIVITY
● Say the number names in order to at least 100, from and back to zero.

VOCABULARY

Numbers 0–100; count on, up; count back, down; count to; ones; twos; more; less; number square; number line; arrow; write in figures.

● **Describe and extend simple number sequences: count on or back in ones or tens, starting from any two-digit number.**

ORAL AND MENTAL STARTER

COUNTING ROUND: Sit the children in a circle. Ask them to count aloud together from 0 to 100 in ones, forwards and backwards, then in tens forwards and backwards to zero. Now explain that you will say a number and choose a child to start counting in ones from that number around the circle. Say: *If I say 23 then Imogen says 24, Patrick says 25, and so on.* The count stops when it gets back to the first child. Have a practice round, prompting children who get stuck. Start the game slowly at first, then speed up. Choose a different child to start the count each time.

MAIN TEACHING ACTIVITY

COUNTING ON/BACK IN ONES: Place the flip chart beside the Number square teaching chart and sit the children in front of them. Tell the children they are going to play another 'number square and cube' game where they count on one and count back one from the number the cube lands on. Write the rule 'Count back 1/Count on 1' on the flip chart and copy the first diagram from photocopiable page 28 on to the flip chart. Demonstrate and explain that the children have to throw a cube on to their number squares, then write the number it lands on in the box in the diagram. They then use their number squares to find the 'Count back 1' and 'Count on 1' numbers and write these numbers in the two circles either side of the arrows:

For example: $\textcircled{26} \leftarrow 27 \rightarrow \textcircled{28}$

Try a few more examples, inviting individuals to contribute the 'Count on 1' and 'Count back 1' numbers. Check that the children know what they have to do before they return to their tables to carry out the activity. Encourage them to write 'Count back 1' and 'Count on 1' in the 'Rule box' on the sheet before they start work.

DIFFERENTIATION

More able: children who finish quickly might try 'Count on 2/Count back 2' with a fresh copy of page 28. Remind them to write in the rule before they start.
Less able: give each child a 0–20 number line and a pile of shuffled cards 0–20 placed face down. Tell the children to take the top card from the pile and write the number in the box on the first diagram on the sheet. Work through an example with the children demonstrating how to find the 'Count back 1' and 'Count on 1' numbers on the number line and writing them in the circles on the sheet. Check that the children understand the task and offer guidance to individuals if necessary.

PLENARY

Play 'Counting round' again, as in the **Oral and mental starter**, counting round the circle on and back in ones from a given number.

Name

Counting in ones

Count on.

Count back.

Name

Two-way counts

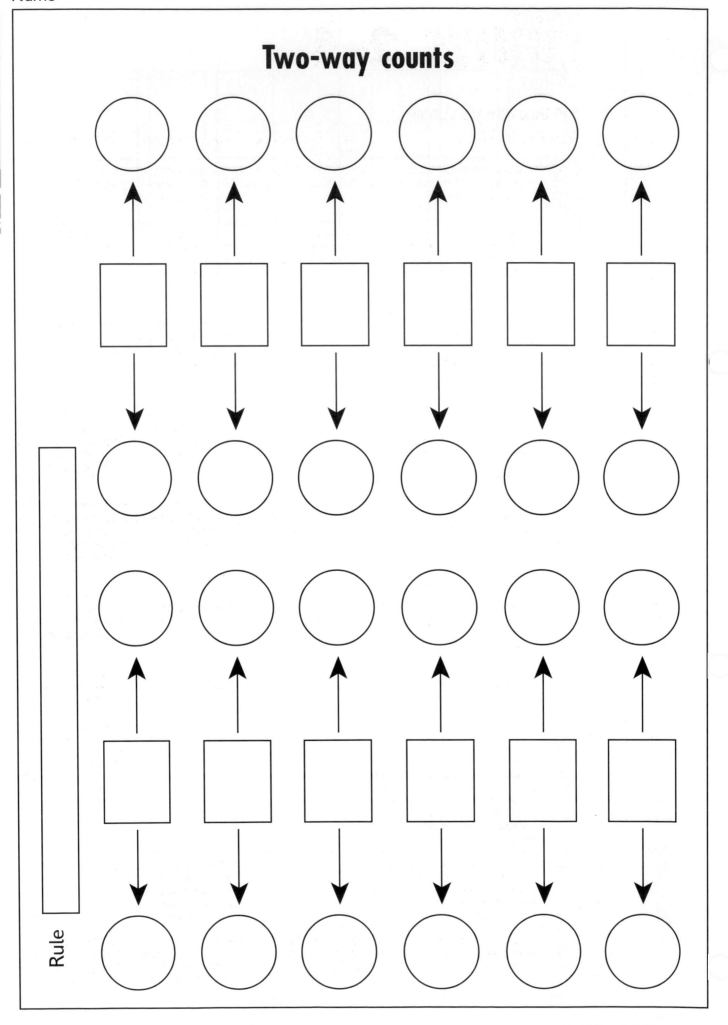

Rule

UNITS 2-4

ORGANISATION (15 LESSONS)

	LEARNING OUTCOMES	ORAL AND MENTAL STARTER	MAIN TEACHING ACTIVITY	PLENARY
LESSON 1	● **Read and write whole numbers to at least 100** in figures and words.	NUMBER WORDS TO 20: Reading numbers.	NUMBER WORDS TO 100: Reading and writing number words.	FIND THE NUMBER (1).
LESSON 2	● Use and begin to read the vocabulary of comparing and ordering numbers, including ordinal numbers to 100.	COUNTING IN ONES: Counting to 100 in ones.	ORDERING NUMBERS: Non-consecutive numbers up to about 30.	COUNTING IN ONES.
LESSON 3	● **Know by heart: all addition and subtraction facts for each number to at least 10.** ● Use the +, – and = signs to record mental additions and subtractions. ● Put the larger number first and count on in ones.	FIND THE NUMBER (1).	ADDING TWO NUMBERS: Adding two numbers in the range 1–10.	ADDING TWO CARDS: Adding two numbers in the range 1–10.
LESSON 4	● **Know what each digit in a two-digit number represents, including 0 as a place holder**, and partition two-digit numbers into a multiple of tens and ones (TU).	ADDING TWO CARDS.	TENS AND UNITS: Drawing numbers as on an abacus.	Reading and explaining TU numbers with a number square.
LESSON 5	● Begin to add three single-digit numbers mentally (totals up to about 20). ● Add three small numbers by putting the largest number first and/or find a pair totalling 10.	10 MORE 10 LESS: Starting to add 10 to multiples of 10.	ADDITION OF THREE (single-digit) NUMBERS.	ALL CHANGE: Adding three single-digit numbers, 1–9.
LESSON 6	● Derive quickly: doubles of all numbers to at least 15. ● Partition additions into tens and units, then recombine.	QUICK DOUBLES: Doubling up to 10.	DOUBLING TWO-DIGIT NUMBERS: Doubling numbers 10–20.	QUICK DOUBLES: Doubling up to 20.
LESSON 7	● Recognise all coins and begin to use £.p notation for money. ● Find totals, give change and work out which coins to pay.	NAMING AND ADDING TWO COINS.	ADDITION OF TWO COINS.	GUESS MY NUMBER: Using one-step operations to guess a number.
LESSON 8	● Use mental addition and subtraction to solve simple word problems involving numbers and money, using one or two steps. ● Find totals, give change and work out which coins to pay. ● **Explain how a problem was solved**.	GUESS MY NUMBER.	50p TO SPEND.	Reviewing results of the Main teaching activity.
LESSON 9	● Partition additions into tens and units, then recombine. ● **Checking results of calculations:** repeat addition in a different order.	ALL CHANGE.	ADDITION IN A DIFFERENT ORDER: Adding two two-digit numbers to get the same answer.	ALL CHANGE.
LESSON 10	● Partition into '5 and a bit' when adding 6, 7, 8 and 9, then recombine.	QUICK DOUBLES: Doubling numbers 1–20.	HARD FACTS: Partitioning '5 and a bit'; single-digit addition patterns.	ADDITION OF TWO NUMBERS: Adding numbers 10–20.

	LEARNING OUTCOMES	ORAL AND MENTAL STARTER	MAIN TEACHING ACTIVITY	PLENARY
LESSON 11	• **Know by heart: all addition and subtraction facts for all numbers to at least 10.**	ALL CHANGE: Adding two two-digit numbers (10–20).	MAKE 20.	ALL CHANGE.
LESSON 12	• **Know by heart:** all pairs of numbers with a total of 20.	FIND THE NUMBER (1).	TAKE FROM 20.	FIND THE NUMBER (2): Identifying numbers from their T and U.
LESSON 13	• Say the number that is 10 more or less than any given two-digit number.	SUBTRACT FROM 20.	ADD 10 TAKE AWAY 10.	SUBTRACT FROM 20.
LESSON 14	• Recognise all coins and begin to use £.p notation for money. • Use mental addition to solve simple word problems involving money, using one or two steps.	ADDITION OF THREE COINS (1p–50p): Variation of 'All change' game.	ADDITION OF THREE COINS (2p–£1.00): Using £.p. notation.	GUESS MY NUMBER: Using numbers 11–20.
LESSON 15	• Use and begin to read the vocabulary of estimation and approximation; give a sensible estimate of at least 50 objects.	HOW TO MAKE 20.	ESTIMATION AND APPROXIMATION: Using numbers of objects and amounts of money.	SUBTRACT FROM 20.

ORAL AND MENTAL SKILLS   Say the number names in order to at least 100, from and back to zero. **Know what each digit in a two-digit number represents, including 0 as a place holder,** and partition two-digit numbers into tens and ones (TU). Say the number that is 10 more or less than any given two-digit number. **Describe and extend number sequences: count on or back in ones or tens starting from any two-digit number. Read and write whole numbers to at least 100** in figures and words. **Know by heart: all addition and subtraction facts for each number to at least 10;** all pairs of numbers with a total of 20. Begin to add three single-digit numbers mentally (totals to about 20). **Use knowledge that addition can be done in any order to do mental calculations more efficiently.**   For example: put the larger number first and count on in ones, then tens or ones. Use mental addition and subtraction to solve simple word problems involving numbers and money, using one or two steps. **Explain how a problem was solved.**

In Unit 2, Lessons 1, 2 and 5 are given in full. In Unit 3, Lessons 6, 7 and 10 are given in full, and in Unit 4, Lessons 11, 14 and 15 are in full. Lessons 3, 4, 8, 9, 12 and 13 are provided in grid form as they develop content that has already been introduced.

RESOURCES

Flip chart and pen; set of word flash cards 'one' to 'twenty'; number words teaching chart (see **Preparation**); Number square teaching chart and individual number squares (from Unit 1, Lesson 2, page 24); sets of numeral cards 0–20; a small easel; small cubes; pencils and paper.

PREPARATION

Make a set of 20 flashcards each showing a number word 'one' to 'twenty'. (These could be printed from the NNS *Mathematical Vocabulary* CD-ROM.) Use a large sheet of paper or card to make a teaching chart headed 'Number words' with a list of number words 'twenty' to 'ninety' and 'zero' to 'nine' in two columns. Attach this chart to a small easel. Place individual number squares, small cubes, sheets of paper and pencils on each table.

LEARNING OUTCOMES

ORAL AND MENTAL STARTER and MAIN TEACHING ACTIVITY
● **Read and write whole numbers to at least 100** in figures and words.

VOCABULARY

Numbers (in numerals and words) 0–100; count; how many?; write in words; number square.

ORAL AND MENTAL STARTER

NUMBER WORDS TO 20: Take the set of number word flash cards and sit the children facing the flip chart. Tell them that you will hold up a card showing a 'number word' and they must say the number aloud. You will then choose a child to write the matching number on the chart each time. Try this for several numbers.

MAIN TEACHING ACTIVITY

NUMBER WORDS TO 100: Sit the children facing the Number words teaching chart and the flip chart. Ask them to count aloud together in ones from 1 to 100. Then ask the children to read the words aloud on the teaching chart as you point to each number word in turn. Next, say that you are going to point to a tens number and a ones number and the children should say the 'whole' number aloud. Choose a child each time to write the number (for example 46) on the flip chart, then ask the class: *Is the number correct? What does the '4' mean? What does the '6' mean?*

Next hold up the Number square teaching chart. Tell the children they are going to play a 'number square and cube game', where they throw the cube on the square and write down the number it lands on, followed by the number word. Demonstrate the method of recording on the flip chart; for example:

35 → thirty-five.

Demonstrate the activity by pointing to a number on your number square, asking the children to say the number aloud, then choosing a child to write the number followed by the number word on the chart. Ask the children to tell you what they have to do before they return to their tables to carry out the activity.

Remind the children to write the heading 'Number words' on their sheets of paper before they start the activity. Challenge them to complete at least 20 examples.

DIFFERENTIATION

More able: challenge the children to complete 50 examples.
Less able: place the set of number word flash cards in a tray on the table so the children can use these for support. Give each child a shuffled pile of cards 1 – 20. Tell them to take the top card and write the number, followed by the number word, for example:

7 → seven.

They should place the used card at the bottom of the pile, take the next, and so on.

PLENARY

FIND THE NUMBER (1): Sit the children facing the Number square teaching chart. Say the name of a number, then choose a child to come and point to it on the number square.

RESOURCES

A shuffled set of numeral cards 1–30 (or equivalent to the number of children in the class); a washing line and pegs; copies of photocopiable page 43 (Ordering numbers); pencils.

PREPARATION

Make a copy of photocopiable page 43 (Ordering numbers) for each child. Hang up the washing line in front of the class within reach of the children. Place copies of the photocopiable sheet and pencils on each table.

LEARNING OUTCOMES

ORAL AND MENTAL STARTER
● **Describe and extend simple number sequences: count on or back in ones, starting from any two-digit number.**

MAIN TEACHING ACTIVITY
● Use and begin to read the vocabulary of comparing and ordering numbers, including ordinal numbers to 100.

VOCABULARY

'Zero' to 'thirty' (or more); ordinal numbers 'first' to 'fifth'; order; place; largest; smallest; more/less; before/ after; between; next; last; last but one; size; correct place; write in figures.

ORAL AND MENTAL STARTER

COUNTING IN ONES: Sit the children in a circle. Explain that they will be counting round the circle in ones to 100 as quickly as possible. Any child who says a wrong number must sit in the middle of the circle and is 'out'. Choose a child to start the count. When the count reaches 100, let any child sitting out rejoin the circle. Choose another child to start the count again, but this time try a two-digit starting number. Play the game a few times.

MAIN TEACHING ACTIVITY

ORDERING NUMBERS: Sit the children in a semicircle facing the washing line and give each child a numeral card and a peg. Choose five children to peg their cards on the line in turn leaving some space between each card. Ask the children to help you to put the numbers in the correct order from the smallest number to the largest. Stand behind the line and ask questions about the first number: *Is this number in the correct place? Is it more/less than the second number, the third, fourth, fifth number? Where should the number be placed?* Ask a child to move the card (if necessary) to its new position on the line. Repeat this until all the numbers are in the correct order. Ask the children to read the numbers aloud in order before taking the cards off the line. Invite sets of five children to peg their cards on the line until all the cards have been used.

Next show the children a copy of photocopiable page 43. Tell them they have to order each set of numbers on the sheet from smallest to largest. Check that the children know what to do to complete the sheet before they return to their tables to carry out the activity.

DIFFERENTIATION

More able: provide paper and a pile of shuffled 1–50 numeral cards. Tell these children to take five cards each time to put in order, largest to smallest, then write down the numbers. Less able: use a shuffled set of 1–20 numeral cards. Give each child a sheet of paper and deal out five cards for them to arrange in order, smallest to largest. They can then write the numbers on their sheet. Collect in cards, shuffle and deal out again. Repeat five times.

PLENARY

Play the 'Counting in ones' game again as in the **Oral and mental starter**.

RESOURCES	Flip chart and pen; Number square teaching chart (page 13); sets of numeral cards 1–10 (enough for two cards for each child); paper, pencils.
LEARNING OUTCOMES	**ORAL AND MENTAL STARTER** ● **Read and write whole numbers to at least 100** in figures and words. **MAIN TEACHING ACTIVITY** ● **Know by heart: all addition and subtraction facts for each number to at least 10.** ● Use the +, – and = signs to record mental additions and subtractions. ● Put the larger number first and count on in ones.
ORAL AND MENTAL STARTER	FIND THE NUMBER (1): Children face the Number square teaching chart. Explain that you will say the name of a number and will then choose a child to come and point to the number on the number square each time.
MAIN TEACHING ACTIVITY	ADDING TWO NUMBERS: Show two numeral cards. Ask: *Which is the larger number?* Write the larger number followed by the second number in an addition 'sum' on the flip chart. Ask a child to add the number on the second card onto the first number by counting on from the larger number in ones. Repeat this a few times, asking: *Which numbers can you add in your head? Who can add 1?* Then: *Who can add 2?* and so on. Lay two sets of numeral cards 1–10 in two rows in the centre of each table. Ask the children to record as many addition sums as they can using numbers on two cards each time (including double numbers). Check they put the larger number first and add on the second number mentally. They should write an 'H' beside any sum they have done entirely in their heads.
DIFFERENTIATION	More able: include additions using numbers on three cards. Less able: use two sets of cards 1–5 to record additions. Provide rods or cubes for children requiring additional support.
PLENARY	ADDING TWO CARDS: Sit the children in a circle and give two numeral cards to each. Ask each in turn to add their two numbers.

RESOURCES	A copy of photocopiable page 44 (Tens and units) for each child; 1–10 numeral cards; pencils; Number square teaching chart (page 13); flip chart. For more able children: number squares; small cubes; pencil and paper. For less able children: Base ten or Cuisenaire rods (tens and ones).
LEARNING OUTCOMES	**ORAL AND MENTAL STARTER** ● **Know by heart: all addition and subtraction facts for each number to at least 10.** Put the larger number first and count on in ones. **MAIN TEACHING ACTIVITY** ● **Know what each digit in a two-digit number represents, including 0 as a place holder**, and partition two-digit numbers into a multiple of tens and ones (TU).
ORAL AND MENTAL STARTER	ADDING TWO CARDS: See the **Plenary** session of Lesson 3, page 32.
MAIN TEACHING ACTIVITY	TENS AND UNITS: Show the children photocopiable page 44 and use the flip chart to demonstrate an example of beads on an abacus. Ask a child to count the tens beads and units beads and write the tens and units numbers underneath on the chart. Ask: *What does each number mean?* Then show an example of an abacus without beads, with a number written underneath. Ask what each number means, then ask a child to draw in beads to match the number. Check that the children know how to complete the sheets before they return to their tables.
DIFFERENTIATION	More able: children who finish quickly can play a 'number square and cube game' where they throw a cube on to the square, write down the number it lands on, then write the number as tens and units, for example: 43 → 4 tens and 3 units. Less able: encourage the use of Base 10 or Cuisenaire rods, matching each bead with a tens rod or a unit rod before writing the numbers. For the second half of the sheet, suggest that the children make the number with tens and units rods, then draw in the number of beads to match the rods.
PLENARY	Children sit facing the Number square teaching chart. Point to different numbers on the number square. Choose a child to say the number, and then the number as tens and units each time, for example: '36 is 3 tens and 6 units'.

RESOURCES

Flip chart and pen; numeral cards 1–9 shuffled into a pack (one card for each child); a pack of numeral cards 1–9 for each group; paper and pencils; three different colours of sorting hoops (red, yellow, blue); sets of numeral cards 1–20; elastic bands.

PREPARATION

Place a pack of numeral cards secured with an elastic band, sheets of paper and pencils on each table.

LEARNING OUTCOMES

ORAL AND MENTAL STARTER
● Say the number that is 10 more or less than any given two-digit number.

MAIN TEACHING ACTIVITY
● Begin to add three single-digit numbers mentally (totals up to about 20).
● Add three small numbers by putting the largest number first and/or find a pair totalling 10.

ORAL AND MENTAL STARTER

10 MORE 10 LESS: Tell the children they are going to play a game adding 10 to 'tens' numbers. Explain that you will say a 'tens' number, then choose a child to say the number that is 10 more, for example: *My number is 30. Nalma, what is your number?* Give each child a turn, then change the rule to '10 less'.

MAIN TEACHING ACTIVITY

ADDITION OF THREE NUMBERS: Sit the children facing the flip chart and tell them that they are going to add three numbers between 1 and 9. Demonstrate on the chart how to add three one-digit numbers together by putting the numbers in the easiest order to find the total (by putting the larger number first and/or finding a pair of numbers totalling 10) for example:

$$3 + 5 + 1 = 5 + 3 + 1 = 9 \qquad \text{or} \qquad 4 + 3 + 6 = \underline{6} + \underline{4} + 3 = \underline{10} + 3 = 13$$

Give each child a card from a shuffled set of numbered 1–9 cards. Invite three children to stand in a line facing the group and show and say the number on their cards. As they do so write the numbers as a sum on the flip chart in the order that the children are standing, then ask the group to say the numbers in the easiest order to find the total. Ask: *Who can tell me what the total is?* Write the total on the chart. Then say: *Can you tell everybody how you did the sum?* Repeat this a few times choosing three different children to stand and face the group each time.

Explain that they are now going to play an 'Add three numbers' game. Each group will use the set of numeral cards on the table. Explain the rules of the game. Check that the children understand them before they return to their tables to play the game.
- Take turns to deal out three cards to each child including yourself.
- Write down the numbers on your cards on a sheet of paper in the easiest order, then add the numbers together to find the total.
- Give the cards back to the next dealer, who places them at the bottom of the pile before dealing three new cards to everyone.

DIFFERENTIATION

More able: try a harder version of the game with sets of cards 1– 20.
Less able: deal only two numeral cards to each child.

PLENARY

ALL CHANGE: Use a shuffled set of numeral cards (1–9) and three coloured hoops placed in a line (red, yellow, blue). Sit the children in a semicircle facing the hoops. Give each child a numeral card. Ask the first three children in the semicircle each to stand in a hoop and show their cards to the group. Ask a fourth child to add the numbers. If the answer given is correct, this child changes places with the child in the red hoop. A fifth child re-totals the numbers, this time changing places with the child in the yellow hoop if correct, and so on. If an incorrect answer is given, play passes to the next child.

RESOURCES

Flip chart and pen; numeral cards 1–10 (one card for each child); sets of numeral cards 10–20 (at least two for each group); Cuisenaire rods; paper and pencils.

LEARNING OUTCOMES

ORAL AND MENTAL STARTER
- **Know by heart: all addition and subtraction facts for each number to at least 10.**

MAIN TEACHING ACTIVITY
- Derive quickly: doubles of all numbers to at least 15.
- Partition additions into tens and units, then recombine.

ORAL AND MENTAL STARTER

QUICK DOUBLES: Sit the children in a circle. Tell them that they are going to play a number doubling game. Give each child a 1–10 numeral card and ask them, in turn around the circle, to double their number and say the double, for example: 'Double 4 is 8.' Ask the children to respond quickly, after each other, to encourage rapid recall. When they have all doubled their numbers successfully, collect in the cards, shuffle them and give them out again. Repeat the game. Finish by choosing children at random to double their number.

LESSON 6

VOCABULARY

Double; add; addition; make; sum; total; more; altogether; equals; explain your method; how you got your answer; show how you....

MAIN TEACHING ACTIVITY

DOUBLING TWO-DIGIT NUMBERS: Sit the children in a semicircle in front of the flip chart and give each child a 10–20 card. Start by asking one child to say the number on his or her card, then write the number as a 'double' sum on the board, for example: 14 + 14.

Next, write the 'sum' showing the tens grouped and added together, followed by the units added together, then the total; for example: 10 + 10 + 4 + 4 = 20 + 8 = 28.

Ask another child to say the number on his or her card and again write the number as a double sum on the flip chart. Then ask the children to tell you how to write the sum by grouping the tens and units together. Choose a child to say the total and write the method on the flip chart. Repeat this a few times.

Explain that the children are going to work, in groups, with a pile of 10–20 cards on their tables. Demonstrate, using a pile of cards, how they are to place the pile of cards face down in front of them, then turn over one card at a time and write the double sum for the number on the card. They then rewrite the sum grouping the tens and units together. Finally they add the numbers together and write the total before turning over another card.

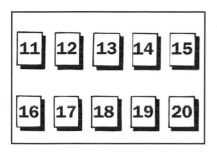

DIFFERENTIATION

More able: tell children who finish quickly to lay the cards out in front of them in two lines of five (11–15 and 16–20). They should then make as many different addition sums as they can with two cards, using the grouping tens and units method.

Less able: provide Cuisenaire rods. If the children have problems with the addition, tell them to make each number with tens and ones rods, then group the tens and ones together, add the tens and count on the ones.

PLENARY

QUICK DOUBLES: Repeat the 'Quick doubles' game from the **Oral and mental starter**, but this time use shuffled sets of 1– 20 cards.

RESOURCES

Sets of coins 1p – 50p (preferably real), flip chart and pen; paper and pencils. For each pair of children: three money dice or cubes marked 1p, 2p, 5p, 10p, 20p, 50p and a small margarine tub.

PREPARATION

Place sets of dice, margarine tubs, paper and pencils on each table.

LEARNING OUTCOMES

ORAL AND MENTAL STARTER

● Use mental addition and subtraction to solve simple word problems involving numbers and money, using one or two steps.

MAIN TEACHING ACTIVITY

● Recognise all coins and begin to use £.p notation for money.
● Find totals, give change and work out which coins to pay.

VOCABULARY

Names of coins; add; plus; equals; change; totals; how much altogether?; pound, £; show how you ...; rearrange amounts; money dice.

ORAL AND MENTAL STARTER

NAMING AND ADDING TWO COINS: Use sets of 1p–20p coins. Sit the children in a circle and give each child a coin. Tell them that you will choose two children to say the names of their coins. You will then ask them to add the two coins together by putting the larger coin first and then adding on the second coin. Demonstrate an example. Ask two children to stand facing the group, then hold up and name their coins. Ask the group to tell you how they would add the coins together. Now ask the children in turn, around the circle, to hold up and name their coins. Select two children to stand up and name their coins. Ask a seated child to say the total of the two coins. Repeat, making sure each child takes a turn.

MAIN TEACHING ACTIVITY

ADDITION OF TWO COINS: Sit the children in a semicircle facing a flip chart. Give each child a coin, making sure that at least one of each coin 1p–50p is included. Choose two children to stand in front of the group, hold up and name their coins. Write the value of each coin on the flip chart as a 'sum' in the order they are given, for example: 5p + 50p. Ask the children to sit down again and then show the group how to find the total by putting the larger number first; for example:

50p + 5p = 55p

Demonstrate the notation for £1.00 when 50p is added to 50p; for example:

50p + 50p = £1.00

Then tell the children that they will be playing a game with two money dice. Explain the rules of the game and check that they all follow them before they return to their tables to play the game.
● Working in pairs, take turns to throw the dice.
● Each child writes down the amounts shown on the dice as a 'money sum'. These should be written in the easiest order to find the total each time.
● If amounts already used are thrown, the child should throw again.

DIFFERENTIATION

More able: challenge children to play the game with three, or even four, dice.
Less able: use two dice marked 1p, 2p, 5p, 10p, 20p, 20p to start with. Extend by using two dice marked 1p–50p.

PLENARY

GUESS MY NUMBER: Tell the class that they are going to play a game where you think of a number, give them a clue, and they have to guess the number. For example: *I am thinking of a number. When I add 3 to the number, the answer is 9. What is my number?* Choose a child to say the answer. Repeat this several times, making the 'clue' a number added to your number each time.

LESSON 8

RESOURCES	Flip chart and pen; a copy of page 45 (50p to spend at the School Fair) for each child; pencils and paper; sets of coins.
LEARNING OUTCOMES	**ORAL AND MENTAL STARTER** ● Use mental addition and subtraction to solve simple word problems involving numbers in real life, using one or two steps. **MAIN TEACHING ACTIVITY** ● Use mental addition and subtraction to solve simple word problems involving money, using one or two steps. ● Find totals, give change and work out which coins to pay. ● **Explain how a problem was solved.**
ORAL AND MENTAL STARTER	GUESS MY NUMBER: See Lesson 7, **Plenary** session above. Make each 'clue' a number subtracted from your number each time. For example: *I am thinking of a number. When I subtract 3 from the number, the answer is 6. What is my number?* Repeat this several times.
MAIN TEACHING ACTIVITY	50P TO SPEND: Sit the children facing a flip chart. Start by giving each child a copy of photocopiable page 45 so they can look at the picture at the top. Tell the children to imagine they have some money to spend at this school fair. Encourage them to look at each stall in the picture in turn and ask, for example: *How much for an ice-cream?* Do this for each stall, then on the flip chart write an example like the first one on the sheet and work through it with the children. Ask: *What are they buying? How much will each item cost. How much will it cost altogether? How much change from 50p?* Check that the children understand how to complete the sheet.
DIFFERENTIATION	More able: encourage the children to work mentally where they can, but tell them they can write any 'working out' on the sheet if they are unsure. Less able: provide sets of coins as additional support.
PLENARY	Copy the first problem from the sheet on to the flip chart. Ask questions as before. Encourage the children to explain how they found out how much money had been spent and how much change there was from 50p.

RESOURCES	A set of shuffled cards 1–10 (one card for each child); three coloured sorting hoops (red, yellow, blue); flip chart and pen; sets of numbered cards 10–20; paper and pencils; Cuisenaire rods.
LEARNING OUTCOMES	**ORAL AND MENTAL STARTER** ● Begin to add three single-digit numbers mentally (totals up to about 20). **MAIN TEACHING ACTIVITY** ● Partition additions into tens and units, then recombine. ● **Checking results of calculations:** repeat addition in a different order.
ORAL AND MENTAL STARTER	ALL CHANGE: Play this game from the **Plenary** session of Lesson 5, Unit 2, on page 34, using shuffled sets of 1–10 cards.
MAIN TEACHING ACTIVITY	ADDITION IN A DIFFERENT ORDER: Place a set of 10–20 cards face up in two rows in the middle of each table. Tell the children to select two different numbers each time, add the numbers together by grouping tens and units, then repeat the addition by writing the numbers in a different order. Highlight that the answers *should* be the same! Demonstrate how to record this on the flip chart, for example: $11 + 15 \rightarrow 20 + 1 + 5 = 26$ $15 + 11 \rightarrow 20 + 5 + 1 = 26$
DIFFERENTIATION	More able: invite children to try adding three numbers, recording, for example: $17 + 14 + 12 \rightarrow 30 + 7 + 4 + 2 = 43$ $12 + 14 + 17 \rightarrow 30 + 6 + 7 = 43$ Less able: provide Cuisenaire rods for children who need additional support.
PLENARY	Repeat the 'All change' game from the **Oral and mental starter**.

RESOURCES

Flip chart and pen; paper and pencils; sets of shuffled numeral cards 1–20 (one card for each child); two plastic hoops; Cuisenaire rods.

PREPARATION

Write the following sums on the board or flip chart:

6 + 6	6 + 7	6 + 8	6 + 9	7 + 6	7 + 7	7 + 8	7 + 9
8 + 6	8 + 7	8 + 8	8 + 9	9 + 6	9 + 7	9 + 8	9 + 9

Place sheets of paper and pencils on each table.

LEARNING OUTCOMES

ORAL AND MENTAL STARTER

● **Know by heart: all addition facts for each number to at least 10.**
● Derive quickly: doubles of all numbers to at least 15.

MAIN TEACHING ACTIVITY

● Partition into '5 and a bit' when adding 6, 7, 8 or 9, then recombine
(e.g. $6 + 8 = 5 + 1 + 5 + 3 = 10 + 4 = 14$).

ORAL AND MENTAL STARTER

QUICK DOUBLES: Repeat this game from the **Plenary** session of Lesson 6, Unit 3, on page 34.

MAIN TEACHING ACTIVITY

HARD FACTS: Sit the children facing the flip chart. Start by reminding them of the activity when they were adding two numeral cards together (Lesson 3, Unit 2, on page 32). Some numbers were easy to add in their heads, but others were not so easy and they had to count on the number on the second card in ones. Ask the children if they know the special way to add difficult numbers in their heads by splitting those numbers into '5 and a bit'. Use the flip chart to demonstrate and explain the method, if necessary, using an example such as: $9 + 6 = \underline{5} + 4 + \underline{5} + 1 = 1\underline{0} + 5 (4 + 1) = 15$.

VOCABULARY

Add; addition; partition into '5 and a bit'; sum; equals; totals; makes; altogether; more; plus; change; rearrange, explain your method; explain how you got the answer; show how you ; rods.

Point to each number in the statement and explain how each number has been split. Then write another example on the chart and ask the children to tell you how the numbers can be split into '5 and a bit'. Repeat with another example.

Next tell the children that they are to write down and complete the sums on the board or flip chart by partitioning the numbers into '5 and a bit'. Check that they all know what to do before they return to their tables to carry out the activity.

DIFFERENTIATION

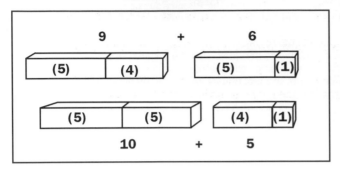

More able: invite these children to try some addition patterns where they change the first number in each sum to a 'teens' number and partition it into '15 and a bit', for example:

$19 + 6 = \underline{15} + 4 + \underline{5} + 1 = \underline{20} + 5 \ (4+1) = 25$

Less able: have Cuisenaire rods available for children who may require support. Tell them to partition each number into a five-rod and another rod. Group the five-rods together to make 10, then group and combine the others to find the total, as shown on the left.

PLENARY

ADDITION OF TWO NUMBERS: Sit the children in a semicircle and give each child a card from a shuffled set of 10–20 cards. Tell them that they are to add two numbers between 10 and 20 by grouping the numbers into tens and ones, adding the tens together and then adding on the ones. Choose two children to stand facing the group and show their cards, then ask another child to say the total of the two numbers. Choose two more children and repeat this.

RESOURCES

Sets of cards numbered 1–10 (one card for each child) and four sets of numeral cards 1–20; two coloured sorting hoops (red and yellow); tubs of interlocking cubes.

LEARNING OUTCOMES

ORAL AND MENTAL STARTER
● Put the larger number first and count on in tens or ones.

MAIN TEACHING ACTIVITY
● **Know by heart: all addition and subtraction facts for each number to at least 10.**

ORAL AND MENTAL STARTER

ALL CHANGE: In this version of the familiar game, the children will be adding two two-digit numbers.

Shuffle a set of cards 0–20 and have ready two hoops. Sit the children in a semicircle and place the hoops side by side in front of the group. Tell the children they are going to play an addition game with hoops where they will change places each time. Explain that in this game they will be taking turns to add two numbers between 10 and 20. They will do this by putting the larger number first and counting on in tens or ones.

Give each child a numeral card and invite the first two children in the semicircle to stand in the hoops and show their cards to the group. The third child in the semicircle has to add the two numbers together by putting the larger number first, then counting on in tens and ones. If the child answers correctly, he or she changes places with the child in the first hoop and shows his or her card. The fourth child then totals these two numbers and, if correct, changes places with the child in the second hoop. If a child answers incorrectly play passes to the next child. Continue around the semicircle with children changing places alternately with the children in the two hoops.

MAIN TEACHING ACTIVITY

MAKE 20: Tell the children that they are going to play a game with sets of cards 1–20 and a tub of interlocking cubes. The cards will be spread out face up and they will take turns to pick up two cards that total 20.

Explain the rules of the game:
- Spread the cards out face up on the table.
- Each time a child picks up two cards they must be shown to the other players.
- The other players check to see if the two numbers total 20.
- If correct, the player keeps the pair of cards. If incorrect, the cards are replaced and play passes to the next child.
- At the end of each game, the children count up the pairs. The player with most pairs is the winner and takes a cube from the tub.
- The cards are shuffled and spread out again. The game is repeated five times.
- At the end of the session the child with most cubes is the overall winner.

Encourage the children to tell you what they have to do before they return to their tables to play the game.

DIFFERENTIATION

More able: these children might try playing the game as 'Pelmanism', starting with all the cards spread out face down. They take turns to pick up one card, then have a second go to try to find another card that will make 20 when added to the first card. When they have picked a correct pair, if the other children agree, they keep the cards and take another turn. Incorrect cards are replaced face down and play passes to the next child.
Less able: use sets of cards 1–10 and change the game to finding pairs of numbers to make 10.

PLENARY

Repeat the 'All change' addition game from the **Oral and mental starter**, with cards numbered 10–20.

LESSON 12

RESOURCES	Number square teaching chart (page 13); sets of 1–20 cards for each group; interlocking cubes; pencils and paper; Base 10 apparatus or Cuisenaire rods.
LEARNING OUTCOMES	**ORAL AND MENTAL STARTER** ● **Know what each digit in a two-digit number represents, including 0 as a place holder**, and partition two-digit numbers into tens and ones (TU). **MAIN TEACHING ACTIVITY** ● **Know by heart:** all pairs of numbers with a total of 20.
ORAL AND MENTAL STARTER	FIND THE NUMBER: play this game from Lesson 3, Unit 2, on page 32. Use tens and units numbers on a 0–99 number square.
MAIN TEACHING ACTIVITY	TAKE FROM 20: Each group needs a set of cards numbered 1–20 and some interlocking cubes. They play the game in the same way as 'Make 20' (Lesson 11), but this time the cards are spread out face down. Children take turns to turn over one card and subtract the number from 20, for example: '20 take away 5 leaves 15.' If the other children agree that the answer is correct, the card remains face up and the child who turned it over takes a cube. If the answer is incorrect, the card is turned face down again and play passes to the next child. At the end the children count their cubes to see who is the winner. Play the game a few times.
DIFFERENTIATION	More able: lay out a set of cards 1–20 in two lines of ten cards 1–10 and 11–20 in the centre of the table. Give each child a sheet of paper to write as many addition and subtraction facts about 20 as they can using a number from each row, for example: 6 + 14 = 20 or 20 – 8 = 12. Less able: use sets of cards 1–10 and change the game to 'Take from 10'.
PLENARY	FIND THE NUMBER (2): Sit the children facing the 0–99 Number square teaching chart. Tell them you are going to say a number in tens and units and then choose a child to come to the chart and point to the number; for example: *Find 4 tens and 6 units* (46).

LESSON 13

RESOURCES	Shuffled set of numeral cards 1–20 (one card for each child); a copy of photocopiable page 28 (Two-way counts) for each child; the 0–99 Number square teaching chart (page 13); small cubes; pencils.
LEARNING OUTCOMES	**ORAL AND MENTAL STARTER** ● **Know by heart:** all pairs of numbers with a total of 20. **MAIN TEACHING ACTIVITY** ● Say the number that is 10 more or less than any given two-digit number.
ORAL AND MENTAL STARTER	SUBTRACT FROM 20: Sit the children in a circle and give each child a card from a shuffled set of 1–20 cards. Each child, in turn, subtracts the number on his or her card from 20, saying, for example: '20 subtract 4 leaves 16'.
MAIN TEACHING ACTIVITY	ADD 10/TAKE AWAY 10: Repeat the number square and cube game ('Counting on/back in ones') from Lesson 3, Unit 1, on page 26 with the new rule of 'Add 10/Take away 10'. Use the 0–99 Number square teaching chart to explain and demonstrate the rule. Point to a few numbers on the chart for children to say the 'Take 10' and 'Add 10' numbers. Remind the children how to record on the sheet, for example: 39 ← 49 → 59
DIFFERENTIATION	More able: these children might try 'Count on (Add) 20/ Count back (Take) 20' with fresh copies of the sheet. Less able: use the rule 'Add 1/Take away 1'. Offer guidance to individuals if necessary.
PLENARY	Repeat the 'Subtract from 20' game from the **Oral and mental starter**.

LESSON 14

RESOURCES

Sets of coins 1p–£1.00; flip chart and pen; sets of three six-sided money dice or cubes marked 2p, 5p, 10p, 20p, 50p, £1.00 (see **Preparation**, below); small plastic trays for throwing dice; three coloured hoops; paper and pencils.

PREPARATION

Mark sets of three cubes with the amounts 2p–£1.00 (prepare at least one set of three dice between two children working in small groups.

LEARNING OUTCOMES

ORAL AND MENTAL STARTER
● **Use knowledge that addition can be done in any order to do mental calculations more efficiently.**

MAIN TEACHING ACTIVITY
● Recognise all coins and begin to use £.p notation for money.
● Use mental addition to solve problems involving money, using one or two steps.

VOCABULARY

Names of coins to £1.00; add; plus; equals; subtract; sign; coin; money; pence; total; altogether; equals; rearrange in a different order; rearrange in easiest order; money dice.

ORAL AND MENTAL STARTER

ADDITION OF THREE COINS: Play a version of the 'All change' game with sets of coins 1p–50p (one coin for each child) and three coloured hoops. Sit the children in a circle and place the three hoops in a line in the middle. Give each child a coin and play the game, as in the **Plenary** session of Lesson 5, Unit 2, on page 34, but with three coins to add each time rather than numerals.

MAIN TEACHING ACTIVITY

ADDITION OF THREE COINS (2p–£1.00): Sit the class in a semicircle facing the flip chart and give each child a coin. Ask: *Who has a 2p coin?* to *Who has a £1.00 coin?* and encourage the children to hold up the appropriate coin if they have it. Show them the notation for £1.00 and £2.00 and the notation for amounts with pounds and pence, for example £1.50 (or 150p). Invite individual children to write different given amounts on the flip chart using £.p notation, for example: £1.20, £3.80, £0.50, 38p. Next, choose three children to stand in a line facing the group and hold up and say the name of their coin.

Scribe the value of each coin on the chart as an addition sum in the order they are given, using £.p notation, for example:

50p + £1.00 + 20p =

Ask the group to rearrange the 'sum' to show the easiest way to find the total. Scribe the new 'sum' on the flip chart and choose a child to say the total. Write this total on the chart, pointing out the method of notation (for example: £1.00 + 70p = £1.70). Highlight that £ and p are never used together. Repeat this a few times.

Tell the children they are going to play a game with three money dice now. Explain the rules of the game and check that the children understand them before they return to their tables to play. Tell them to:

● Work in pairs, taking turns to throw the three dice.
● Write down the amounts on the dice as a 'money sum' on paper each time in the easiest order to find the total. Use £.p notation where appropriate.
● The first pair to complete 20 money sums with the dice wins the game.

DIFFERENTIATION

More able: try playing the game again with four dice.
Less able: just play with two dice.

PLENARY

GUESS MY NUMBER: Ask addition and subtraction questions with numbers between 11–20. For example: *I am thinking of a number. When I add 5 to the number the answer is 18. What is my number?; I am thinking of a number. When I subtract 2 from the number the answer is 12. What is my number?*

RESOURCES

A shuffled set of numeral cards 1–20 (one card for each child); large plastic screwtop jars containing between 40 and 50 cubes; a plastic bank bag containing 1p coins, (between 50p and £1.00 in value); teaching charts as shown in **Preparation** below.

PREPARATION

Copy the following onto a flip chart or large sheets of paper as teaching charts:

Estimate and approximate the number of cubes in a jar		
Approximately less than 30	Approximately more than 30	Approximately more than 50
'Exact' estimates	'Exact' estimates	'Exact' estimates

Estimate and approximate how much money in a bag		
Approximately less than 50p	Approximately more than 50p	Approximately more than £1.00
'Exact' estimates	'Exact' estimates	'Exact' estimates

LEARNING OUTCOMES

ORAL AND MENTAL STARTER
● **Know by heart:** all pairs of numbers with a total of 20.

MAIN TEACHING ACTIVITY
● Use and begin to read the vocabulary of estimation and approximation; give a sensible estimate of at least 50 objects.

VOCABULARY

Estimate; guess how many; approximate; count; nearest; closest; nearly; roughly; close to; about the same as; just over; just under; exact; exactly; actual number; too many; too few; enough; not enough; cubes; money bags; coins.

ORAL AND MENTAL STARTER

HOW TO MAKE 20: Stand the children in a circle and give each child a card numbered 1–20. Tell them that they are going to play a game where they take turns, around the circle, to say the number on the card and then the number needed to make 20 in an addition sentence, for example: '13 add 7 equals 20'. Children who answer correctly may sit down. If the answer is incorrect, they remain standing. At the end of the round give any child still standing another turn with a different card. If they hesitate, invite a seated child to say the answer. Collect the cards, shuffle them, give them out again, then repeat the game.

MAIN TEACHING ACTIVITY

ESTIMATION AND APPROXIMATION: Numbers of objects and amounts of money:
Sit the children in a semicircle facing the 'Cubes' teaching chart. Explain that *approximate* numbers are 'about', but *estimates* are a 'guess' of the 'exact' number: so 'about 30' or '32' respectively, when there might actually be 31 or 33 cubes. Tell the children that you will be passing a jar of cubes around. They should look carefully and say their estimate of the exact number of cubes in the jar. Each child, in turn, holds the jar and says the estimate, then ask the group to say which column that estimate should be written in. Scribe the child's first name and number in the appropriate 'approximate' column on the chart. When all the children have made their estimates, tip the cubes into a hoop on the floor in front of the chart and choose a child to count the exact number by grouping and counting the cubes in tens, adding on any remaining ones. Then ask the children to look at the chart to find, first, which set of children made the closest approximation, then the child who made the nearest estimate to the actual number of cubes in the jar. Repeat the activity with the 'Money chart' and the money bag, asking each child to give the exact amount of money in the bag each time.

DIFFERENTIATION

More able: when all the cubes in each jar have been counted, tip the contents of two jars into one jar for children to estimate, then count, the larger number of cubes. Do this with all the jars.
Less able: choose two children to work together to count the contents of each jar.

PLENARY

Repeat 'How to make 20' changing the rule to 'Subtract from 20'. Ask the children to subtract the number on their card from 20 and say the answer as a subtraction sentence, for example: '20 subtract 4 leaves 16.'

Name

Ordering numbers

smallest → largest

6	3	8	2	5

13	19	11	15	10

27	22	24	28	26

14	25	3	10	29

24	4	21	7	16

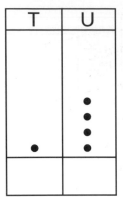

Tens and units

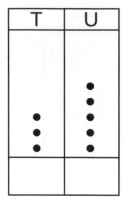

Write the value underneath each abacus.

T	U
.	.
i	i

Row 1:

T	U
.	⋮

T	U
⁝	⁞

T	U
⁝	.

T	U
⁝	⁞

Row 2:

T	U
:	⋮

T	U
.	⁞

T	U
⁝	

T	U
	⁞

Complete each abacus.

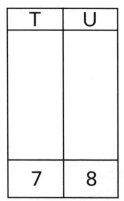

Row 3:

T	U
1	2

T	U
4	3

T	U
7	8

T	U
9	0

Row 4:

T	U
6	6

T	U
	7

T	U
3	9

T	U
2	1

Name

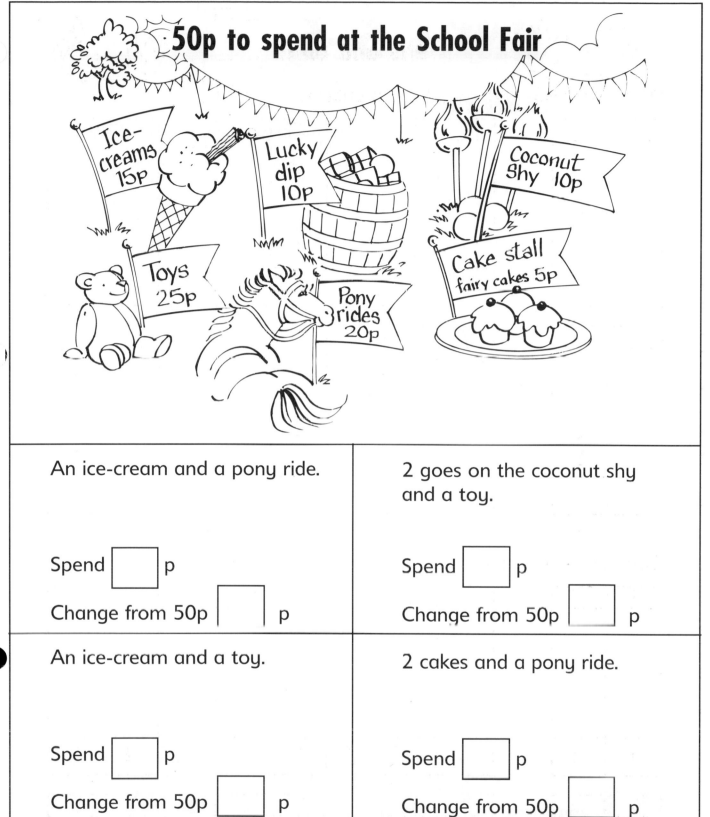

50p to spend at the School Fair

Ice-creams 15p

Lucky dip 10p

Coconut Shy 10p

Toys 25p

Pony rides 20p

Cake stall fairy cakes 5p

An ice-cream and a pony ride. Spend ☐ p Change from 50p ☐ p	2 goes on the coconut shy and a toy. Spend ☐ p Change from 50p ☐ p
An ice-cream and a toy. Spend ☐ p Change from 50p ☐ p	2 cakes and a pony ride. Spend ☐ p Change from 50p ☐ p
A lucky dip and a toy. Spend ☐ p Change from 50p ☐ p	A pony ride, a lucky dip and a go on the coconut shy. Spend ☐ p Change from 50p ☐ p

UNITS 5-6

ORGANISATION (8 LESSONS)

LEARNING OUTCOMES	ORAL AND MENTAL STARTER	MAIN TEACHING ACTIVITY	PLENARY
LESSON 1 +2 +3 +4 +5 ● Use mental addition and subtraction to solve simple word problems involving measures, using one or two steps. Explain how the problem was solved. ● Use and begin to read the vocabulary related to length. ● **Estimate, measure and compare lengths using standard units** (m, cm); **suggest suitable units and equipment for such measurements**. ● **Read a simple scale to the nearest labelled division, including using a ruler to draw and measure lines to the nearest centimetre,** recording estimates and measurements as '3 and a bit metres long' or 'about 8 centimetres'.	HOW TO MAKE 20 or ALL CHANGE.	Comparing heights visually; measuring in metres, decimetres and centimetres; estimating and measuring large numbers of centimetres; using, reading and recording from a range of measuring equipment.	Reviewing work from all the Main teaching activities.
LESSON 6 +7 +8 ● **Use the mathematical names for common 3-D and 2-D shapes.** ● **Sort shapes and describe some of their features.** ● Make and describe shapes, pictures and patterns. ● Relate solid shapes to pictures of them. ● Solve mathematical problems or puzzles, recognise simple patterns and relationships, generalise and predict. Suggest extensions by asking 'What if ...?' or 'What could I try next?'.	10 MORE 10 LESS.	Naming 2-D and 3-D shapes; making designs, patterns and models with 2-D and 3-D shapes; drawing pictures of models; making shapes using a geoboard.	Reviewing work from all the Main teaching activities.

ORAL AND MENTAL SKILLS Say the number that is 10 more or less than any given two-digit number. **Know by heart:** all pairs of numbers with a total of 20. **Use knowledge that addition can be done in any order to do mental calculations more efficiently.** For example: put the larger number first and count on in tens or ones.

In Unit 5 (Lessons 1–5) and Unit 6 (Lessons 6–8), the lessons may be given as separate, whole-class lessons, or presented to different groups of children on a circus basis.

RESOURCES

Flip chart and pen; a small easel; a shuffled set of cards 1–20 (one card for each child); three hoops; a beanbag; paper and pencils; photocopiable pages 51 (Measuring length), 52 (Measuring with a tape measure) and 53 (Length problems). For practical activities: metre sticks; chalk; decimetre rods/sticks; centimetre rulers; centimetre tape-measures; a tray of small objects that can be measured in cm.

PREPARATION

Put the resources for each activity on a different table. Copy pages 51, 52 and 53 for each child. You might like to consider making enlarged copies for demonstration purposes.

COMPARING HEIGHTS: Copy this chart on to a large sheet of paper for each group to complete:

Comparing heights with a metre stick		
Taller	Shorter	About the same

ESTIMATING AND MEASURING LONG LENGTHS: Copy this chart on to A4 paper and make a copy for each child. Charts like this can be easily prepared on the class computer.

Estimating, measuring and comparing in centimetres			
Object	Estimate in cm	Actual measure in cm	Estimate – Actual more/less/same

Make a copy on A4 paper for each child.

THROW A BEANBAG: Copy the following chart on to a large sheet of paper and attach this to a small easel.

	Throwing a beanbag
Too short	
In the hoop	
Too long	

LEARNING OUTCOMES

ORAL AND MENTAL STARTER
● **Know by heart:** all pairs of numbers with a total of 20.
● Put the larger number first then count on in tens or ones.

MAIN TEACHING ACTIVITIES
● Use mental addition and subtraction to solve simple word problems involving measures, using one or two steps.
● Explain how the problem was solved.
● Use and begin to read the vocabulary related to length.
● **Estimate, measure and compare lengths using standard units** (m, cm); **suggest suitable units and equipment for such measurements**.
● **Read a simple scale to the nearest labelled division, including using a ruler to draw and measure lines to the nearest centimetre,** recording estimates and measurements as '3 and a bit metres long' or 'about 8 centimetres'.

ORAL AND MENTAL STARTER

Select each day to play either 'How to make 20' (see Lesson 15, Unit 4, page 42) or 'All change' adding two numbers 1–20 (see Lesson 11, Unit 4, page 38).

MAIN TEACHING ACTIVITIES

The following activities can be planned as whole class or group work over five days depending on the availability of resources. If activities are planned as group work on a circus basis, it will be necessary to plan a brief introduction to each activity at the beginning of the lesson and to decide which of the activities will require high, medium or low teacher/adult input during each session.

1. COMPARING HEIGHTS: Ask two children to stand up in their places and challenge the class to say which child is taller. Check by asking the selected children to come to the front of the class and stand back to back. Ask two more children to stand up.

Demonstrate how to hold a metre stick upright with one end on the floor. Ask several children to name an object in the room that is taller than the metre stick and write the names of the objects on the chart. Ask a different child to check each object using the metre stick. If the object is in the correct column put a 'tick' beside it. If it is in the wrong column, cross the name out and rewrite it in the correct column.

Tell the group to try this activity again, taking turns to name objects taller than, and then

VOCABULARY

Estimate; compare; nearly; measure; size; about the same as; around; half; height; higher; taller; low; lower; about the same; length; short; shorter; not enough; too much; too little; shortest; long; longer; longest; wide; metres (m); metre stick; decimetres (dm); rods; centimetres (cm); ruler; scale; far; further; furthest; tape measure; near; close; start from.

shorter than, a metre stick. Repeat this again with objects that are about the same height as a metre stick (allow objects that are less than 10cm either way).

2. DECIMETRES TO CENTIMETRES: Demonstrate measuring length in decimetres by inviting a child to lie on the floor and choosing another child to lay decimetre rods alongside him or her. Ask: *How many rods altogether?* Discuss the possibility of 'a bit more' or '½' if whole decimetres rods do not fit exactly. Write a sentence on a displayed sheet to demonstrate the method of recording, for example:

_____ measures [ ]dm long.

Now choose a child to measure a decimetre rod with a ruler to find out how many centimetres are in a decimetre. Explain how they can make their measurements more exact by changing the decimetres to centimetres, counting each rod as a '10'. Ask the children to count the rods that were laid out to measure the child on the floor in tens. This will tell them how long the child is in centimetres. Ask: *How many centimetres altogether?* Write a sentence on a displayed sheet to show the method of recording, for example:

_____ measures [ ]cm long.

Tell the children in the group to work in pairs to measure each other in decimetres. They should write two sentences to show how long each child is in decimetres, then in centimetres. They then change partners until they have each measured five different children. Conclude by discussing the results with the group, comparing their results to find the longest/shortest child, and any children who are the same length.

3. MEASURING WITH STANDARD UNITS: Give each child a copy of photocopiable page 51 and read it aloud with them. Then choose a child to demonstrate one example of each of the first three activities: the width of the classroom; a table; a small book. Complete the first line of each box on the photocopiable sheet together. Then demonstrate how to use a ruler to measure the lines at the bottom of the sheet. If rulers with 'dead ends' are used, point out that the children must measure from the first mark on the ruler and not the edge. Divide the children into small groups and give each group a different part of the task to start. Ask the children working with metre sticks and decimetre rods/sticks to work in pairs. As children finish each activity they can move to another part of the task. Tell them to choose two objects to measure, writing the name of each object and the number of m/dm/cm on the sheet. Check that the children know how to measure with each piece of equipment before they return to their tables to complete the sheet.

4. ESTIMATING AND MEASURING LONG LENGTHS: Choose two children to demonstrate how to measure the length of a table in centimetres using a tape measure (one child holds the tape measure at the starting place, the other holds the tape measure at the ending place and reads the measurement in centimetres).

Give each child a copy of the prepared sheet to look at. Tell them to write the names of five large objects on the sheet and then their estimates of the length of each object in centimetres. They then work in pairs to measure each other's chosen objects to the nearest centimetre with a tape measure, writing the measurement on the sheet. When all the measurements have been carried out, they compare their own estimates with actual measurements and record whether an estimate was more/less/the same.

5. VITAL STATISTICS: Start by demonstrating the activity. Choose two children to measure around each other's chest using a tape measure. Scribe the measurements on an enlarged copy of photocopiable page 52. Ask: *How much is the difference between the two measurements?* Scribe the difference (in cm) on the chart. Next give each child a copy of the photocopiable sheet and ask them to read aloud the different parts of the body they have to measure. Put the children into pairs before sending them back to their tables to carry out the activity. Although this activity focuses on 'difference' rather than particular measurements, it should be approached sensitively.

6. THROW A BEANBAG: Clear some floor space and sit the children in two lines, facing each other with a space in between. Place a hoop between the lines of children. Measure 3m back from the hoop and place the metre stick to mark a 'throwing line'. Place the easel with the prepared chart beside the line. Tell the children to take turns to stand behind the line and try to throw the beanbag into the hoop. When they have thrown the beanbag, they make a tally mark in the correct row on the chart. At the end of the game, ask the children to count up the tally marks and write the number at the end of each row.

7. MEASURING LENGTH PROBLEMS: Give each child a copy of photocopiable page 53 (Length problems). Read through each question on the sheet aloud with the children and ask, for each one: *How will you find the answer? Will you add the numbers together? Take away a number? Count on or count back?* Tell the children that when they return to their tables to complete the sheet they should read through each question and decide how they are going to find the answer before writing anything down. Encourage the children to work mentally where they can and tell them they can write 'sums' or draw pictures to help them if they are unsure.

DIFFERENTIATION

More able: encourage these children to make measurements to the nearest ½cm, to work out differences between pairs of measurements mentally and to compare estimates with actual measurements by working out the differences, writing, for example: '4cm more'. Less able: in 'Vital statistics', if any children are unsure, show them how to work out the difference by finding the number of the smaller measurement on the tape measure, then counting on in ones to the number of the larger measurement.

PLENARY

Review the work done in one of the activities each day, asking individual children to give their results or answers. Use a flip chart to scribe the results given, then discuss these in terms of comparisons. Ask: *Which is the tallest/longest/shortest/the same size?* Display all the resulting charts and completed photocopiable sheets.

LESSON 6 +7 +8

RESOURCES

Teaching charts of the properties of 2-D and 3-D shapes (see **Preparation**) and dotty grids representing geoboard 'pins'; flip chart and pen; sets of 2-D shapes: triangles, circles, rectangles, squares, pentagons, hexagons, octagons, ovals (trapeziums if available); sets of 3-D shapes: cubes, cuboids, pyramids, spheres, cylinders, cones, prisms; 9-pin geoboards; elastic bands (one for each child); photocopiable page 54; paper; pencils; crayons or felt-tipped pens.

PREPARATION

Place the resources related to each activity on different tables.
Copy these grids as teaching charts on to a flip chart or other large sheets of paper:

Properties of 2-D shapes				Properties of 3-D shapes		
Shape	Sides	Corners		Shape	Sides	Corners

Copy four enlarged dotty grids from photocopiable page 54 on to a flip chart page also. Make a copy of photocopiable page 54 for each child.

LEARNING OUTCOMES

ORAL AND MENTAL STARTER
● Say the number that is 10 more or less than any given two-digit number.

MAIN TEACHING ACTIVITY
● **Use the mathematical names for common 3-D and 2-D shapes.**
● **Sort shapes and describe some of their features.**
● Make and describe shapes, pictures and patterns.
● Relate solid shapes to pictures of them.
● Solve mathematical problems or puzzles, recognise simple patterns and relationships, generalise and predict. Suggest extensions by asking 'What if …?' or 'What could I try next?'

VOCABULARY

Shape;
pattern;
triangle;
circle;
rectangle;
square;
diamond;
pentagon;
star; hexagon;
trapezium;
octagon; oval;
sides;
corners;
faces; flat;
curved;
straight; edge;
round;
surface;
hollow; solid;
point; pointed;
make; build;
draw; cube;
cuboid;
pyramid;
sphere; ball;
cone; cylinder;
prism;
geoboard;
elastic bands;
pins; stretch.

ORAL AND MENTAL STARTER

10 MORE 10 LESS: Play this game as in Lesson 5, Unit 2, on page 33.

MAIN TEACHING ACTIVITIES

The following activities may be offered as separate, whole-class lessons or set up as work for different groups on each day so that the children experience a range of activities on a circus basis. Suitable whole class/group introductions are given for each task. You will need to introduce or revise the relevant teaching points each day.

At the start of this unit, and on subsequent days if necessary, sit the children in a semicircle facing the 'Properties of 2-D shapes' teaching chart. Write the name of each shape in the first column and point to different names on the chart for the children to read aloud together. Hold up one of each shape. Ask the children to say the name of the shape. Then give each child a 2-D shape and ask them in turn to name the shape. Repeat this using 3-D shapes and the other teaching chart.

1. PROPERTIES OF 2-D SHAPES: Point to the name of the first shape on the teaching chart of 2-D shapes. Ask all children holding that shape to stand up and count how many sides the shape has. Choose a child to say and write the number in the 'Sides' column. When these children have sat down ask children holding the second shape to stand up, and so on. Repeat the activity, asking the children to count the corners of the shapes this time. Tell the children they are to use 2-D shapes to make a shape design, pattern or picture, then draw and colour a picture of their work on paper. When they have finished their drawings, ask them to count and record the number of different shapes they used beside their picture, for example: triangles 4. (Remind the children to look at the chart if they have difficulty spelling the names of shapes.)

2. PROPERTIES OF 3-D SHAPES: Repeat the first activity using the 3-D shapes chart. The children then make and draw pictures of their 3-D models, finally counting the number of shapes used.

3. MAKING SHAPES WITH 9-PIN GEOBOARDS: Sit the children facing the enlarged dotty grids on the flip chart and give each child a geoboard and an elastic band. Demonstrate how to use the elastic band with the geoboard to make a shape. Then, using the flip chart enlargement, show the children how to copy the shape on to a dotty grid. Repeat this by asking the children to make a shape on their own geoboards, then choose a child to draw the shape he or she has made on a grid on the flip chart. Repeat this two more times.

Next, show the children a copy of photocopiable page 54 and tell them that they are to make different shapes on their geoboards and copy each shape on to the dotty grids. When the sheets are completed, ask the children to colour the shapes, count how many sides each shape has, then write the number of sides in the box underneath each grid. Ask them to write the names of any shapes they know beside the boxes.

DIFFERENTIATION

For 'Making shapes with 9-pin geoboards':
More able: children who finish quickly can be given a fresh sheet to make different shapes with five sides.
Less able: ask children to make different shapes on their geoboards with four sides.

PLENARY

Review the work from one activity each day. For the two 'Properties of shapes' activities, select a few children to show their work to the group. Then go through the names of the shapes on the chart, asking children to stand up if they used that shape in their design/pattern/picture and finding out how many of that shape each child used. For the geoboard activity, ask: *Who made a shape with three sides? What are shapes with three sides called? Shapes with four sides? Shapes with four equal sides?* Find out who made the shape with the most sides.

Measuring length

Choose three objects to measure.

Using a metre stick.

1. A _____ measures [ ] metres long.	
2. A _____ measures [ ] metres long.	
3. A _____ measures [ ] metres long.	

Using decimetre rods.

1. A _____ measures [ ] decimetres long.	
2. A _____ measures [ ] decimetres long.	
3. A _____ measures [ ] decimetres long.	

Using a centimetre ruler.

1. A _____ measures [ ] centimetres long.	
2. A _____ measures [ ] centimetres long.	
3. A _____ measures [ ] centimetres long.	

Measure these lines with a centimetre ruler.

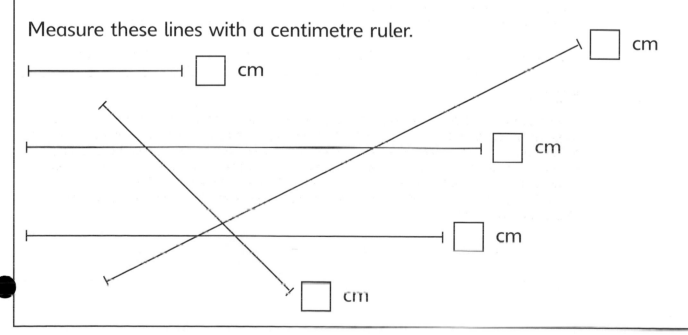

Name

Measuring with a tape measure

Work with
a friend.

	Me	My friend	Difference in cm
Around the waist	cm	cm	cm
Around the head			
Around the wrist			
Length of foot			
Length of arm			
Length of hand			
Around the chest			
Around the leg			
Around the ankle			
Across the back			
Across the chest			

Name

 **Length problems**

Two lines measure 8cm and 7cm.

How many centimetres altogether?

☐ cm

A bookcase has three shelves.
Each shelf is 2m long.

How many metres of shelf altogether?

☐ m

What is:
5cm add 9cm?

☐ cm

15cm subtract 9cm?

☐ cm

A cat is 30cm tall.
A dog is 10cm taller.

How tall is the dog?

☐ cm

A 20cm ribbon is cut into two halves.

How long is one half?

☐ cm

A ruler is 25cm long.
A crayon is 10cm shorter.

How long is the crayon?

☐ cm

A child throws a beanbag:
1st throw = 3 metres
2nd throw = 5 metres.

What is the difference between the two throws?

☐ m

Three crayons measure 6cm, 8cm and 4cm.

How many centimetres altogether?

☐ cm

Making shapes using 9-pin geoboards

UNIT 7: Assess & Review

Choose from the following activities. During the group activities, some of the children can complete assessment worksheets 1a and 1b which assess their skills with reading and writing numbers, with counting, and with addition while others work with you on practical tasks. The specific assessment criteria for the assessment sheets can be found at the bottom of each sheet.

RESOURCES

Sets of numeral cards 1–10; number squares and small cubes; sets of three 1–6 dice; centimetre rulers; tape measures and metre sticks; sets of 2-D and 3-D shapes; pencils and paper; copies of assessment worksheets 1a and 1b, photocopiable page 28 (Two-way counts) and prepared sheets for each child (see **Preparation** below); sorting hoops.

PREPARATION

Copy the following charts on to two sheets of A4 paper. Make a copy of both charts for each child. Such charts are easily produced on the class computer.

Properties of 2-D shapes		
Shape	Sides	Corners

Properties of 3-D shapes		
Shape	Sides	Corners

ORAL AND MENTAL STARTER

ASSESSMENT

● Can the children: Count, read, write and order whole numbers to at least 100? Describe and extend simple number sequences: counting on or back in ones or tens from any two-digit number?

● Do the children: Know what each digit in a two-digit number represents, including 0 as a place holder? Know by heart: all addition and subtraction facts for each number to at least 10?

COUNTING: Count on or back in ones or tens from any two-digit number by playing appropriate 'My number… your number' games and repeating the 'number square and cube' games: Count on 1 or 10/Count back 1 or 10, with copies of photocopiable page 28.

ADDITION: Repeat the 'All change' games with numbers 1–10 and sorting hoops.

GROUP ACTIVITIES

ASSESSMENT

● Can the children: Use knowledge that addition can be done in any order to do mental calculations more efficiently? Estimate, measure and compare lengths, masses and capacities, using standard units; suggest suitable units and equipment for such measurements? Read a simple scale to the nearest labelled division, including using a ruler to draw and measure lines to the nearest centimetre? Use the mathematical names for common 3-D and 2-D shapes; sort shapes and describe some of their features?

ADDITION: Carry out an 'Addition of three numbers' game with three dice. The children throw the dice and record their addition statements on paper, writing the numbers in the easiest order to do the calculation. Check whether children are using mental strategies or simply counting the spots to find the total.

MEASURES: Ask the children, working in pairs, to measure the length of three short and three long items, using suitable units and equipment for each item. They then record their answers in a sentence, for example:

A crayon measures 5 and a bit centimetres long.

The piano measures 2 and a bit metres long.

Ask them to measure and draw lines of various given lengths in centimetres such as 15 cm or 8 cm. Check that children are selecting the appropriate equipment to carry out the measuring (cm ruler or metre stick) and whether their measurements are reasonably accurate.

SHAPES: Give each child a copy of each of the prepared sheets. Ask them to sort and name, using their mathematical names, some common 2-D and 3-D shapes. They should then describe some of their features by completing the chart. Check whether children have named and described the properties of each shape correctly.

Assessment sheet 1a

Write these numbers:

twenty-one → ☐   nineteen → ☐

forty-five → ☐   fifty-seven → ☐

seventy-eight → ☐   eighty → ☐

Write these numbers in words:

25 → ☐   12 → ☐

62 → ☐   99 → ☐

38 → ☐   76 → ☐

Write these numbers as tens and units:

53 →

8 →

81 →

18 →

Count on in tens:

6 → ☐ → ☐ → ☐ → ☐ → ☐ → ☐

Count back in tens:

93 → ☐ → ☐ → ☐ → ☐ → ☐ → ☐

- Count, read, write and order whole numbers to at least 100.
- Know what each digit in a two-digit number represents, including 0 as a place holder.
- Describe and extend simple number sequences: count on or back in ones or tens, starting from any two-digit number.

UNIT 7

Assessment sheet 1b

Make up to 10:

$6 + \triangle = 10$ $\triangle + 5 = 10$ $10 + \triangle = 10$

$3 + \triangle = 10$ $\triangle + 8 = 10$ $\triangle + 9 = 10$

Double these numbers:

$5 \rightarrow \boxed{}$ $4 \rightarrow \boxed{}$ $10 \rightarrow \boxed{}$

$9 \rightarrow \boxed{}$ $8 \rightarrow \boxed{}$ $7 \rightarrow \boxed{}$

$3 \rightarrow \boxed{}$ $6 \rightarrow \boxed{}$ $2 \rightarrow \boxed{}$

Subtract from 10:

$10 - 7 = \boxed{}$ $10 - 6 = \boxed{}$

$10 - 5 = \boxed{}$ $10 - 8 = \boxed{}$

$10 - 2 = \boxed{}$ $10 - 9 = \boxed{}$

Add these numbers:

$3 + 6 + 5 = \boxed{}$ $5 + 4 + 3 = \boxed{}$

$2 + 7 + 9 = \boxed{}$ $1 + 8 + 7 = \boxed{}$

$4 + 3 + 7 = \boxed{}$ $6 + 6 + 6 = \boxed{}$

● Know by heart: all addition and subtraction facts for each number to at least 10.
● Use knowledge that addition can be done in any order to do mental calculations more efficiently.

UNIT 8

ORGANISATION (5 LESSONS)

	LEARNING OUTCOMES	ORAL AND MENTAL STARTER	MAIN TEACHING ACTIVITY	PLENARY
LESSON 1	● **Describe and extend simple number sequences:** count on in twos from and back to zero or any small number.	COUNTING ON AND BACK IN ONES AND TENS.	COUNTING ON AND BACK IN TWOS.	COUNTING ON AND BACK IN TWOS.
LESSON 2	● **Recognise odd and even numbers** to at least 30. ● Investigate a general statement about familiar numbers by finding examples that satisfy it.	COUNTING ON AND BACK IN TWOS.	ODD AND EVEN.	ODD OR EVEN NUMBER?: Using 1–30 cards.
LESSON 3	● **Describe and extend simple number sequences.**	COUNTING ON AND BACK IN TENS.	Missing and next number sequences.	Reviewing work from the Main teaching activity.
LESSON 4	● Solve mathematical puzzles, recognise simple patterns and relationships, generalise and predict. Suggest extensions. ● **Explain how a problem was solved** orally and, where appropriate, in writing.	COUNTING ON AND BACK IN TWOS.	FINDING DIFFERENT WAYS TO SCORE 12 WITH THREE DICE.	Reviewing work from the Main teaching activity.
LESSON 5	● Solve mathematical puzzles, recognise simple patterns and relationships, generalise and predict. Suggest extensions by asking 'What if …?' or ' What could I try next?' ● **Explain how a problem was solved** orally and, where appropriate, in writing.	MAKE 20. TAKE FROM 20.	Working on magic square problems.	Reviewing work from the Main teaching activity.

ORAL AND MENTAL SKILLS Describe and extend simple number sequences; count on or back in ones or tens, starting from any two-digit number; count on in twos from and back to zero or any small number. **Know by heart:** all pairs of number with a total of 20.

In Unit 8 Lessons 1 and 2 are given in full, while Lessons 3, 4 and 5 are given as grids.

RESOURCES

0–99 Number square teaching chart and individual 0–99 (or 0-49) number squares from photocopiable page 13; small cubes; copies of photocopiable pages 13 (0–99 Number square) and 28 (Two-way counts); a small easel; marker pen; pencils; crayons or pens.

PREPARATION

Copy page 13 at least once for each child, and page 28 for more able children.

LEARNING OUTCOMES

ORAL AND MENTAL STARTER
● **Describe and extend simple number sequences: count on or back in ones or tens, starting from any two-digit number.**

MAIN TEACHING ACTIVITY
● Count on in twos from and back to zero or any small number.

ORAL AND MENTAL STARTER

COUNTING ON AND BACK IN ONES AND TENS: Display the 0–99 Number square teaching chart on a small easel. Sit the children around it. Ask them to recite counting back from 30 in ones and back from 100 in tens. Point to a number on the chart. Ask the children to count on in tens from this number to the number nearest to 100, for example 23, 33..., 93. Do this a few times, then change to counting back in tens to the nearest number to 0.

MAIN TEACHING ACTIVITY

COUNTING ON AND BACK IN TWOS: Use the teaching chart to explain and demonstrate colouring the pattern of 'Count on 2'. Start from 0 and record the pattern as a number sequence underneath the square, for example 0 → 2 → 4...: *What number will be coloured after 4? After 6?* Give each child a copy of page 13. Tell the children to copy the work on the chart, then continue colouring and writing the pattern as far as possible.

DIFFERENTIATION

More able: give these children an individual number square and a cube with a copy of photocopiable page 28 to play the number square and cube game 'Counting on/back', but with the rule 'Count on and back 2' (See Lesson 3, Unit 1 of this term, page 26).
Less able: give these children a 0–49 number rectangle with which to carry out the activity. Make 0–49 number rectangles from 0–99 number squares cut off after the 40–49 row.

PLENARY

COUNTING ON AND COUNT BACK IN TWOS: Play a game where you say a number and choose a child to say the 'count on 2' number each time. Repeat this, changing the rule to 'count back 2'.

RESOURCES

Teaching chart (see **Preparation**) and individual A4 copies; flip chart and pen; sets of dominoes; pencils; a set of shuffled numeral cards 1–30 (one card for each child); interlocking cubes.

PREPARATION

Make a teaching chart by copying the following on to a flip chart sheet. Also make a copy on A4 paper and copy one for each child.

Odd	Even

LEARNING OUTCOMES

ORAL AND MENTAL STARTER
● Count on in twos from or back to zero or any small number.

MAIN TEACHING ACTIVITY
● **Recognise odd and even numbers** to at least 30.
● Investigate a general statement about familiar numbers by finding examples that satisfy it.

ORAL AND MENTAL STARTER

COUNTING ON AND BACK IN TWOS: Stand the children in a circle. Ask them to recite counting in twos from 0–30, then back from 30–0; then 1–29, and back from 29–1. Select a child to start a count in twos around the circle from 0. If someone says an incorrect number, he or she sits down and the count passes to the next child. Continue as far as the children left standing can count. Ask any seated children to stand again and repeat.

MAIN TEACHING ACTIVITY

ODD AND EVEN: Sit the children in a semicircle facing the teaching chart. To demonstrate odd and even numbers, ask two children to stand in front of the group and hold hands. Explain that all even numbers have to be 'pair' numbers or a 'number in the 2 family'. Write 2 in the Even column. Ask another child to stand beside the 'pair': *How many now?* (3). Explain that numbers that cannot be paired are called 'odd numbers' because there is an odd one left over. Write 3 in the Odd column. Ask a fourth child to stand, and again ask for the number (4). Encourage the children to say whether the number is odd or even (can be paired), then write 4 in the Even column. Invite a fifth child to stand, and so on.

Next, tell the children they are going to carry out an odd and even number activity with dominoes. Show them a copy of the prepared sheet. Tell them to work in groups and spread out their dominoes face down in the middle of the table. They must pick up one domino each time, add the spots and decide whether the total is odd or even. Each child should draw the domino and write the total beside it in the correct column on the sheet.

Odd	Even
 5	

DIFFERENTIATION

More able: discuss the status of the 'double blank'. Zero is not a number, therefore it cannot be odd or even. These children could also be given a fresh sheet to try totalling the spots on two dominoes each time and deciding whether the number is odd or even.
Less able: encourage the children to work out easier numbers in their heads, but if they need help, provide 12 interlocking cubes. They can match the spots on each domino with cubes to make a stick, then split the stick into twos to see if the number is odd or even.

PLENARY

ODD OR EVEN NUMBER? Give each child a card from a shuffled set of 1–30. Ask the children to stand in a circle and, in turn, say the number on their card and whether it is odd or even. If they answer correctly, they can sit down. At the end of the round, give any child still standing another try. Collect in the cards, shuffle them and play again.

LESSON 3

RESOURCES	A copy of photocopiable page 63 (Number sequences) for each child; 0–99 number squares; pencils.
LEARNING OUTCOMES	**ORAL AND MENTAL STARTER** and **MAIN TEACHING ACTIVITY** ● **Describe and extend simple number sequences.**
ORAL AND MENTAL STARTER	COUNTING ON AND BACK IN TENS. (See Lesson 1, page 60.)
MAIN TEACHING ACTIVITY	Give each child a copy of the photocopiable sheet. Ask about each 'missing number' sequence: *What is the counting pattern? What do you have to do?* Ask about each 'next number' sequence: *What does each arrow ask you to do?* Make sure the children understand what they have to do before sending them to their tables to carry out the task.
DIFFERENTIATION	More able: give each child a set of cards 1–10 and ask them to select a card each time to start a number sequence and choose their own rule – for example 'counting in twos – and write the number sequence as far as they can on their sheet. Less able: provide 0–99 number squares for children who require additional support.
PLENARY	Review the work in the **Main teaching activity** by going through each sequence on the board, inviting children to give their responses and explain their methods.

LESSON 4

RESOURCES	One set of three spotted dice (for each pair of children); paper and pencils; flip chart and pen; interlocking cubes.
LEARNING OUTCOMES	**ORAL AND MENTAL STARTER** ● **Describe and extend simple number sequences.** **MAIN TEACHING ACTIVITY** ● Solve mathematical puzzles, recognise simple patterns and relationships, generalise and predict. Suggest extensions. ● **Explain how a problem was solved** orally and, where appropriate, in writing.
ORAL AND MENTAL STARTER	COUNTING ON AND BACK IN TWOS: (see Lesson 1, on page 60).
MAIN TEACHING ACTIVITY	FINDING DIFFERENT WAYS TO SCORE 12 WITH THREE DICE: Children work in pairs and individually record solutions as spotted dice drawings, writing the addition sum beside each solution: $5 + 5 + 2 = 12$
DIFFERENTIATION	More able: try ways to score 15 with four dice. Less able: give children a stick of 12 interlocking cubes. Ask them to find different ways to break the stick into three pieces, count the cubes in each piece and write an addition sum each time.
PLENARY	Invite individual children to draw a solution to the main activity on a flip chart. Discuss how they knew/found out there were 12 spots in all.

LESSON 5

RESOURCES	Teaching chart of nine-square (3 × 3) grid with numbers 1, 1, 1, 2, 2, 2, 3, 3, 3 written underneath; a shuffled set of numeral cards 1–20 (one card for each child); a flip chart or small easel; sheets of plain and 2cm squared paper and pencils; sets of numbered cards 1, 1, 1, 2, 2, 2, 3, 3, 3.
LEARNING OUTCOMES	**ORAL AND MENTAL STARTER** ● **Know by heart:** all pairs of numbers with a total of 20. **MAIN TEACHING ACTIVITY** ● Solve mathematical puzzles, recognise simple patterns and relationships, generalise and predict. Suggest extensions by asking 'What if …?' or ' What could I try next?' ● **Explain how a problem was solved** orally and, where appropriate, in writing.
ORAL AND MENTAL STARTER	MAKE 20: Give each child a card. Ask the children, round the circle to 'make 20' by adding to the number on their card, saying, for example: '9 add 11 equals 20'. Repeat the game with the rule 'take from 20' where the children subtract the number on their card from 20.
MAIN TEACHING ACTIVITY	MAGIC SQUARE: Tell them they are going to find a way to solve a magic puzzle. Explain the task, using the teaching chart. The children should draw a nine-square grid on their squared paper. Then work out where to place each number shown in one of the nine squares so that all lines — across, down and diagonal — add up to the magic number '6'. They can draw as many grids as they need to try out their ideas until they find a solution. Let the children choose whether to work alone or with a partner.
DIFFERENTIATION	More able: invite them to try the same problem with: 2, 2, 2, 3, 3, 3, 4, 4, 4 to give the magic number '9'; then 3, 3, 3, 4, 4, 4, 5, 5, 5 to give the magic number '12', and so on. Can they explain the rule? Less able: let the children work in pairs. Give each pair a set of cards, 1, 1, 1, 2, 2, 2, 3, 3, 3 so they can physically move the numbers around. If they require help, give them this clue: *Sort the two diagonal lines first.*
PLENARY	Ask the children to demonstrate using grids on the flip chart and explain how they solved the Magic square problem. Can they tell you a special clue to help anyone solve the problem?

Number sequences

Complete these:

1		3		5			8		

20	18			10				

	20	30			70		

90			50				0

3	13			43			73	

$6 \xrightarrow{+10} \bigcirc \xrightarrow{+10} \bigcirc \xrightarrow{+10} \bigcirc \xrightarrow{+10} \bigcirc$

$84 \xrightarrow{-10} \bigcirc \xrightarrow{-10} \bigcirc \xrightarrow{-10} \bigcirc \xrightarrow{-10} \bigcirc$

$2 \xrightarrow{+10} \bigcirc \xrightarrow{+1} \bigcirc \xrightarrow{+10} \bigcirc \xrightarrow{+1} \bigcirc$

$93 \xrightarrow{-10} \bigcirc \xrightarrow{-1} \bigcirc \xrightarrow{-10} \bigcirc \xrightarrow{-1} \bigcirc$

$5 \xrightarrow{+2} \bigcirc \xrightarrow{+10} \bigcirc \xrightarrow{+2} \bigcirc \xrightarrow{+10} \bigcirc$

UNIT 9

ORGANISATION (5 LESSONS)

LEARNING OUTCOMES	ORAL AND MENTAL STARTER	MAIN TEACHING ACTIVITY	PLENARY
LESSON 1 • **Know what each digit in a two-digit number represents, including 0 as a place holder.** • Round numbers less than 100 to the nearest 10.	ADD 10.	TO THE NEAREST TEN: Rounding single- and two-digit numbers.	FIND THE NUMBER (2).
LESSON 2 • Use and begin to read the vocabulary of comparing and ordering numbers, including ordinal numbers to 100.	TO THE NEAREST 10.	ORDERING ORDINAL AND CARDINAL NUMBERS: Ordinal numbers to 30.	TO THE NEAREST 10.
LESSON 3 • **Use knowledge that addition can be done in any order to do mental calculations more efficiently.** For example: add three small numbers by putting the largest number first and/or find a pair totalling 10; partition additions into tens and units, then recombine.	ALL CHANGE: With 10–20.	ADDING TRIOS.	ALL CHANGE: With three numbers 1–20.
LESSON 4 • Recognise all coins and begin to use £.p notation for money. • Find totals,... and work out which coins to pay. • Add three small numbers by putting the largest number first and/or find a pair totalling 10. • Use mental addition and subtraction to solve simple word problems involving money, using one or two steps.	ADDITION OF TWO COINS: with money cards.	ADDITION OF THREE COINS.	Reviewing the work of the Main teaching activity.
LESSON 5 • Find totals, give change and work out which coins to pay. • Add three small numbers by putting the largest number first and/or find a pair totalling 10.	ALL CHANGE: Adding three numbers 1–20.	SPEND AND CHANGE FROM 50p.	SAVING UP 50p PROBLEMS.

ORAL AND MENTAL SKILLS   Say the number that is 10 more or less than any given two-digit number. Round numbers less than 100 to the nearest 10. **Use knowledge that addition can be done in any order to do mental calculations more efficiently.** For example: add three small numbers by putting the largest number first and/or find a pair totalling 10; partition additions into tens and units, then recombine. Recognise all coins. Find totals,... and work out which coins to pay.

In Unit 9, Lessons 1, 3, 4 and 5 are given in full. Lesson 2 is provided in grid form.

RESOURCES

0–99 Number square teaching chart and a 0–99 number square for each child (photocopiable page 13); small cubes; paper and pencils.

PREPARATION

Place individual number squares, cubes, paper and pencils on each table.

LEARNING OUTCOMES

ORAL AND MENTAL STARTER
● Say the number that is 10 more or less than any given two-digit number.

MAIN TEACHING ACTIVITY
● **Know what each digit in a two-digit number represents, including 0 as a place holder.**
● Round numbers less than 100 to the nearest 10.

VOCABULARY

Numbers 1–100; round; round to the nearest ten; tens and units; rule; calculate; mental calculation; describe the rule; number square; number rectangle; cube.

ORAL AND MENTAL STARTER

ADD 10: Say a number between 1 and 100 and choose one of the children to say the number that is 10 more: *My number is 45; Luke, what is your number?* Try '10 less' too.

MAIN TEACHING ACTIVITY

TO THE NEAREST 10: Sit the children in a semicircle facing the teaching chart. Remind them of their previous work (Lesson 15, Unit 4 on page 42) on approximating: *What does 'about 36' mean?* Explain and demonstrate how any two-digit number ending in 1–4 is rounded down to the nearest 10 below, for example 43 → 40. Numbers ending in 5–9 (numbers 5 and above) are rounded up to the nearest 10, for example 45 → 50; 47 → 50. So 36 could be 'about 40' with this new rule. Point to numbers on the chart and encourage the children, in turn, to say, for example: '34 rounded to the nearest 10 is 30'.

Next tell the children they will be playing a number square and cube game. This time they will throw the cube on to the square, write down the number it lands on, then round the number to the nearest 10, for example: 78 → 80. Challenge the children to complete more than 20 examples. Check that the children understand what they have to do.

DIFFERENTIATION

More able: challenge the children to complete more than 30 examples.
Less able: give children a 0–49 number rectangle to carry out the activity.

PLENARY

FIND THE NUMBER (2): Sit the children facing the Number square teaching chart. Say a number as tens and units, for example: *5 tens and 6 units,* and ask each child in turn to come to the chart and point to the number. Verify with the group that he or she is correct. Extend this to rounding the numbers to the nearest 10, if the children seem confident.

LESSON 2

RESOURCES	0–99 Number square teaching chart (photocopiable page 13); sets of ordinal number cards 1st–30th or more; individual number squares; small cubes; pencils and paper.
LEARNING OUTCOMES	**ORAL AND MENTAL STARTER** ● Round numbers less than 100 to the nearest 10. **MAIN TEACHING ACTIVITY** ● Use and begin to read the vocabulary of comparing and ordering numbers, including ordinal numbers to 100.
ORAL AND MENTAL STARTER	ROUNDING NUMBERS: Sit children facing the chart. Point to a number and choose a child to round the number to the nearest 10. Remind them of the rule: *Numbers ending in 1–4 are rounded down to the tens number below, numbers ending in 5–9 are rounded up to the tens number above.* Repeat.
MAIN TEACHING ACTIVITY	ORDERING ORDINAL AND CARDINAL NUMBERS: Sit the children in a circle. Give out the ordinal number cards in order to each child in the circle. Say: *Will the child holding the fourth card stand up?* Repeat this until all the children are standing. Collect in cards, and hand them out again to repeat the process starting with a different child. After the second round, ask children to say the numbers in order round the circle, 1st to 30th. Give each group a shuffled set of ordinal number cards. One child in each group deals out the set. Children take turns to lay a card in a line in order, starting with the child holding the '1st' card (if the next child does not have '2nd' play passes to the third child). First child to put down all his or her cards is the winner. Tell the children to play the game a few times.
DIFFERENTIATION	More able: play a number square and cube game where children throw a cube on to a square and write the number it lands on, followed by that number in ordinal form, for example 23 → 23rd. Less able: use ordinal cards 1st–10th or 1st–20th for the group game.
PLENARY	Repeat 'To the nearest 10' from Lesson 1, above.

LESSON 3

RESOURCES

Flip chart and pen; two different-coloured sorting hoops; sets of numeral cards 1–20 and 10–20 (one card for each child); photocopiable page 69 (Trios); pencils.

PREPARATION

Make a copy of page 69 for each child. Lay a set of shuffled numeral cards 1–20 in two lines of ten in the middle of each table together with copies of page 69, and pencils.

LEARNING OUTCOMES

ORAL AND MENTAL STARTER

● **Use knowledge that addition can be done in any order to do calculations more efficiently.** For example: partition additions into tens and units, then recombine.

MAIN TEACHING ACTIVITY

● **Use knowledge that addition can be done in any order to do calculations more efficiently.** For example: add three small numbers by putting the largest number first and/ or find a pair totalling 10; partition additions into tens and units, then recombine.

ORAL AND MENTAL STARTER

ALL CHANGE: Play with two hoops and numbers 10–20 (see Lesson 11, Unit 4, page 38).

MAIN TEACHING ACTIVITY

ADDING TRIOS: Sit the children around the flip chart. Give each child a card from the set of 1–20. Tell the children they are going to add three numbers between 1 and 20. Ask three children to stand facing the group, hold up their cards and say the numbers. Scribe the numbers on the flip chart as a sum in the order the children are standing. Ask the class what order the numbers should be written in to find the total most easily: *What number should come first? Second? Last?* Rewrite the sum in the new order and ask the children to find the total. Discuss how they did this. Repeat this a few times.

Next tell the children they are going to add three numbers using the 1–20 cards on their tables. Show them a copy of page 69. Tell them to choose three different numbers, including one 'teens' number, then write these numbers in the squares of a trio diagram and find the total. Tell them to start with the largest number then count on the other numbers in ones, and write the answer in the centre of the diagram. Demonstrate the method of recording on the chart. When they finish, tell them to exchange sheets with a partner and mark each other's work.

DIFFERENTIATION

More able: challenge them to use two 'teens' number cards and the mental strategy of partitioning numbers into tens and units, writing 'method workings' on the sheet.
Less able: provide a set of shuffled numeral cards 1–10, or alternatively two rows of 1–5.

PLENARY

Play 'All change' (Lesson 11, Unit 4, on page 38) with three hoops and numbers 1–20.

VOCABULARY

Numbers 1–30; add; plus; total; equals; makes; sum; altogether; one-digit, two-digit numbers; re-arrange; change round; first, second; teens numbers; tens and units; numeral cards.

13

18

2   **3**

LESSON 4

RESOURCES

Flip chart and pen, photocopiable pages 15 (Coin cards) and 69 (Trios); sets of three money dice or cubes (two dice marked 1p, 2p, 5p, 10p, 20p, 50p, and one dice marked 50p, 50p, £1.00, £1.00, £2.00, £2.00); small tubs (for throwing dice); paper and pencils.

PREPARATION

Make three photocopies of page 15 (Coin cards) on A4 card, laminate these and cut them into individual cards (48 cards). Secure each set with a rubber band.

Make a copy of photocopiable page 69 (Trios) for each child. Place a copy of the sheet, sets of dice, tubs and pencils on each table.

LEARNING OUTCOMES

ORAL AND MENTAL STARTER
● Find totals,... and work out which coins to pay.

MAIN TEACHING ACTIVITY
● Recognise all coins and begin to use £.p notation for money.
● Find totals, ... and work out which coins to pay.
● Add three small numbers by putting the largest number first and/or find a pair totalling 10.
● Use mental addition and subtraction to solve simple word problems involving money, using one or two steps.

VOCABULARY

Names of coins 1p to £2.00; add; plus; subtract; equals; total; makes; pound; £1.00; rearrange; change round; best way; money dice; trio diagram.

ORAL AND MENTAL STARTER

ADDITION OF TWO COINS: Give each child in the circle a card from a shuffled set of coin cards: 1p, 2p, 5p, 10p, 20p, 50p. Ask two children to stand in front of the group and show their cards, then choose a third child to say the total money. Repeat this a few times.

MAIN TEACHING ACTIVITY

ADDITION OF THREE COINS: Use a shuffled set of coin cards (1p, 2p, 5p, 10p, 20p, 50p, £1.00, £2.00). Sit the children in a semicircle facing the flip chart and give one card to each child. Ask them, in turn, to name the coin on their card. Remind them of £.p notation for amounts £1.00 and above. Ask three children to stand at the front in a line to show and say the name of the coin on their cards. Write the amounts as an addition sum on the flip chart in the order the children are standing. Ask the class to find the total by the easiest method. Choose one child to say the total and describe the method she or he used. Scribe this method on the flip chart, then ask if any child used a different method and invite others to write their methods on the flip chart. Choose three more children to stand in a line to repeat this activity.

Next, tell the children that they are going to play a game with three money dice. Show the children that two of the dice have the amounts 1p, 2p, 5p, 10p, 20p and 50p while the third dice has 50p, £1.00 and £2.00. Show them a copy of photocopiable page 69 and explain the rules of the game:
● Work in pairs, taking turns to throw the dice in a tub.
● Both write the amounts on the dice in a trio diagram (as in Lesson 3 on page 66).
● Find the total amount using the easiest method and write the total in the centre of the diagram each time, for example: The first pair of children to complete their sheets are the winners.

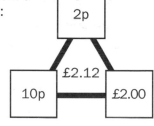

DIFFERENTIATION

More able: pairs of children who finish the sheet quickly could be given a sheet of paper and an extra dice marked 1p, 2p, 5p, 10p, 20p and 50p. Tell the children to throw four dice each time and record the amounts shown as a sum on their sheet, placing the amounts in the easiest order to find the total.
Less able: give children two money dice or two sets of coin cards instead of three and a sheet of paper. Encourage them to record a sum, writing the numbers in the easiest order to find the total (putting the larger number first).

PLENARY

Review the work of the **Main teaching activity** by drawing some trio diagrams on a flip chart. Ask the children to sit with their completed sheets in front of the chart and invite pairs of children to copy one of their completed trios on to a diagram on the chart. They should then tell the group how they found the total.

RESOURCES

Shuffled set of numeral cards 1–20 (one card for each child); three sorting hoops; flip chart and pen; sets of coin cards 1p, 2p, 5p, 10p, 20p (photocopiable page 15) (one for each child); sets of coins: 1p, 2p, 5p, 10p, 20p, 50p; sets of three money dice: 1p, 2p, 5p, 10p, 10p, 20p for each group; photocopiable page 70 (Spend and change from 50p); money dice: 1p, 2p, 5p, 1p, 2p, 5p; a tray.

PREPARATION

Photocopy page 70 for each child. Also make an enlarged copy or draw the chart on page 70 on the flip chart or a large sheet of paper headed 'Spend and change from 50p'.

LEARNING OUTCOMES

ORAL AND MENTAL STARTER

● Add three small numbers by putting the largest number first and/or find a pair totalling 10.

MAIN TEACHING ACTIVITY

● Add three small numbers by putting the largest number first and/or find a pair totalling 10.
● Use mental addition and subtraction to solve simple word problems involving money, using one or two steps.
● Find totals, give change, and work out which coins to pay.

ORAL AND MENTAL STARTER

ALL CHANGE: Play with three hoops and numbers 1–20 (see Lesson 11, Unit 4, page 38).

MAIN TEACHING ACTIVITY

SPEND AND CHANGE FROM 50P: Sit the children in a semicircle facing the flip chart. Tell them they are going to add three coins together and find the change from 50p. Shuffle the coin cards (1p, 2p, 5p, 10p, 20p) and give each child a card. Ask three children to stand up and say the name of the coin on their cards. Ask the class to find the total. Discuss the easiest method. Sketch this method as coins onto the chart and write in the total (see example). Next, ask the group to work out the change from 50p, then how the change could be given in coins. Choose a child to say the total change and possible coins. Draw this on the chart too. Repeat this with three different children. Three 20p cards may be shown together. If this happens, discuss the principle of having a set amount to spend (50p). Suggest that it is best not to spend more than you have to avoid borrowing.

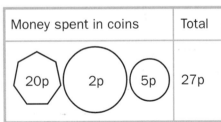

Money spent in coins	Total
20p 2p 5p	27p

Next show the children a copy of page 70. Tell them to work in pairs, taking turns to throw the three money dice to find out which coins are spent each time. They should draw round coins onto the sheet in the easiest order for finding the total and write it in. Then they must work out how much change would be given from 50p, writing in the total change and drawing possible coins in the Change column, again in the easiest order for finding the total. Check that the children know what to do before they return to their tables.

DIFFERENTIATION

More able: play 'First to 50p'. Provide a tray of coins. Children take turns to throw a dice marked 1p, 1p, 2p, 2p, 5p, 5p and take the coin thrown. They may change each 10p collected in coins for a 10p coin. The first child to change five 10p coins for a 50p wins.
Less able: children use two dice instead of three.

PLENARY

SAVING UP 50p PROBLEMS: Ask oral questions, such as: *Tom has 30p. How much more money does he need to save? Vicky has 48p. How much more does she need to save?*

VOCABULARY

Names of coins 1p–50p; numbers 1–50; total amount; cost; pay; change; saving up; spend; spent; add; subtract; count on; difference; coins and coin cards; draw round.

Name

Trios

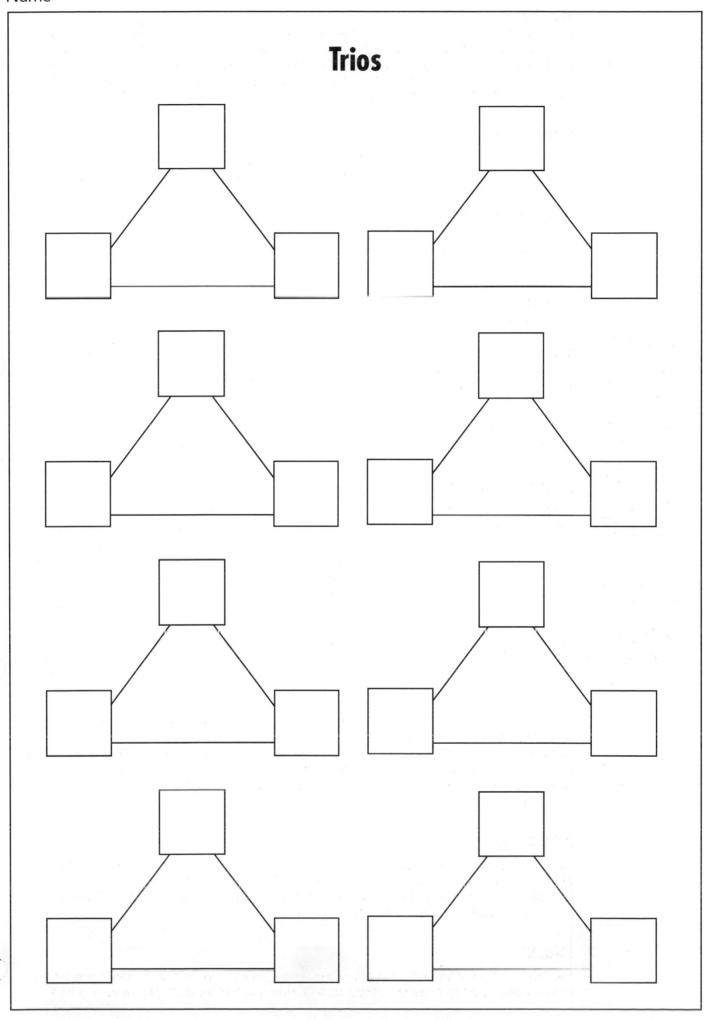

Spend and change from ___

Money spent in coins	Total	Change in coins	Total change

UNITS 10-11

ORGANISATION (10 LESSONS)

	LEARNING OUTCOMES	ORAL AND MENTAL STARTER	MAIN TEACHING ACTIVITY	PLENARY
LESSON 1	● **Understand the operation of multiplication as repeated addition or as describing an array.** ● Use and begin to read the related vocabulary.	COUNTING IN TWOS.	MULTIPLES OF 2: Grouping into twos, including counting 2p coins.	Reviewing the work done in the Main teaching activity.
LESSON 2	● **Understand the operation of multiplication as repeated addition or as describing an array.** ● Use and begin to read the related vocabulary.	COUNTING IN TENS.	MULTIPLES OF 10.	MULTIPLES OF 10 QUESTIONS: Asking oral questions.
LESSON 3	● Begin to understand division as sharing. ● Use and begin to read the related vocabulary.	2× AND 10× TABLES: Reciting the tables facts.	GROUPING AND SHARING INVESTIGATIONS.	Reviewing the work done in the Main teaching activity.
LESSON 4	● Begin to understand division as grouping (repeated subtraction) or sharing. ● Use and begin to read the related vocabulary. ● Use the ÷ and = signs to record mental calculations in a number sentence.	2× AND 10× TABLES.	DIVISION BY GROUPING IN TENS: Dividing multiples of 10 by 10 and recording in number sentences.	2× AND 10× TABLES AND DIVISION BY 10 QUESTIONS: Asking oral questions.
LESSON 5	● Use mental addition and subtraction, simple multiplication and division to solve simple word problems including problems with numbers in 'real life'.	QUICK-FIRE TABLES: 2× and 10× oral questions using a variety of language.	MULTIPLICATION AND DIVISION WORD PROBLEMS: Oral and written delivery.	Reviewing the work of the Main teaching activity.
LESSON 6	● Find totals, give change, and work out which coins to pay. ● Recognise all coins and begin to use £.p notation for money.	SPEND AND CHANGE FROM 50P: Asking oral questions.	SPEND AND CHANGE FROM £1.00.	SAVING UP £1.00: Asking oral problems.
LESSON 7	● Find totals, give change, and work out which coins to pay. ● Recognise all coins and begin to use £.p notation for money. ● Use mental addition and subtraction to solve simple word problems involving money.	SPEND AND CHANGE FROM £1.00: Asking oral questions.	£1.00 TO SPEND AT THE ZOO SHOP.	SAVING UP £1.00: Asking oral problems.
LESSON 8 +9	● Begin to recognise and find one half and one quarter of shapes and small numbers of objects. ● Begin to recognise that two halves make one whole.	BUILDING UP DOUBLING.	DIVIDING INTO HALVES: Using simple shapes and small numbers. Progressing to quarters.	Practising halving numbers.

LEARNING OUTCOMES	ORAL & MENTAL STARTER	MAIN TEACHING ACTIVITY	PLENARY
● Begin to recognise and find one half and one quarter of shapes and small numbers of objects.	DOUBLE AND HALF.	HALVING INVESTIGATION: Putting three 'eggs' in a half-dozen egg-box.	Reviewing the work of the Main teaching activity.

LESSON 10

ORAL AND MENTAL SKILLS Describe and extend simple number sequences: **count on or back in tens, starting from any two-digit number;** count on in twos from and back to zero or any small number. **Know by heart: multiplication facts for the 2 and 10 times tables**. Derive quickly: division facts corresponding to the 2 and 10 times tables; doubles of all numbers to at least 15. **Know and use halving as the inverse of doubling.** Use mental addition and subtraction, simple multiplication and division to solve simple word problems involving numbers in 'real life' or money. Find totals, give change, work out which coins to pay.

Lessons 1, 3, 4, 8 and 10 are given in full. Lessons 2, 5, 6 and 7 are provided as grids as they develop into problem-solving the number concepts previously introduced. Lesson 9 is an extension of Lesson 8, repeating the content with quarters rather than halves.

LESSON 1

RESOURCES

Teaching chart (see **Preparation**, below) and copies for the children; bricks for demonstration ('enlarged cubes'); 12 transparent plastic bank bags; self-adhesive address labels; a large number of 2p coins; four trays; flip chart and pen; paper and pencils.

PREPARATION

Draw (or use the class computer to make) two copies of the following chart on a sheet of A4 (or A3) paper. Make a copy for each child cut into two separate charts.

Moneybags					
Bag	Number of coins	Amount	Bag	Number of coins	Amount
1 2 3 4 5 6			7 8 9 10 11 12		

Use self-adhesive address labels to label and number the set of plastic bags 1–12. Place different numbers of 2p coins, from 10p to 50p in value, in the bags. Place three numbered bags of coins into each of four trays. Place each tray in the centre of a table.

LEARNING OUTCOMES

ORAL AND MENTAL STARTER
● Count on in twos from and back to zero or any small number.
● Derive quickly: doubles of all numbers to at least 15.

MAIN TEACHING ACTIVITY
● **Understand the operation of multiplication as repeated addition or as describing an array**.
● Use and begin to read the related vocabulary.

ORAL AND MENTAL STARTER

COUNTING IN TWOS: Sit the children in a circle to recite together, then count round the circle, in twos. Start from zero. Then try counting from larger, odd numbers – quite tricky!

MAIN TEACHING ACTIVITY

MULTIPLES OF 2: Demonstrate grouping bricks into sets of two (two, then four). Write a × sign on the board with what it means underneath (lots of, groups of, times, multiply by).

VOCABULARY

Count; double; lots of; groups of; times; multiply by; amount; total; How much altogether?; equals; check total; coins; money bags.

Then demonstrate the method of recording multiplying groups of two objects using the × sign on a flip chart, for example: 2 × 1 = 2. Point to the numbers and say: *2 times 1, or, one group of 2 equals 2.* For 2 × 2 = 4, say: *2 times 2 equals, or, two groups of 2 equals 4. 2 × 2? What should come next?* Ask the children to say what should be written next and then ask them to read the multiplication sentence aloud as you point to the numbers. Tell the children that when they return to their tables they are to copy the 'times 2 number sentences' on the chart on to a sheet of paper, and then continue writing the pattern of 'times 2' as far as they can.

Show them a copy of the 'Moneybags' sheet you have prepared and the trays of bags of 2p coins. Tell them that when they finish the 'times 2' work, they should work in pairs, take a numbered bag, count the coins and write the total number of coins and the amount of money in the correct columns on the sheet. When the money has been counted, they should put the coins back in the bag, replace the bag in the tray and take another bag. When they have counted all the bags on their table they should move to another table.

DIFFERENTIATION

More able: children can go on to add together the amounts in two bags each time.
Less able: give each child a set of 20 cubes for them to break into twos and count when writing the pattern of 'times 2' on their sheet.

PLENARY

Review the work in the **Main teaching activity** by asking the children how far they managed to get with writing the 'times 2' pattern. Ask: *Who got to 10 times 2? How much is 10 times 2? Who got to 15 times 2?* Then ask the children to tell you how much money was in each bag. Invite individual children to write an amount on the flip chart, for example: 'Bag 1 → 8 coins = 16p', and then write the appropriate 'times two': '2 × 8 = 16'. Conclude by asking the children to look at their 'times 2' sheet and recite the 2 times table. This activity could be followed up by using these sheets as homework so that the children can learn the tables by heart.

RESOURCES	A set of cards marked '10' (one for each child); interlocking cubes; 10 transparent plastic bags; a large set of 10p coins; paper and pencils.
LEARNING OUTCOMES	**ORAL AND MENTAL STARTER** ● **Count on or back in tens, starting from any two-digit number.** **MAIN TEACHING ACTIVITY** ● **Understand the operation of multiplication as repeated addition or as describing an array.** ● Use and begin to read the related vocabulary.
ORAL AND MENTAL STARTER	COUNTING IN TENS: Start by counting around the circle in tens, from 0–100 and 100–0. Then give each child a card marked '10'. Ask a number of children to stand up and show their cards, for example five children. Ask the group: *How many tens? How many altogether?* Ask a different number of children to stand up and repeat.
MAIN TEACHING ACTIVITY	MULTIPLES OF 10: Repeat activity as Lesson 1 above, but grouping cubes into tens and counting different amounts of 10p coins.
DIFFERENTIATION	As in Lesson 1, but using tens.
PLENARY	MULTIPLES OF 10 QUESTIONS: such as, *2 groups of 10? How many altogether?* Repeat multiples of 2 questions: *3 groups of 2?* etc.

RESOURCES

Flip chart and pen; trays of interlocking cubes; plain and squared paper; pencils, crayons or felt-tipped pens.

PREPARATION

Place a tray of interlocking cubes, plain and squared paper, and pencils, crayons or felt-tipped pens on each table.

LEARNING OUTCOMES

ORAL AND MENTAL STARTER

● **Know by heart: multiplication facts for the 2 and 10 times tables.**

MAIN TEACHING ACTIVITY

● Begin to understand division as sharing; use and begin to read the related vocabulary.

ORAL AND MENTAL STARTER

2 AND 10 TIMES TABLES: Recite the tables together. Ask questions: *Three twos are...?*

MAIN TEACHING ACTIVITY

GROUPING AND SHARING INVESTIGATIONS: Tell the children they are going to work with a partner to find different ways to group and share 24 cubes. To help them with this, tell the children to split the cubes into equal sticks, then make the sticks into a rectangle (demonstrate an example with two sticks of 12 cubes). Then they should draw the rectangle on squared paper, using one square on the paper for one cube. Repeat splitting the cubes into different equal sticks until all the different rectangles that can be made with 24 cubes have been found. When this has been done tell the children to work by themselves to find different ways to share 24 interlocking cubes equally. Again they should split the 24 cubes into equal sticks each time, but should record, for example: 24 → shared into two = 12 each. Demonstrate this method of recording on the flip chart before the children start this part of the activity.

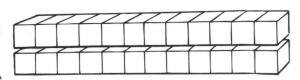

DIFFERENTIATION

More able: discuss rectangle arrays in terms of multiplication and division statements. Ask the children to count the number of rows of cubes and the number of cubes in each row, for example: 24 cubes arranged in a rectangle of 2 rows of cubes → 24 ÷ 2 = 12. Ask them to write a multiplication statement for each rectangle too, for example: 24 = 2 × 12. Less able: children might carry out the investigations with 12 cubes instead of 24.

PLENARY

Review the work done in the **Main teaching activity** on the flip chart. Invite individual children to draw different rectangles they have made and write a number statement.

RESOURCES

Flip chart and pen; two '10' cards and a set of numeral cards for each pair (see below); a set of dominoes for each group; paper and pencils; Base 10 or Cuisenaire rods.

PREPARATION

Make a set of cards numbered '10' (one for each child) and a set of cards numbered in twos 2–20, and in tens to 100 for each pair. Discard the double six and six/five dominoes from each set.

LEARNING OUTCOMES

ORAL AND MENTAL STARTER

● **Know by heart: multiplication facts for the 2 and 10 times tables.**

MAIN TEACHING ACTIVITY

● Begin to understand division as grouping (repeated subtraction) or sharing; use and begin to read the related vocabulary.

● Use the ÷ and = signs to record mental calculations in a number sentence.

VOCABULARY

Divide; divided by; divided into; tens number; count spots; group; equals.

ORAL AND MENTAL STARTER

2 AND 10 TIMES TABLES: Recite these times tables together. Then give each pair of children a set of cards: twos 2–20, then tens 30–100. Ask quick-fire questions, such as: *3 × 2? 5 × 10?* Ask the pairs to choose an answer card to hold up. Try giving some children the twos and others the tens. Ask: *What happens when I ask 2 × 5? or 1 × 10?*

MAIN TEACHING ACTIVITY

DIVISION BY GROUPING IN TENS: Sit children in a semicircle facing the flip chart. Give each child a 10 card. Ask a number of children, perhaps five, to stand, and ask one of the class to count the total number in tens (50). Then ask: *How many tens in 50?* Write the division statement on the board (50 ÷ 10 = 5). Ask a different number of children to stand up, then choose another child to count the total number, say how many tens and then write the division statement on the board. Repeat this a few times.

Tell the children they are going to carry out an activity with dominoes. They need to spread out their set of dominoes face down in the middle of the table. Select one domino, draw around it on a sheet of paper and mark in the spots. By calling each spot on the domino a 'ten', they should find the total number by counting in tens, write it underneath the domino drawing and then divide the number by 10, recording, for example:

Replace the domino and select another. They should aim to record 6–10 dominoes like this. Check that the children know what to do before they return to their tables.

 70 ÷ 10 = 7

70

DIFFERENTIATION

More able: challenge the children to complete 20 or more examples.
Less able: provide 'ten' rods for children who need additional support. They can match one rod to each spot. For numbers less than 5 use sets of Ace–5 playing cards.

PLENARY

Recite the 2 times and 10 times table. Then ask quick-fire multiplication and division by 10 questions, such as: *How many tens in 60?*

LESSON 5

RESOURCES	A copy of photocopiable page 79 (Word problems) for each child; numeral cards; pencils and paper; flip chart and pen; Cuisenaire rods; interlocking cubes.
LEARNING OUTCOMES	**ORAL AND MENTAL STARTER** and **MAIN TEACHING ACTIVITY** ● Use mental ad1dition and subtraction, simple multiplication and division, to solve simple word problems involving numbers in 'real life'.
ORAL AND MENTAL STARTER	QUICK-FIRE TABLES: Oral questions, for example: *6 × 2? 4 × 10? How many twos in 14? How many tens in 60?* Repeat '2 and 10 times tables' from Lesson 4 above.
MAIN TEACHING ACTIVITY	MULTIPLICATION AND DIVISION WORD PROBLEMS: Start by asking some oral questions using variations of the written questions on page 79 such as: *Chews cost 2p. How much will three chews cost?* Tell children that they are to complete other similar questions. Give each child a copy of photocopiable page 79. Read through each question with the children and ask if they have to *multiply* or *divide* the numbers to find the answer each time.
DIFFERENTIATION	More able: encourage the children to solve problems mentally where they can, drawing an 'H' beside any problem they have done entirely in their heads. Tell them they will be asked to describe orally (to the rest of the class) their methods of solving any problem they have done in their head. Less able: suggest that children should write number sentences where they can. Tell them they can draw a picture or use rods or cubes to model a problem if they are unsure.
PLENARY	Review the work done in the **Main teaching activity** on a flip chart. Go through each question, inviting children to give answers and explain methods. Scribe methods and answers on the chart.

LESSON 6

RESOURCES	A copy of photocopiable page 70 (Spend and change from £1.00) for each child; sets of coin cards: 1p, 2p, 5p, 10p, 20p, 50p; sets of three dice or cubes marked 1p, 2p, 5p, 10p, 20p, 50p; dice marked 2p, 5p, 10p, 2p, 5p, 10p; assorted coins.
LEARNING OUTCOMES	**ORAL AND MENTAL STARTER** ● Use mental addition and subtraction to solve simple word problems involving money. **MAIN TEACHING ACTIVITY** ● Find totals, give change, and work out which coins to pay. ● Recognise all coins and begin to use £.p notation for money.
ORAL AND MENTAL STARTER	SPEND AND CHANGE FROM 50P: Ask questions such as: *Ben spent 35p. How much change from 50p?*
MAIN TEACHING ACTIVITY	SPEND AND CHANGE FROM £1.00: Start by asking some oral questions, for example: *Peter spent 60p. How much change from £1.00? Jenny spent 75p. How much change from £1.00?* Then use photocopiable page 70 to carry out the activity in the same way as in Lesson 5, Unit 9, on page 68.
DIFFERENTIATION	More able: these children might play the game: 'First to £1.00' with a dice marked 2p, 5p, 10p, 2p, 5p, 10p (see Lesson 5, Unit 9). Less able: repeat the 'Spend and change' activity changing the rule to 'Change from 50p' (See Lesson 5, Unit 9).
PLENARY	SAVING UP £1.00: Set some oral problems, for example: *Fiona has saved 75p. How much more does she need to save?*

LESSON 7

RESOURCES	A copy of photocopiable page 80 (£1.00 to spend at the zoo shop) for each child; paper and pencils; sets of coins.
LEARNING OUTCOMES	**ORAL AND MENTAL STARTER** and **MAIN TEACHING ACTIVITY** ● Find totals, give change, and work out which coins to pay. ● Recognise all coins and begin to use £.p notation for money. ● Use mental addition and subtraction to solve simple word problems involving money.
ORAL AND MENTAL STARTER	SPEND AND CHANGE FROM £1.00: Ask oral questions such as: *Jo spends 40p. How much change will she get from £1.00?*
MAIN TEACHING ACTIVITY	£1.00 TO SPEND AT THE ZOO SHOP: Give each child a copy of photocopiable page 80. Ask how much each item costs, then read through the sheet with the children to make sure they understand what they have to do. Remind children to find the total of each list by putting the largest amount first, and so on.
DIFFERENTIATION	More able: encourage children to work mentally where they can but tell them they can write 'workings' on a separate sheet if they are unsure. Less able: provide sets of coins for children who may require additional support.
PLENARY	SAVING UP £1.00: Set some oral problems; for example: *The children in 2M are trying to save up £1.00 to spend on a school trip. Ahmed has saved up 60p. How much more does he need to save?*

LESSON 8 +9

RESOURCES

A flip chart and pen; numeral cards 1–10 (one card for each child), also even-numbered 2–20 cards; gummed paper squares; 2-D circles and squares; scissors; 12 interlocking cubes and a paper plate for each child; paper and pencils.

PREPARATION

Draw a line with a marker pen down the centre of each plate to 'cut' it in half. Place gummed paper squares, 2-D circles and squares, interlocking cubes, paper plates, paper, pencils and scissors on the tables.

LEARNING OUTCOMES

ORAL AND MENTAL STARTER
- **Know by heart : multiplication facts for the 2 and 10 times tables.**
- Derive quickly doubles of all numbers to at least 15.

MAIN TEACHING ACTIVITY
- Begin to recognise and find one half and one quarter of shapes and small numbers of objects.
- Begin to recognise that two halves make one whole.

VOCABULARY

Part; equal parts; half; halves; quarter(s); one whole; fractions; shapes; circles; squares; fold and cut; draw a line.

ORAL AND MENTAL STARTER

BUILDING UP DOUBLING: Sit the children in a circle and recite the 2 and 10 times tables. Then give each child one of a shuffled set of numeral cards 1–10. Tell them they are to take turns round the circle to double the number on their cards saying, for example: 'Double 4 equals 8'.

MAIN TEACHING ACTIVITY

DIVIDING INTO HALVES: Sit the children facing the flip chart and ask them if they know what 'half' means. Think together about 'half full', 'half way up', 'I'm six and a half' and 'half an hour'. Explain that they are going to cut shapes in half and find halves of numbers.

Demonstrate dividing shapes into halves (two equal parts) by drawing two circles on the flip chart, then drawing a line to cut one of the circles in half. Label the circles ½ and ½ (two halves) and 1 whole. Do the same with two squares.

Show the children how to draw round and cut out two circles from a gummed paper square, then fold and cut one in half. Do the same with a square. Tell them to stick the shapes on their sheets and label them like the ones on the flip chart.

Explain that when they have finished cutting and sticking their shapes, they are to take a paper plate and 12 interlocking cubes. They should put half on one side of the plate and half on the other side. Demonstrate this, using a plate and cubes, starting with two, then four. Demonstrate the method of recording on the flip chart, for example:

½ of 2 = 1
½ of 4 = 2 and so on.

DIFFERENTIATION

More able: challenge these children to find more ways of cutting the square (for example, into halves: corner to corner). Ask them to continue writing the ½ statements beyond 12. Can they do these mentally by predicting what will come next? You may like to make explicit the link between × 2 and ÷ 2 as 'opposites' (inverse operations).
Less able: tell children to work in pairs to carry out the plate and cubes activity.

PLENARY

Play a halving numbers game with even numbered cards 2–20. Tell the children you will hold up a card and choose a child to halve the number each time.

LESSON 9

Repeat Lesson 8, but in the **Main teaching activity** move on to 'quartering' by folding and cutting shapes, then sharing four cubes (then eight and sixteen cubes) into quarters by placing them on a paper plate with two lines drawn on to 'cut' the plate into quarters, recording '¼ of 4 = 1' and so on.

More able children may spot the similarity between two quarters and one half of the circle or square for themselves.

LESSON 10

RESOURCES

A shuffled pack of even-numbered cards 2–20 (one card for each child); flip chart and pen; squared paper; pencils, crayons or felt-tipped pens; a half dozen egg box and a lump of Plasticine for each child; dozen egg boxes for more able children.

PREPARATION

Place the materials for the children on the tables.

LEARNING OUTCOMES

ORAL AND MENTAL STARTER
● Derive quickly: doubles of all numbers to at least 15.
● **Know and use halving as the inverse of doubling.**

MAIN TEACHING ACTIVITY
● Begin to recognise and find one half and one quarter of shapes and small numbers of objects.

VOCABULARY

Double; half; halve; split; divide; share; share equally; two equal groups; investigate; find; different.

ORAL AND MENTAL STARTER

DOUBLE AND HALF: Stand the children in a circle and give them each an even numeral card. In turn, they should double their number, for example: 'Double 4 is 8'. If correct, they sit down. Give each child still standing another turn. Ask the whole class to stand again. Change to halving (or 'dividing by 2'). Try some quick-fire questions: *Double 3 is...?* Ask all the children with the correct answer card to hold it up: this is useful assessment.

MAIN TEACHING ACTIVITY

HALVING INVESTIGATION: Sit the children facing the flip chart. Explain that they are going to investigate how many different ways there are to place half of six eggs in a six-egg (half-dozen) egg box. Use a lump of Plasticine to make three balls, roughly the same size. Tell the children that the balls are pretend eggs. Hold up a six-egg egg box. Ask: *How many eggs will fit in the box?* Invite a child to place the three 'eggs' in the box and ask how much of the box is filled (one half). Draw a diagram of the egg box on the flip chart showing the position of the eggs in the box with coloured circles, for example:

Tell the children their task is to find different ways to place three eggs in the box. Tell them to use squared paper to draw rectangles of six squares (2 × 3 squares) as the 'egg boxes' and colour a circle for each egg.

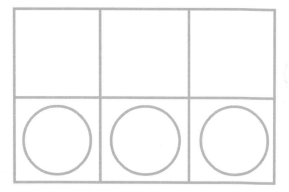

DIFFERENTIATION

More able: can find different ways to place three eggs in a 12-egg box (one quarter).
Less able: make a master sheet showing six 'egg boxes'. Copy one for each child.

PLENARY

Invite individual children to draw their different ways to place the eggs in the box on the flip chart. Ask: *What is the same about each egg box?* (There are three eggs in each box.) *What is different...?* (The three eggs are in different places.) Highlight that when halving numbers or shapes there always have to be two equal parts or two equal numbers. 'Half' shapes can be in any position as long as there are two halves or two equal parts.

Name

Word problems (× and ÷)

Chews cost 2p each.
How much will 7
chews cost?

Two children share
20 sweets equally.
How many sweets
each?

Felt-tipped pens are in
packs of 10.
How many pens are there
in 6 packs?

Two children can sit at
each table.
How many children sit
at 8 tables?

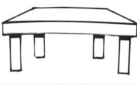

These stamps cost 2p.
How many stamps can
you buy for 20p?

Cereal bars cost 10p.
How many cereal bars
can be bought for 50p?

10 apples in a bag.
How many apples
in 7 bags?

10 chairs in a row.
How many rows for
40 chairs?

£1.00 to spend at the zoo shop

badge	book	notepad	postcard	pencil	sticker
25p	75p	30p	15p	10p	5p

Choose three items to buy. What change will you get from £1.00?
Try this five more times.

Item	Cost

UNITS 12–13

ORGANISATION (10 LESSONS)

	LEARNING OUTCOMES	ORAL AND MENTAL STARTER	MAIN TEACHING ACTIVITY	PLENARY
LESSON 1 +2 +3	● Use and begin to read the vocabulary related to mass. ● **Estimate, measure and compare masses using standard units** (kg)**; suggest suitable units and equipment for such measurements.** ● **Read a simple scale to the nearest labelled division.**	2 AND 10 TIMES TABLES PRACTICE: Asking both quick-fire and 'real-life' questions.	ESTIMATE AND COMPARE MASSES; ORDERING OBJECTS LIGHTEST TO HEAVIEST; CHOOSING EQUIPMENT TO MEASURE MASSES.	Reviewing the work of the Main teaching activities.
LESSON 4	● Read the time to the hour and half hour on an analogue clock.	ALL CHANGE: Adding two two-digit numbers with numbers 10–30.	TIMES TO THE HOUR.	ALL CHANGE: With numbers 10–30.
LESSON 5	● Order the months of the year.	ORDERING THE WEEK: Reading and reciting the names of the days of the week.	MONTHS OF THE YEAR.	ORDERING THE WEEK.
LESSON 6	● Read the time to the hour and half hour on an analogue clock. ● Use mental addition and subtraction to solve simple word problems involving numbers in 'real life'.	ORDERING THE YEAR: Reading and reciting the names of the months of the year.	ONE HOUR LATER AND EARLIER: Playing a game with time cards.	ORDERING THE YEAR.
LESSON 7	● Use mental addition and subtraction to solve simple word problems involving numbers in 'real life'. ● Find a small difference by counting up from the smaller to the larger number.	ONE HOUR LATER AND EARLIER.	PLANE JOURNEYS: Exploring 'how much time does it take?'	Reviewing the work done in the Main teaching activity.
LESSON 8 +9	● Use mental addition and subtraction to solve simple word problems. ● Solve a given problem by sorting, classifying and organising information in simple ways.	ORDERING THE WEEK and ORDERING THE YEAR.	HOW MANY CHILDREN HAVE BIRTHDAYS IN EACH MONTH? Birthday-related investigations to reinforce the months, and time calculation.	Reviewing the work done in the Main teaching activity.
LESSON 10	● Use and begin to read the vocabulary related to time. ● Suggest suitable units to estimate or measure time.	ALL CHANGE: Adding two two-digit numbers with numbers 10–30.	TIMING COMPETITIONS: Estimating and measuring time.	Reviewing the work done in the Main teaching activity.

ORAL AND MENTAL SKILLS   Know by heart: multiplication facts for the 2 and 10 times tables; doubles of all numbers to 10 and the corresponding halves. Derive quickly: division facts corresponding to the 2 and 10 times tables; doubles of all numbers to at least 15. **Know and use halving as the inverse of doubling.** Partition additions into tens and units, then recombine. Use known number facts and place value to add/subtract mentally. Find a small difference by counting up from the smaller to the larger number. Use and begin to read the vocabulary related to time. Order the months of the year. Use mental addition and subtraction to solve simple word problems involving numbers in 'real life'.

In Unit 12 Lessons 1 and 5 are given in full. Lessons 2 and 3 continue the work of Lesson 1 and may be given as separate lessons or used with Lesson 1 on a circus basis. Lesson 4 is provided in grid form. In Unit 13 Lessons 7, 8 and 10 are given in full. Lesson 6 is provided as a grid, while Lesson 9 continues the work of Lesson 8.

RESOURCES

Flip chart and pen, photocopiable page 89 (Ordering objects); a shuffled set of even-numbered cards 2–20 (one card for each child); a pan balance; cooking scales with pans and a range of weights in kg and g; kitchen scales with a dial; bathroom scales; spring balances; digital scales (for weighing letters and very small objects); a collection of objects of different masses; sheets of paper, folded in half; pencils, crayons or felt-tipped pens.

PREPARATION

Decide whether to work through these activities as separate lessons, or on a circus basis. Lay out the materials appropriate for the approach you have chosen.

LEARNING OUTCOMES

ORAL AND MENTAL STARTER
● **Know by heart: multiplication facts for the 2 and 10 times tables;** doubles of all numbers to 10 and the corresponding halves.
● Derive quickly: division facts corresponding to the 2 and 10 times tables.
● **Know and use halving as the inverse of doubling.**

MAIN TEACHING ACTIVITY
● Use and begin to read the vocabulary related to mass.
● **Estimate, measure and compare masses using standard units** (kg)**; suggest suitable units and equipment for such measurements.**
● **Read a simple scale to the nearest labelled division**.

VOCABULARY

Names of equipment for measuring mass; weigh; weight; kilogram; half kilogram; gram; order; estimate; too many; too few; not enough; balance; scales; heavy; heavier; heaviest; light; lighter; lightest; more; less; about the same as; exactly.

ORAL AND MENTAL STARTER

2 AND 10 TIMES TABLES PRACTICE: Recite the 2 and 10 times tables. Ask quick-fire questions, such as: *5 × 2?; 7 × 10?,* and then questions in words (and in context for more able children), for example: *How many twos in 10? How many tens in 50?* Play 'Double and half' with even-numbered cards 2–20 as in Lesson 10, Unit 11 on page 78.

MAIN TEACHING ACTIVITY

You may wish to carry out the following as separate, whole-class lessons or organise the work for different groups over three days on a circus basis. In the latter case, revisit the main teaching points of the activities at the start of each session.

Show the children how they can estimate which is the lighter or heavier object of two by simply handling them. Pass two objects around so the children can hold them, then take a vote on which object they thought was heavier. Check their estimate by balancing the two objects against each other on a pan balance. Can they now put a third object in the right place to order the three from lightest to heaviest? And a fourth? Discuss whether this is a good way to measure 'mass': what about when mass matters, for example when cooking? Display and demonstrate using the equipment for measuring mass, one item at a time. As you talk, write a list on the board of the names of the equipment. Ask the children to suggest things which each piece of equipment might be suitable to weigh. Also talk about equipment, such as a weighbridge, used to weigh very heavy items (lorries and elephants!) Then introduce the following activities, making sure that the children know what to do.

1. ESTIMATE AND COMPARE MASSES BY DIRECT COMPARISON: Let the children try choosing two objects and estimating which is heavier by handling them and then checking their estimates by balancing the two objects against each other on a pan balance.

2. ORDERING OBJECTS LIGHTEST TO HEAVIEST: Organise the children into groups of four to carry out this activity. Show them a copy of page 89. Tell them to work as a group to order four different objects from lightest to heaviest, but they should each complete a recording sheet. By handling each object in turn or holding an object in each hand (as many times as required) they should put the objects in order by mass. When the order is decided, they should draw and label the objects in the first half of their sheets. They should then repeat the activity, using a pan balance to balance the objects against each other (as many times as required), recording in the second half of the sheet. When they have completed the sheet, ask them to compare their two sets of results and write a sentence underneath, such as: 'We thought the book was heavier than the stone, but it was lighter.'

3. CHOOSING SUITABLE EQUIPMENT TO MEASURE MASSES: Give each child a sheet of paper folded in half. Tell them to write the name of a piece of weighing equipment at the top of each half, and then draw and label four things which could be weighed with each.

DIFFERENTIATION

More able: extend 'Ordering objects' by making (on your computer) a version of page 89 with five-column charts for ordering five objects. The children should work in fives.

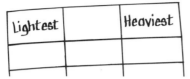

Less able: provide a three column chart for each child. Working in threes, they should order three objects by handling only and then draw a picture of each object in the correct column on the sheet. They should aim to repeat the activity twice more.

PLENARY

Review one **Main teaching activity** each day. Ask each group to present their results.

RESOURCES	A shuffled set of numeral cards 10–30 (one card per child); two coloured sorting hoops (red and blue); a large teaching clock with moveable hands; a copy of photocopiable page 16 (Clock faces) for each child; pencils, crayons or felt-tipped pens. For each group: a shuffled set of 12 time cards in words, such as 'Two o'clock' and 'Half past two' for each hour and half hour time from 1–12 o'clock; cardboard clocks.
LEARNING OUTCOMES	**ORAL AND MENTAL STARTER** ● Partition additions into tens and units, then recombine. ● Use know number facts and place value to add/subtract numbers mentally. **MAIN TEACHING ACTIVITY** ● Read the time to the hour and half hour on an analogue clock.
ORAL AND MENTAL STARTER	ALL CHANGE: Adding two two-digit numbers 10–30 (see Lesson 11, Unit 4, page 38).
MAIN TEACHING ACTIVITY	TIMES TO THE HOUR: Using a large teaching clock, remind the children of the position of the hands on a clock for times to the hour or half hour. Children then draw in hands on clocks and write times to the hour or half-hour on copies of photocopiable page 16 according to the time cards.
DIFFERENTIATION	More able: these children might be asked to illustrate the clock diagrams on the sheets, making them into different designs, such as a cuckoo clock or a face clock. Less able: use only time cards to the hour for children who require more practice with reading and recording times to the hour.
PLENARY	Repeat 'All change' with numbers 10–30.

RESOURCES
Flash cards of the names of days and months; flip chart and pen.
For each group: A set of month cards, paper and pencils.

PREPARATION

Make the flash cards by printing out the appropriate words from the NNS *Mathematical Vocabulary* CD-ROM, if available. Spread a set of month cards out, face up, on each table.

LEARNING OUTCOMES

ORAL AND MENTAL STARTER
● Use and begin to read the vocabulary related to time.

MAIN TEACHING ACTIVITY
● Order the months of the year.

UNITS 12–13

VOCABULARY

Names of the days of the week and months of the year; before; after; in between; next; last; birthdays; earlier/later.

ORAL AND MENTAL STARTER

ORDERING THE WEEK: Ask the children if they can remember the names of the days of the week. Hold up the flash card for today and ask a child to read it. Show the other cards, out of order, for them to read. Tell the children to say a day of the week each, in order, round the circle (the first child says 'Monday', the next says 'Tuesday' and so on. After 'Sunday', the next child says 'Monday'). Next, ask some questions about the days of the week and choose individuals to answer, for example: *What day comes after Tuesday? What day comes before Friday? What day comes between Friday and Sunday?*

MAIN TEACHING ACTIVITY

MONTHS OF THE YEAR: Sit the children facing the flip chart. Hold up the 'January' card. Ask the children to read it aloud. Then hold up 'February' and so on, in order. Repeat this once. Shuffle the cards and hold up one at a time. Choose a child to read each one. Give out the cards to different children. Write 'January' on the flip chart and ask the child holding that card to stand up: *What month comes next?* Ask the child holding that card to stand up, while you write 'February' on the flip chart and so on. Collect in the cards and recite the names of the months together while you point to each word. Tell the children now they are to go and write the names of the months, in order, January to December, then December to January, using the flash cards on their tables if they need help.

DIFFERENTIATION

More able: children who finish quickly can be given a shuffled pile of month cards (and a fresh sheet of paper if required). Children take a card from the pile each time, write the name of the month, followed by the name of the next month – March, April, and so on.
Less able: lay out a set of month cards in order in three lines of four cards. Children write the names of the months in order from January to December on their sheet.

PLENARY

Repeat the 'Ordering the week' activity from the **Oral and mental starter**.

LESSON 6

RESOURCES	Flash cards with the names of the months; a small easel and black felt-tipped pen; a large teaching clock with moveable hands; photocopiable page 90 (Later and earlier); sets of 12 time cards showing each hour from 1–12 o'clock; cardboard clocks; pencils; storage trays.
PREPARATION	Make flash cards by printing out the appropriate words from the NNS *Mathematical Vocabulary* CD-ROM, if available. Make an A3 copy of photocopiable page 90 and attach it to the easel. Make an A4 copy for each child. Place a storage tray with copies of the sheet, time cards, cardboard clocks and pencils in the centre of each table.
LEARNING OUTCOMES	**ORAL AND MENTAL STARTER** ● Use and begin to read the vocabulary related to time. ● Order the months of the year. **MAIN TEACHING ACTIVITY** ● Read the time to the hour and half hour on an analogue clock. ● Use mental addition and subtraction to solve simple word problems involving numbers in 'real life'.
ORAL AND MENTAL STARTER	ORDERING THE YEAR: Repeat the **Oral and mental starter** of Lesson 5 of this unit (above), but using the months flash cards.
MAIN TEACHING ACTIVITY	ONE HOUR LATER AND EARLIER: Use the enlarged photocopiable page and the teaching clock to demonstrate. Tell the children to pick a different time card each time and write that time underneath the first middle clock. They draw the hands on the clock, then use the two clocks either side to show 'one hour later and earlier', again writing the times underneath.
DIFFERENTIATION	More able: children who finish early can be given a fresh copy of the sheet to carry out the activity with the rule '2 hours later and earlier'. Less able: use cardboard clocks to count on or back one hour.
PLENARY	Repeat 'Ordering the year' and, if you do not do so already, start a rota for writing the date on the board every day, offering the flash cards as help.

RESOURCES

Teaching chart (See **Preparation**, below) and an A4 copy for each child; a teaching clock; cardboard clocks; sets of time cards marked with different times to the hour; pencils; flip chart and pen.

PREPARATION

Make a teaching chart by copying the one shown on to a flip chart sheet, then make an A4 version for each child. (Charts like this are easily made on a computer.) Place copies of the sheet, a set of timecards, cardboard clocks and pencils on each table.

Plane journeys		
Take off time	Landing time	Flight time

LEARNING OUTCOMES

ORAL AND MENTAL STARTER

● Use mental addition and subtraction to solve simple word problems involving numbers in 'real life'.

MAIN TEACHING ACTIVITY

● Use mental addition and subtraction to solve simple word problems involving numbers in 'real life'.

● Find a small difference by counting up from the smaller to the larger number.

ORAL AND MENTAL STARTER

ONE HOUR LATER AND EARLIER: Sit the children in a semicircle facing the teaching clock. Set the hands on the clock to different times to the hour. Choose a child to say the time one hour later each time. Change the rule to one hour earlier.

MAIN TEACHING ACTIVITY

PLANE JOURNEYS: Sit the children facing the 'Plane journeys' chart. Talk briefly about their experiences of air travel. Explain to them that they will be working out how long a flight takes by looking at the time the plane takes off and the time it lands. Demonstrate this with the time cards in hours and the teaching clock. Select two time cards. Show the children the card with the smaller number, ask them to read the time together then choose a child to write this time in the chart's 'Take off' column. Repeat this with the second card for the 'Landing time'. Set the hands on the teaching clock to the 'Take off time'. Ask the children to say the 'Landing time', then show them how to count on round the clock in ones while you point to each number until the 'Landing time' is reached. Ask: *How long is the flight time?* Choose a child to write the 'Flight time' on the chart (see example below).

Plane journeys		
Take off time	Landing time	Flight time
3 o'clock	8 o'clock	5 hours

Repeat this with a few more examples, then tell the children they are to carry out the activity in the same way with the time cards and sheets on their tables. Tell them to choose two cards from the tray each time, write the smaller number as the 'Take off time' and the larger number as the 'Landing time'.

Encourage them to work out the flight times mentally where they can, writing an 'H' beside each flight time they have worked out in their heads. Alternatively they could use a cardboard clock and count round the clock in ones. They should aim to do the activity ten times.

DIFFERENTIATION

More able: give these children a fresh copy of the sheet and ask them to select two cards, putting the larger number as the 'Take off time' and the smaller number as the 'Landing time'. Can they think of a situation where this could happen? (One time before midday, for example 11 o'clock, and the other after, for example 3 o'clock — avoid getting involved in time differences!) Tell them they will have to count from the larger number around the clock in ones through 12 to find the flight time.

Less able: show children how to set the hands on a cardboard clock to the 'Take-off' time and count round the clock in ones to the 'Landing' hour to work out the flight time.

PLENARY

Review the work of the **Main teaching activity** with the enlarged chart. Invite individual children to give different examples of a plane journey (Take off and Landing times) from their sheet. Scribe each journey on the chart and ask the class to say the flight time each time. Ask the children to look at the chart and say which journey was the longest or shortest? Were there any plane journeys that took the same time?

RESOURCES

Photocopiable page 17 (Faces); a recording sheet for each child titled 'How long until your birthday?'; large sheets of paper or card; paper paste and spreaders; paper, pencils, crayons or felt-tipped pens.

PREPARATION

On a large sheet of paper or card prepare a chart displaying a list of the names of the months of the year. Use a second sheet to prepare a birthday graph. Draw a grid with 12 columns and 12 rows, ensuring that the face diagrams on photocopiable page 17 will fit in the cells on the grid. Write the names of the months along the bottom of the grid and number the cells 1–12 at the left side of the grid. Make sufficient copies of page 17 for each child to have one face diagram. Cut the sheets up into individual faces.

Make a copy of the recording chart below for each child. The class computer can be very useful for making such charts.

How long until your birthday?		This month is _____
Name	Birthday month	Number of months to next birthday

LEARNING OUTCOMES

ORAL AND MENTAL STARTER
● Use and begin to read the vocabulary related to time.
● Order the months of the year.

MAIN TEACHING ACTIVITY
● Use mental addition and subtraction to solve simple word problems.
● Solve a given problem by sorting, classifying and organising information in simple ways.

ORAL AND MENTAL STARTER

ORDERING THE WEEK and ORDERING THE YEAR: Repeat these activities from Lessons 5 and 6 of this unit (page 84). Try saying, for example: *My day/month is Tuesday/June. Nadia, what will the next day/month be?* Change the rule to 'last month was…'.

MAIN TEACHING ACTIVITY

To reinforce the month work, these two activities use the children's knowledge of the months and their order, as well as giving a 'real-life' context for organising data about themselves. You may wish to carry out these activities as separate, whole-class lessons or organise them as work for different groups over two days on a circus basis.
1. HOW LONG UNTIL YOUR NEXT BIRTHDAY? Place the chart displaying the names of the months where all children can see it. Give each child a copy of the recording sheet you have made. Start by asking them to write the name of the current month at the top of the sheet. Then tell them to ask ten different children which month their birthday is in. They should write the name of each child and the birthday month on the sheet (remind them that they can look at the chart if they are unsure of how to spell a month). They should then work out the number of months until each child's next birthday, saying the months while counting on their fingers (they can use the chart to help them if necessary).
2. HOW MANY CHILDREN HAVE A BIRTHDAY IN EACH MONTH OF THE YEAR?
Pose this question and guide the children towards making a graph to find out.

VOCABULARY

Names of the months of the year; next month; how many altogether? total.

Tell them that they are going to make a class birthday graph showing a picture of each child, then count the number of children in each month. Show them the graph chart and a face diagram and tell them to make the diagram into a picture of their face and colour it. When they have finished, they paste their face in the appropriate column on the birthday graph and write a sentence about the number of birthdays in each month on a sheet of paper. Demonstrate the recording on the class board. For example 'In January there are — birthdays.' Tell the children, if they are unsure how to spell a month, to look at the chart showing the names of the months. Display the finished graph, with the original question and the children's statements.

January	✓
February	
March	✓ ✓
April	
May	
June	
July	
August	
September	
October	
November	
December	

DIFFERENTIATION

More able: children who finish making the graph quickly can be given a sheet listing the names of each month as a tally chart and a clipboard. Tell them to go round the class asking each child their birthday month, putting a tick against the month on their chart. When they have finished they count the number of ticks for each month and write the total.
Less able: in 'How long until your next birthday?' tell the children to ask five different children the month of their birthday rather than ten. If they finish quickly, invite them to try another five.

PLENARY

Display the completed birthday graph where everyone can see it. Ask questions, such as: *Which month shows the most/least number of birthdays? Are there any months showing the same number of birthdays? How many more birthdays in — than — ? What is the total number of birthdays in — and —? If two more children had birthdays in —, how many would there be altogether?*

LESSON 10

RESOURCES

For each child: a copy of photocopiable page 18 (Blank number square) , a sheet of plain paper and a pencil. For each group: a copy of photocopiable page 91 (Timing games result sheet) and a 1-minute sand timer. Paper and colouring pencils (red, green, blue).

PREPARATION

Make a copy of photocopiable page 18 (Blank number square) for each child and a copy of photocopiable page 91 for each group. Place the resources for each group on the tables and write the following tasks on the board:
    Using the 1-minute timer:
WRITING NUMBERS: How many numbers can you write on a 0–99 number square in one minute, counting in ones?
WRITING NAMES: How many times can you write your name in one minute (first name and family name)?

LEARNING OUTCOMES

ORAL AND MENTAL STARTER
● Use and begin to read the vocabulary related to time.
● Order the months of the year.

MAIN TEACHING ACTIVITY
● Use and begin to read the vocabulary related to time.
● Suggest suitable units to estimate or measure time.

Minute timer; minute; estimate; count; more; less; highest/ lowest number; closest/ nearest estimate; actual result; more; less; quick; quicker; quickest; quickly; fast; faster; fastest; slow; slower; slowest; takes longer; takes less time.

ORAL AND MENTAL STARTER

ALL CHANGE: Adding two two-digit numbers 10–30 (see Lesson 11, Unit 4, page 38).

MAIN TEACHING ACTIVITY

TIMING COMPETITIONS: Ask the children how long they think a minute is. Can they remember what special word is used to mean making a best exact guess? Let them try 'estimating' one minute. How could they find out how long exactly one minute really was? What would they 'measure' it with? (Expect to be shown every digital watch in the room!) Explain to the children they will be working together in small groups to carry out two timing games with a minute timer. Read the tasks on the board together and check that the children understand what needs to be done:

Writing numbers
● Write your name on your results sheet and then write your estimated number for the first task: Writing numbers.
● Work with a partner, taking turns to carry out the task (one person writes the numbers on a number square sheet while the other works the minute timer and says 'Ready steady go' and 'Stop').
● As you complete each task write the result on your results sheet.

Writing names
● When all the children in the group have completed the first task, they complete the second task in the same way, using plain paper to write their names and recording their results on the sheet.

Organise the children into groups of four or six and give each group a number. Tell the children to choose a partner to work with, then give each group a recording sheet for their results. While children are completing the timing games, clean the board and prepare it for the plenary session (see **Plenary** notes below).

DIFFERENTIATION

More able: any group that finishes quickly should discuss the results on the chart as a group. Ask them to use a red pencil to colour the box showing the highest number and the largest number of names written. Then colour the boxes showing the lowest number and the least number of names in blue. Finally, they should colour the boxes showing the closest/nearest estimated numbers to the actual results for each task in green.
Less able: children should all complete the writing numbers activity. If there is time ask them to try the writing names activity.

PLENARY

Draw this chart on the class board twice. Tell the children that when we have lots of results from investigations like these (from science experiments, for example) we need to look at how our estimates matched what really happened.

Writing numbers	Group 1		Group 2		Group 3		Group 4	
Highest number								
Lowest number								
Closest estimate to actual result	E	A	E	A	E	A	E	A

Repeat with the chart for the second task, changing the wording on it accordingly.
Review the results of each task in turn by asking each group to call out the results while you scribe the numbers on the chart. Then ask the children:
● *Which group had the highest number, lowest number, and the closest estimate to the actual result in each task?*
● *Did everyone have a fair chance? What about children with short/long names?*
● *Which was the fairer competition?*

Name

Ordering objects

Order four objects from lightest to heaviest by handling them.

lightest			heaviest

Order four objects from lightest to heaviest by balancing them.

lightest			heaviest

Compare the results and write a sentence.

Later and earlier

Rule

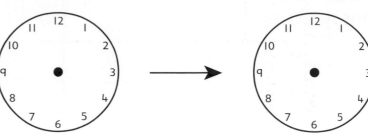

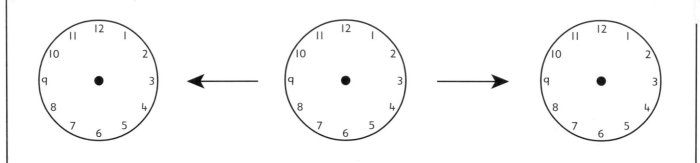

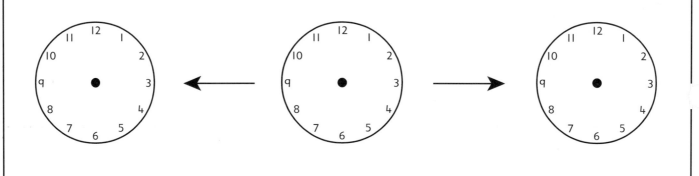

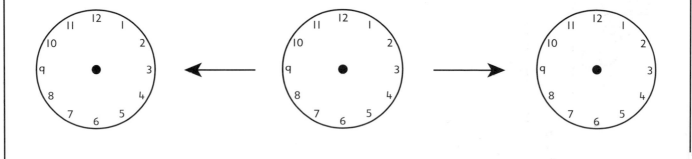

Name

UNITS 12-13

Timing games results sheet

Name	Writing numbers		Writing names	
	Estimated number	Actual number	Estimated number	Actual number

UNIT 14: Assess & Review

Choose from the following activities over the two lessons. During the group activities, some of the children can complete assessment worksheets 2a and 2b which assess addition and multiplication skills, including 2 and 10 times tables, while others work with you on practical tasks. The specific assessment criteria for the assessment sheets can be found at the bottom of each sheet.

RESOURCES

Sets of numeral cards 1–30, in various combinations; three coloured hoops; pan balances; ½ kg weights and a collections of objects for balancing; photocopiable page 69 (Trios); assessment worksheets 2a and 2b; flip chart and pen; pencils and paper.

Sorting objects by mass		
Less than $\frac{1}{2}$ kg	About $\frac{1}{2}$ kg	More than $\frac{1}{2}$ kg

PREPARATION

Copy assessment worksheets 2a and 2b and photocopiable page 69 for each child. Set up a demonstration table with the balances and weights. Draw this teaching chart on a flip chart . Make an A4 paper copy for each child.

ORAL AND MENTAL STARTER

ASSESSMENT

● Can the children: Use knowledge that addition can be done in any order to do mental calculations more efficiently?
● Do the children: Know and use halving as the inverse of doubling? Know by heart facts for the 2 and 10 times tables?

ALL CHANGE: Play this with two hoops and numeral cards 10–30, then the same game again with three hoops and numeral cards 1–20.
DOUBLE AND HALF: (See Unit 11, Lesson 10, on page 78.) Play with even numbered cards 2–20.
2 AND 10 TIMES TABLES: Ask the children to recite the tables, then count round the circle, forward and back, in twos and tens. Ask questions such as: *What are 5 twos? 6 tens?*

GROUP ACTIVITIES

ASSESSMENT

● Can the children: Use knowledge that addition can be done in any order to do mental calculations more efficiently? Estimate, measure and compare masses using standard units; suggest suitable units and equipment for such measurements?

ADDITION OF THREE COINS/NUMBERS: Repeat these activities from Lessons 3 and 4, Unit 9, on pages 66 and 67 using photocopiable page 69 (Trios).
SORTING OBJECTS BY MASS: Sit the children facing the teaching chart and demonstration table. Pass a ½ kg weight around so the children can handle it. Invite a child to choose an object in the classroom that will balance it, then use equipment on the table to check. Ask the children in the group to judge whether the pans look balanced (or nearly so) or whether the object clearly weighs more or less than ½ kg. Scribe the name of the object in the appropriate column on the teaching chart. Repeat the demonstration with another child. Next, tell the children to work in small groups. Give each child a copy of the teaching chart. Tell them each to choose an object in the classroom they think will balance ½ kg. Take turns to balance the objects against the ½ kg weight, and then, as a group, discuss each result and write the name of the object in the appropriate column on their sheet.

Name

Assessment sheet 2a

Complete:

$3 + 15 =$ ☐ $12 + 14 =$ ☐

$6 + 12 =$ ☐ $4 + 18 =$ ☐

$13 + 15 =$ ☐ $7 + 13 =$ ☐

$4 + 14 =$ ☐ $11 + 16 =$ ☐

$5 + 9 =$ ☐ $21 + 24 =$ ☐

$10 + 7 + 7 =$ ☐ $4 + 6 + 13 =$ ☐

$5 + 13 + 5 =$ ☐ $2 + 16 + 8 =$ ☐

$7 + 13 + 16 =$ ☐ $9 + 1 + 18 =$ ☐

$8 + 11 + 11 =$ ☐ $2 + 11 + 2 =$ ☐

$4 + 10 + 4 =$ ☐ $8 + 17 + 3 =$ ☐

$2 + 9 + 9 =$ ☐ $6 + 8 + 6 =$ ☐

Write two additions for each domino:

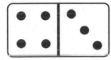   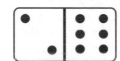   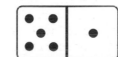   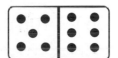

● Use knowledge that addition can be done in any order to do mental calculations more efficiently.

Name

Assessment sheet 2b

Complete:

2 + 2		2 × 2	4
2 + 2 + 2 + 2			
		2 × 3	
2 + 2 + 2 + 2 + 2 + 2			
		2 × 7	
2 + 2 + 2 + 2 + 2			
		2 × 8	

2 × 5 = ☐   2 × 3 = ☐   2 × 7 = ☐

2 × 10 = ☐   2 × 8 = ☐   2 × 4 = ☐

2 × 6 = ☐   2 × 1 = ☐   2 × 9 = ☐

10 × 3 = ☐   10 × 7 = ☐   10 × 8 = ☐

10 × 6 = ☐   10 × 2 = ☐   10 × 1 = ☐

10 × 4 = ☐   10 × 5 = ☐   10 × 9 = ☐

How many pence?

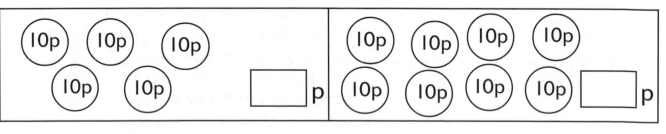

- Understand the operation of multiplication as repeated addition or as describing an array.
- Know by heart: multiplication facts for the 2 and 10 times tables.

TERM 2

Term 2 continues to extend children's knowledge of number sequences, ordering numbers to 100, use of ordinal numbers, place value (tens and units), odd and even numbers and rounding numbers to the nearest 10. Understanding addition and subtraction and understanding multiplication and division are developed and extended further through taught and practised mental strategies, solving related numerical and practical 'real life' problems, including using money up to £2.00. Children are taught to recognise symmetry in 2-D shapes and to solve simple mathematical puzzles. They are also taught to estimate and measure capacity using standard units, read the time to the quarter hour on an analogue clock, and to carry out simple timing games and data-handling activities.

ENLARGE THIS SHEET TO A3 AND USE IT AS YOUR MEDIUM-TERM PLANNING GRID.

Oral and mental skills: Say the number names in order to at least 100, from and back to zero. **Describe and extend number sequences: count on or back in ones or tens;** count on in twos from and back to zero or any small number. Count in hundreds from and back to zero. Compare two given two-digit numbers, say which is more or less, and give a number which lies between them. Round numbers less than 100 to the nearest 10. Say the number that is 10 more or less than any two-digit number. **Know by heart: all addition and subtraction facts for each number to at least 10;** all pairs of numbers with a total of 20; doubles of all numbers to 10 and the corresponding halves. **Use knowledge that addition can be done in any order to do mental calculations more efficiently.** For example: put the larger number first and count on in tens or ones. Partition into '5 and a bit' when adding 6, 7, 8 or 9, then recombine (e.g. 16 + 8 = 15 + 1 + 5 + 3 = 20 + 4 = 24); partition additions into tens and units, then recombine. Add three numbers mentally by putting the largest number first, and count on it tens or ones, and/or find a pair totalling 10, look for doubles or partition into '5 and a bit' when adding 6, 7, 8 or 9. Identify near doubles, using doubles already known. **State the subtraction corresponding to a given addition and vice versa.** Recognise all coins and begin to use £.p notation for money (for example, know that £4.65 indicates £4 and 65p). Find totals, give change, and work out which coins to pay. Use mental addition and subtraction to solve simple word problems involving money.

Unit	Topic	Objectives: Children will be taught to...
1	Counting and properties of numbers	● Use and begin to read the vocabulary of estimation and approximation; give a sensible estimate of at least 50 objects. Count reliably up to 100 objects by grouping them: for example, in tens, then in fives or twos. **Describe and extend number sequences: recognise odd and even numbers** to at least 30; count in hundreds from/back to zero.
2–4	Place value, ordering, estimating, rounding Understanding + and – Mental calculation strategies (+ and –) Money and 'real life' problems Making decisions and checking results	● Use and begin to read the vocabulary of comparing and ordering numbers, including ordinal numbers to 100. **Order whole numbers to at least 100,** and position them on a 100 square. **Know what each digit in a two-digit number represents, including 0 as a place holder,** and partition two-digit numbers into a multiple of ten and ones. ● Use the +, – and = signs to record mental additions and subtractions in a number sentence, and recognise the use of a symbol such as □ or △ to stand for an unknown number. Begin to add three single digit numbers mentally or three two-digit numbers with the help of apparatus. Recognise that addition can be done in any order, but not subtraction: for example, 3 + 21 = 21 + 3, but 21 – 3 does not equal 3 – 21. **Understand that subtraction is the inverse of addition. State the subtraction corresponding to a given addition,** and vice versa. ● **Use knowledge that addition can be done in any order to do mental calculations more efficiently.** For example: put the larger number first and count on in tens and ones; partition additions into tens and units, then recombine; add three small numbers by putting the largest number first, and/or find a pair totalling ten; partition into '5 and a bit' when adding 6, 7, 8 or 9, then recombine. **Understand that subtraction is the inverse of addition. State the subtraction corresponding to a given addition,** and vice versa. ● Recognise all coins and begin to use £.p notation for money (for example, know that £4.65 indicates £4 and 65p). Find totals, give change, and work out which coins to pay. Use mental addition and subtraction to solve simple word problems involving numbers in 'real life' and money, using one or two steps. **Choose and use appropriate operations and efficient calculation strategies.** ● Repeat addition in a different order. Check with an equivalent calculation.
5–6	Measures, including problems Shape and space Reasoning about shapes	● Use and begin to read the vocabulary related to capacity. **Estimate, measure and compare capacities using standard units** (l); **suggest suitable units for such measurements. Read a simple scale to the nearest labelled division,** recording estimates and measurements as 'a bit', 'about', 'nearly …'. Solve simple word problems involving capacity. Explain how the problem was solved. ● **Use the mathematical names for common 2-D and 3-D shapes. Sort shapes, and describe some of their features.** Begin to recognise line symmetry. Make and describe shapes, pictures and patterns. ● **Explain how a problem was solved** orally.
7	Assess and review	● **Read and write whole numbers to at least 100. Know what each digit in a two-digit number represents (including 0 as a place holder). Describe and extend simple number sequences; recognise odd and even numbers. Understand that subtraction is the inverse of addition. State the subtraction corresponding to a given addition.Choose and use appropriate operations and efficient calculation strategies. Estimate, measure and compare capacities using standard units** (l); **suggest suitable units for such measurements. Read a simple scale to the nearest labelled division. Use the mathematical names for common 2-D and 3-D shapes. Sort shapes, and describe some of their features. Explain how a problem was solved.**

Oral and mental skills: Describe and extend simple number sequences: count on in twos from and back to zero or any small number and **recognise odd and even numbers** to at least 30; **count on or back in tens starting from any two digit number;** count on in steps of 3 to at least 30, from and back to zero, then from and back to any given small number. **Choose and use efficient calculation strategies.** Use known number facts and place value to carry out mentally simple multiplications. **Know by heart: all addition and subtraction facts for each number to at least 10;** doubles of all numbers to 10 and the corresponding halves; all pairs of numbers with a total of 20; **multiplication facts for the 2 and 10 times tables;** all pairs of multiples of 10 with a total of 100. Derive quickly: division facts corresponding to the 2 and 10 times tables; doubles of all numbers to at least 15. Put the larger number first and count on in tens or ones; partition additions into tens and units, then recombine. Add three small numbers by putting the largest number first and/or find a pair totalling 10. Identify near doubles, using doubles already known. Add/subtract 9: add/subtract 10 and adjust by 1. Use mental addition, subtraction and simple multiplication to solve simple word problems involving numbers in 'real life' or money, using one or two steps. Explain how the problem was solved.

Unit	Topic	Objectives: Children will be taught to...
8	Counting and properties of numbers Reasoning about numbers	● Use and begin to read the vocabulary of estimation and approximation; give a sensible estimate of at least 50 objects. Count reliably up to 100 objects by grouping them: for example, in tens, then in fives or twos. **Describe and extend simple number sequences:** count on in twos from and back to zero or any small number and **recognise odd and even numbers** to at least 30; **count on or back in tens starting from any two digit number;** count on in steps of 3 to at least 30, from and back to zero, then from and back to any given small number.
9	Place value, ordering, estimating, rounding Understanding + and – Mental calculation strategies (+ and –) Money and 'real life' problems Making decisions and checking results	● **Order whole numbers to at least 100,** and position them on a 100 square. ● Know by heart: all pairs of multiples of 10 with a total of 100 (e.g. 30 + 70). Begin to add three two-digit numbers with the help of apparatus (totals up to 100). ● Use patterns of similar calculations. Add/subtract9: add/subtract 10 and adjust by 1. ● Investigate a general statement about familiar numbers by finding examples that satisfy it. Recognise all coins and begin to use £.p notation for money (for example, know that £4.65 indicates £4 and 65p). Find totals, give change, and work out which coins to pay.
10	Understanding × and ÷ Mental calculation strategies (× and ÷) Money and 'real life' problems Making decisions and checking results Fractions	● Understand the operation of multiplication as repeated addition or as describibg an array. Use the × and = signs to record mental calculations in a number sentence. ● Use known number facts to carry out mentally simple multiplications. ● Use mental addition, subtraction and simple multiplication to solve simple word problems involving numbers in 'real life' or money, using one or two steps. Solve mathematical problems or puxxles. Suggest extensions by asking 'What if...?' or 'What could I try next?' Explain how the problem was solved. ● Check with an equivalent calculation. ● Begin to recognise and find one half of shapes.
11–12	Measures and time, including problems Handling data	● Use and begin to read the vocabulary related to length, mass and capacity. **Estimate, measure and compare lengths, masses and capacities using standard units** (m, cm, kg, l); **suggest suitable units for such measurements. Use a ruler to draw and measure lines to the nearest centimetre.** Order the months of the year. Read the time to the quarter hour on an analogue clock. se mental addition and subtraction to solve simple word problems. ● Solve a given problem by sorting, classifying and organising information in simple ways, such as: in a list or simple table; in a pictogram; or in a block graph. Discuss and explain results.
13	Assess and review	● **Describe and extend simple number sequences: count on or back in tens starting from any two digit number; recognise odd and even numbers. Choose and use efficient calculation strategies. Know by heart: all addition and subtraction facts for each number to at least 10; multiplication facts for the 2 and 10 times tables; Order whole numbers to at least 100. Estimate, measure and compare lengths, masses and capacities using standard units** (m, cm, kg, l); **suggest suitable units for such measurements. Use a ruler to draw and measure lines to the nearest centimetre.**

100 MATHS LESSONS ● **YEAR 2** TERM 2

UNIT 1

ORGANISATION (3 LESSONS)

	LEARNING OUTCOMES	ORAL AND MENTAL STARTER	MAIN TEACHING ACTIVITY	PLENARY
LESSON 1	● Use and begin to read the vocabulary of estimation and approximation; give a sensible estimate of at least 50 objects. ● Count reliably up to 100 objects by grouping them: for example, in tens, then in fives or twos.	ALL CHANGE: Playing with two hoops and numbers 1–10.	SCOOP A CUPFUL: Approximating, estimating and counting.	Reviewing work from the Main teaching activity.
LESSON 2	● **Describe and extend simple number sequences: recognise odd and even numbers** to at least 30.	COUNTING IN TWOS: Counting round the circle in twos from 0, then from 1.	ODD AND EVEN NUMBERS: Making totals of two dominoes.	COUNTING IN TWOS.
LESSON 3	● **Describe and extend simple number sequences:** count in hundreds from and back to zero.	COUNTING IN STEPS: Counting in ones, twos and tens from and back to zero.	COUNT ON AND COUNT BACK 100: Counting with a number line and cards.	MY NUMBER/ YOUR NUMBER: Counting in 100s.

ORAL AND MENTAL SKILLS Say the number names in order to at least 100, from and back to zero. **Describe and extend simple number sequences: count on or back in ones or tens,** count on in twos from and back to zero or any small number. **Know by heart: all addition and subtraction facts for each number to at least 10.**

RESOURCES

A set of shuffled numeral cards 1–10 (one card for each child); two coloured PE hoops; a flip chart and pen; photocopiable page 100; pencils; for each group – a paper or plastic cup, a sorting hoop, and a large margarine tub half-filled with small countable objects, such as pasta shells, buttons, counters or centimetre cubes.

PREPARATION

Copy photocopiable page 100 on to a flip chart sheet (or large sheet of paper) and make an A4 copy of the sheet for each group. Place the materials for each group on their tables.

LEARNING OUTCOMES

ORAL AND MENTAL STARTER
● Say the number names in order to at least 100, from and back to zero.
● **Know by heart: all addition facts for each number to at least 10.**

MAIN TEACHING ACTIVITY
● Use and begin to read the vocabulary of estimation and approximation; give a sensible estimate of at least 50 objects.
● Count reliably up to 100 objects by grouping them: e.g., in tens, then in fives or twos.

VOCABULARY

Approximate; estimate; guess; exact; exactly; nearly; close to; too many; too few; about the same as; enough; not enough; exact; exactly; objects.

ORAL AND MENTAL STARTER

ALL CHANGE: Sit the children in a circle and count round in ones to 100, then play the game with two hoops and numeral cards 1–10 (see Lesson 5, Unit 2, Term 1 on page 34).

MAIN TEACHING ACTIVITY

SCOOP A CUPFUL: Sit the children facing the enlarged copy of page 100. Show them a paper cup, a sorting hoop and a tub filled with countable objects. Use the photocopiable sheet to remind the children of the difference between 'approximate' and 'estimate'.

Tell the children that they will be working together in small groups to make an approximation of the number of objects from the tub that will fill a cup, then give a close estimate of the number of objects, then scoop a cupful to find out the exact number. Invite two children to write their names on the chart. Ask them to say, then write, their estimate in the appropriate 'Approximately' column on the chart, for example:

Scoop a cupful				
	Approximately less than 30	Approximately more than 30 and less than 50	Approximately more than 50	
Name	Close estimate	Close estimate	Close estimate	Exact number
David		45		
Sara			62	

Then explain to the children how they should continue:
● Take turns to scoop a cupful of objects, and tip these into the sorting hoop.
● Count the objects by grouping them first into tens, with any objects left over in five, twos, or one. Write the total in the 'Exact number' column on the chart.
● The rest of the group watch to check that the number is counted correctly each time.
● Replace the objects in the tub before another child takes a turn.
Organise the children into groups of four to six, number the groups, and check that the children know what to do before they return to their tables to carry out the task.

DIFFERENTIATION

More able: give the children a larger cup to carry out the activity.
Less able: let children try the activity with a smaller cup initially.

PLENARY

Review the **Main teaching activity**. Ask each group in turn : *Who made the correct approximation to the number in the cup (e.g. more than 30 and less than 50)? Who chose an approximate number that was too few/too many? Who made the closest estimate to the exact number in the cup? Who had an estimated number that was too few/too many?*

RESOURCES	A set of dominoes for each group; paper and pencils.
LEARNING OUTCOMES	**ORAL AND MENTAL STARTER** ● **Describe and extend simple number sequences:** count on in twos from and back to zero or any small number. **MAIN TEACHING ACTIVITY** ● **Describe and extend simple number sequences: recognize odd and even numbers** to at least 30.
ORAL AND MENTAL STARTER	COUNTING IN TWOS: Count around the circle in twos from 0, then from 1, to 100 or as far as possible.
MAIN TEACHING ACTIVITY	ODD AND EVEN NUMBERS: Remind the children about odd and even numbers: *What is an odd/even number?* (All even numbers are numbers in the 'two' family, while odd numbers are not.) Give each group of children a set of dominoes. Tell them to spread out the dominoes face down, select two each time, count all the spots on each domino, then write the two numbers as a 'sum' and find the total, writing whether the total is an odd or even number. For example: '9 + 8 = 17. 17 is an odd number.'
DIFFERENTIATION	More able: try selecting three dominoes each time. Less able: tell the children to select one domino each time.
PLENARY	Repeat counting round the circle in twos from 0, then from 1. Ask after each round: *Were the numbers in the counting sequence odd or even?*

LESSON 3

RESOURCES

Flip chart and pen; photocopiable page 20 (number lines marked in 100s); sets of cards 100, 200 … 1000; paper and pencils; photocopiable page 28 (Two-way counts).

PREPARATION

Make a large number line marked in 100s, or peg cards in multiples of 100 in order, 100–1000, on a washing line in front of the class. Make sets of cards numbered in 100s. Laminate the cards and secure each set with an elastic band. Make copies (enlarged, if possible) of photocopiable page 20 and cut them into separate number lines. Place a 100s number line, paper and pencils, and a set of shuffled cards marked in 100s in two lines, face up, on each table.

LEARNING OUTCOMES

ORAL AND MENTAL STARTER

● **Describe and extend simple number sequences: count on and back in ones or tens,** count on in twos from and back to zero or any small number.

MAIN TEACHING ACTIVITY

● **Describe and extend simple number sequences:** count in hundreds from and back to zero.

ORAL AND MENTAL STARTER

COUNTING IN STEPS: Revise counting in twos, then count in ones and tens from and back to zero to 100, or beyond.

MAIN TEACHING ACTIVITY

COUNT ON AND COUNT BACK 100: Use the 100s number line or washing line and cards to demonstrate counting in hundreds from and back to zero. Ask the children to recite counting in hundreds from and back to zero, then count around the circle in hundreds to 1000 and back to zero.

   Next, tell the children that they are going to count on 100 with cards numbered in 100s. Demonstrate the activity by holding up a numeral card and asking the children to say the number. Scribe the number on the chart. Then ask the children to say the 'count on 100' number. Scribe this number on the chart, demonstrating the method of recording, for example:

   300 → 400.

Tell the children that when they return to their tables, they should look at the cards on the table, choose a number and write it down, then count on 100 from the number and write that down (using a number line if they need help), then take another card, and so on. When they have used each number once, tell them to repeat the activity with the rule 'Count back 100', recording, for example:

   300 → 200.

Ask the children to tell you what they have to do, then send them back to their tables to carry out the activity.

DIFFERENTIATION

More able: give each child a copy of photocopiable sheet 28 (Two-way counts). Ask them to choose a card, write the number in the centre box, then count back and count on 100 from the number each time.

Less able: give out the set of cards numbered in 100s and ask the children to peg them on the line in order. Ask: *Who has the 100 card? 200 card?* etc.

PLENARY

MY NUMBER/YOUR NUMBER: Start by counting round the class in 100s. Then ask questions such as: *My number is 300. (Katie), so your number is?* Change the rule to 'Count back 100'. You could try 'Count on/count back 200'.

VOCABULARY

Numbers to 100, numbers in hundreds to one thousand; zero; count on; count back.

Name

Scoop a cupful

	Approximately less than 30	Approximately more than 30 and less than 50	Approximately more than 50	
Name	Close estimate	Close estimate	Close estimate	Exact number

UNITS 2-4

ORGANISATION (15 LESSONS)

	LEARNING OUTCOMES	ORAL AND MENTAL STARTER	MAIN TEACHING ACTIVITY	PLENARY
LESSON 1	● Partition into '5 and a bit' when adding 6, 7, 8 or 9, then recombine (e.g. 16 + 8 = 15 + 1 + 5 + 3 = 20 + 4 = 24).	Playing circle games with 1–20 cards. MAKE 20 and SUBTRACT FROM 20.	HARD FACTS: Partitioning into '5 and a bit' when adding 6, 7, 8, 9 to two-digit numbers.	Reviewing work from the Main teaching activity.
LESSON 2	● Put the larger number first and count on in tens or ones.	10 MORE 10 LESS. Adding and subtracting two-digit numbers.	ADDING TWO TWO-DIGIT NUMBERS: Adding with 10–30 cards.	ALL CHANGE.
LESSON 3	● **Order whole numbers to at least 100,** and position them on a 100 square.	GIVE ME A NUMBER.	Positioning numbers on a blank number square with 0–99 cards.	GIVE ME A NUMBER.
LESSON 4	● Use and begin to read the vocabulary of comparing and ordering numbers, including ordinal numbers to 100.	NEAREST 10: Playing a game with a number square.	ORDERING NUMBERS: Ordering numbers to 100.	CHANGING PLACES.
LESSON 5	● Recognise all coins and begin to use £.p notation for money. ● Find totals, give change, and work out which coins to pay.	SPEND AND CHANGE FROM £1.00: Asking oral questions.	MONEY BAGS: Counting money in money bags to £2.00.	Reviewing work from the Main teaching activity.
LESSON 6	● Partition additions into tens and units, then recombine.	ALL CHANGE: Playing with two hoops and 1–20 cards.	ADDITION OF TWO TWO-DIGIT NUMBERS: With numbers 10–30.	ADD BY GROUPING TENS AND UNITS: With cards 10–50.
LESSON 7	● Add three small numbers by putting the largest number first, and/or find a pair totalling 10. ● Solve mathematical problems or puzzles, recognise simple relationships, generalise or predict. Suggest extensions by asking 'What if...?' or 'What could I try next?' ● Repeat addition in a different order.	ALL CHANGE: Playing with three hoops and cards 1–20.	TRIOS: Finding three numbers to total 30.	Reviewing work from the Main teaching activity.
LESSON 8	● Put the larger number first and count on in tens and ones. ● **Know what each digit in a two-digit number represents, including 0 as a place holder**, and partition two-digit numbers into a multiple of ten and ones.	ADD BY COUNTING ON TENS AND UNITS: Adding by counting on tens and ones, with cards 10–30.	CHANGING TENS AND UNITS INTO WHOLE NUMBERS: Using sets of cards (0 tens to 9 tens and 0 to 9 units).	NAME THE NUMBER.
LESSON 9	● Use the +, − and = signs to record mental additions and subtractions in a number sentence.	ALL CHANGE: Playing with three hoops and cards 1–10.	TWO STEP OPERATIONS: Adding and subtracting.	Setting oral problems – passengers on a bus.
LESSON 10	● Recognise all coins and begin to use £.p notation for money. ● Find totals, give change, and work out which coins to pay. ● Use mental addition and subtraction to solve simple word problems involving money.	SPEND AND CHANGE FROM £1.00: Asking oral questions and addition by counting.	MONEY BAGS: Counting money bags with amounts from 50p to £3.00.	Reviewing work from the Main teaching activity.

	LEARNING OUTCOMES	ORAL AND MENTAL STARTER	MAIN TEACHING ACTIVITY	PLENARY
LESSON 11	● Begin to add three two-digit numbers with the help of apparatus.	ALL CHANGE: Playing with three hoops and cards 1–20.	Adding three two-digit numbers.	Adding by grouping tens and units, with cards 10–50.
LESSON 12	● Recognise that addition can be done in any order, but not subtraction: for example, 3 + 21 = 21 + 3, but 21 – 3 does not equal 3 – 21. ● **Understand that subtraction is the inverse of addition.** ● **State the subtraction corresponding to a given addition, and vice versa.** ● Check results of calculations with an equivalent calculation. ● **Choose and use appropriate operations and efficient calculation strategies.**	Playing circle games with cards 1–20. MAKE 20 and SUBTRACT FROM 20.	EQUIVALENT AND NON-EQUIVALENT CALCULATIONS: Working with numeral cards 1–20.	Setting oral addition and subtraction problems – making sandwiches.
LESSON 13	● Use the +, – and = signs to record mental addition and subtractions in a number sentence, and recognise the use of a symbol such as ☐ or △ to stand for an unknown number. ● **Choose and use appropriate operations and efficient calculation strategies.**	COUNT THE TENS, THEN THE ONES: Adding by counting on ten, then ones, playing with cards 10–30.	MISSING NUMBERS, SIGNS AND WORD PROBLEMS: Adding and subtracting.	COUNT THE TENS, THEN THE ONES.
LESSON 14	● Recognise all coins and begin to use £.p notation for money (for example, know that £4.65 indicates £4 and 65p). ● Find totals, give change, and work out which coins to pay. ● Use mental addition and subtraction to solve simple word problems involving money.	SPEND AND CHANGE FROM £1.00: Asking oral questions.	Spend and change from £2.00.	SAVING UP £2.00 PROBLEMS.
LESSON 15	● Use mental addition and subtraction to solve simple word problems involving money. ● Recognise all coins and begin to use £.p notation for money (for example, know that £4.65 indicates £4 and 65p). ● Find totals, give change, and work out which coins to pay.	SPEND AND CHANGE FROM £2.00: Asking oral questions.	BURGER BAR MEALS.	Reviewing work from the Main teaching activity.

ORAL AND MENTAL SKILLS   Compare two given two-digit numbers, say which is more or less, and give a number which lies between them. Round numbers less than 100 to the nearest 10. **Know by heart: all addition and subtraction facts for each number to at least 10;** all pairs of numbers with a total of 20. Say the number that is 10 more or less than any two-digit number. Put the larger number first and count on in tens and ones. Partition into '5 and a bit' when adding 6, 7, 8 or 9, then recombine (e.g., 16 + 8 = 15 + 1 + 5 + 3 = 20 + 4 = 24). Partition additions into tens and units then recombine. Add three numbers mentally by putting the larger number first, and count on in tens or ones, and/or finding a pair totalling 10, look for doubles or partition into '5 and a bit' when adding 6, 7, 8 or 9. Recognise all coins and begin to use £.p notation for money (for example, know that £4.65 indicates £4 and 65p). Find totals, give change, and working out which coins to pay. Use mental addition and subtraction to solve simple word problems involving money.

In Unit 2 Lessons 1, 3 and 4 are given in full, Lessons 2 and 5 are provided, briefly, in grid form. In Unit 3 Lessons 6 and 8 are given in full, while Lessons 7, 9 and 10 are given as grids. In Unit 4 Lessons 11 and 12 are given in full, while the remaining three lessons are provided as grids.

RESOURCES

Flip chart and pen; a set of numeral cards 1–20 (one card for each child); plastic hoops; paper and pencils; Cuisenaire rods.

PREPARATION

Write the following additions on the board:

16 + 6	16 + 7	16 + 8	16 + 9
17 + 6	17 + 7	17 + 8	17 + 9
18 + 6	18 + 7	18 + 8	18 + 9
19 + 6	19 + 7	19 + 8	19 + 9

LEARNING OUTCOMES

ORAL AND MENTAL STARTER
● **Know by heart: all addition and subtraction facts for each number to at least 10;** all pairs of numbers with a total of 20.

MAIN TEACHING ACTIVITY
● Partition into '5 and a bit' when adding 6, 7, 8 or 9, then recombine (e.g. 16 + 8 = 15 + 1 + 5 + 3 = 20 + 4 = 24).

VOCABULARY

Add; addition; make; group into 5 and a bit; plus; sum; equals; total; altogether; change; re-arrange; best way; easiest way; explain your method; explain how you got your answer; give an example of; show how you ....

ORAL AND MENTAL STARTER

Sit the children in a circle and give each child a 1–20 numeral card. Then ask each child in the circle, in turn, to:

MAKE 20: Children say the number on their card followed by the number required to make 20, for example, '16 and 4 make 20', then:

SUBTRACT FROM 20: Children subtract the number on their card from 20 saying, for example, '20 subtract 16 equals 4'.

MAIN TEACHING ACTIVITY

HARD FACTS: partitioning into '5 and a bit'. Sit the children facing the flip chart. Briefly remind them of the method of adding by partitioning numbers into '5 and a bit' and give a few examples. Ask the children what to do and scribe their method on the flip chart. Then use the flip chart to demonstrate the method of adding larger numbers by changing 'teens' numbers into '15 and a bit' and smaller numbers into '5 and a bit'. Work through a few examples, asking the children to tell you the method each time, for example:

19 + 6 = <u>15</u> + 4 + <u>5</u> + 1 = <u>20</u> + 5 (from the 4 + 1) = 25

Then tell the children to return to their tables to copy and complete the sums on the board, using the method they have been shown.

DIFFERENTIATION

More able: invite these children to try changing the first number in each sum to a 'twenties' number, then partitioning the first number into '25 and a bit', for example:

29 + 6 = <u>25</u> + 4 + <u>5</u> + 1 = <u>30</u> + 5 (from the 4 + 1) = 35.

Less able: write the sums as single-digit sums on a flip chart, like this:

6 + 6	6 + 7	6 + 8	6 + 9
7 + 6	7 + 7	7 + 8	7 + 9

Provide Cuisenaire rods for children who may require additional support. Let them partition each number rod into a 'five-rod' and another rod. They then group five-rods together, followed by the other rods to find the total, for example:

7 + 6 = 5 + 2 + 5 + 1 = 10 + 3 = 13

PLENARY

Review the work done in the **Main teaching activity** by going through each example on the board, choosing children to say how they found the total. Scribe their method on the board each time.

RESOURCES	A set of numeral cards 10–30 for each group (10–40 cards for more able children); paper and pencils; Cuisenaire rods.
LEARNING OUTCOMES	**ORAL AND MENTAL STARTER** ● Compare two-digit numbers, say which is more or less and give a number which lies between them. **MAIN TEACHING ACTIVITY** ● Put the larger number first and count on in tens or ones.
ORAL AND MENTAL STARTER	10 MORE 10 LESS: Play in the same way as '10 more/10 less' starting from any two-digit number. See Lesson 5, Unit 2, Term 1 on page 33.
MAIN TEACHING ACTIVITY	ADDING TWO TWO-DIGIT NUMBERS: Demonstrate adding two two-digit numbers by putting the larger number first, counting on the tens and then adding the ones: 24 + 23 → 24, 34, 44 + 3 → 47. Lay a set of 10–30 numeral cards face up on each table. Tell the children to record as many 'sums' as they can using two numbers each time (including doubles).
DIFFERENTIATION	More able: try using sets of cards 10–40. Less able: have Cuisenaire rods available to help these children.
PLENARY	ALL CHANGE: Using two hoops and numeral cards 10–30 as on page 34.

RESOURCES

Photocopiable page 18 (Blank number square); a water-based marker; a small easel; a shuffled set of 0–99 cards for each group; pens; pencils; individual 0–99 number squares.

PREPARATION

Make an enlarged copy of photocopiable page 18 (Blank number square) on card and laminate it. Attach the chart to a small easel. Make an A4 copy of this sheet for each child.

LEARNING OUTCOMES

ORAL AND MENTAL STARTER

● Compare two given two-digit numbers, say which is more or less, and give a number which lies between them.

MAIN TEACHING ACTIVITY

● **Order whole numbers to at least 100,** and position them on a 100 square.

ORAL AND MENTAL STARTER

GIVE ME A NUMBER: Ask questions, such as: *Give me a number more than 20, …less than 50, …in between 30 and 40, …*and so on.

MAIN TEACHING ACTIVITY

NUMBERS ON A NUMBER SQUARE: Sit the children facing the blank number square chart. Tell them that they are going to help you to write on the numbers. Ask for *a number between 0 and 99* and show the children how to find its place: count down the first column in tens, then count along in ones. Write in the number with the coloured marker. Choose other numbers and invite a child to find the correct box for each and write the number in.

Now tell the children to fill in their own blank number squares. Deal ten 0–99 cards to each child. They should write these numbers in with a coloured pen and the rest in pencil.

DIFFERENTIATION

More able: deal these children 20 cards each.
Less able: provide individuals with completed 0–99 number squares.

PLENARY

Fill in the whole sqaure. Repeat 'Give me a number' from the **Oral and mental starter**.

RESOURCES

Photocopiable page 13 (0–99 Number square) teaching chart; for each group: a set of shuffled cards 1–100, a small rectangular margarine tub, paper and pencils.

PREPARATION

Enlarge, then laminate a copy of photocopiable page 13 to use as a teaching chart. Place a shuffled set of cards 1–100 face down in the centre of the table, along with a margarine tub and paper and pencils. Give each child a sheet of paper.

LEARNING OUTCOMES

ORAL AND MENTAL STARTER
● Round numbers less than 100 to the nearest 10.

MAIN TEACHING ACTIVITY
● Use and begin to read the vocabulary of comparing and ordering numbers, including ordinal numbers to 100.

VOCABULARY

Numbers 1–100; round to the nearest 10; ordinal numbers 1st to 8th; first; last; order; size; position; before; after; more; less; next; in-between.

ORAL AND MENTAL STARTER

NEAREST 10: Sit the children in a semicircle facing the enlarged 0–99 square. Tell the children you will point to a number on the square and choose a child to round the number to the nearest 10 each time. Try this a number of times, checking that the children remember which way to round numbers ending in 5 and digits greater than or less than 5: 5 or less round down; more than 5 round up.

MAIN TEACHING ACTIVITY

ORDERING NUMBERS: Choose ten children to stand in a line in front of the class. Ask the children in the line to number themselves in order 1 to 10 aloud. Ask the seated children to try to remember these numbers and then ask the children in the line to repeat numbering themselves. Ask questions, such as: *What position in the line is the second boy? The third girl?; What position is (Amy)? Who is first/last in the line?* Repeat this activity with another ten children.

Next, tell the children they are to carry out an ordering numbers activity with the 1–100 cards on their tables. Explain what they have to do.
● Take turns to count out seven cards from the pile, place the cards in order, lowest to highest number, in a line, then write the numbers in order on the sheet of paper.
● Place the used cards face up in the tub, then take seven more cards from the pile.
● When all the cards have been used, shuffle the pile of cards in the tub and place them face down beside the tub to start over again.
● The activity finishes when everyone has ordered ten sets of cards.
Ask the children to tell you what they have to do before they return to their tables to carry out the activity.

DIFFERENTIATION

More able: take 10 cards instead of seven.
Less able: provide 0–99 number squares for children who require additional support.

PLENARY

CHANGING PLACES: Sit the children in a semicircle and choose ten of them to stand in a line facing the group. Ask the standing children to number themselves in ordinal numbers 1st to 10th. Then give instructions to seated children, such as: *(Chloe) change places with the 4th child, …the 2nd girl, …the first/last child…*and so on.

LESSON 5

RESOURCES	A set of 20 plastic money bags (numbered 1–20) each containing different amounts of money from 50p to £2.00; self-adhesive address labels; trays; flip chart and pen; paper and pencils.
LEARNING OUTCOMES	**ORAL AND MENTAL STARTER** and **MAIN TEACHING ACTIVITY** ● Recognise all coins and begin to use £.p notation for money (for example, know that £4.65 indicates £4 and 65p). ● Find totals, give change, and work out which coins to pay.
ORAL AND MENTAL STARTER	SPEND AND CHANGE FROM £1.00: Tell the children you are going to ask questions about spending money and will choose a child to say how much change each time, for example: *(Ryan) spends 30p. How much change will he have from £1.00?*
MAIN TEACHING ACTIVITY	MONEY BAGS: Place five money bags in a tray on each table. Use one bag to demonstrate finding the total by first sorting coins into type, then finding the total of the largest value coins, adding the total of the next value coin, and so on, down to the smallest value. Demonstrate £.p notation on a flip chart for amounts over £1.00, e.g. £1.45. Children work in pairs to find the total in each bag by sorting and counting the coins, then checking the total by counting the money in a different way. They then record, for example, Money Bag 4 → 76p. Each bag of money is replaced in the tray after it has been counted. As children finish counting the bags on one table they can move to another table. Check that they understand this before they start the activity.
DIFFERENTIATION	More able: ask these children to find the total amount of money in pairs of money bags. Less able: any pair of children having difficulty should be reminded to sort the coins into type, find the total of each type of coin starting with the largest value, e.g. £1 coins → £2.00.
PLENARY	Review the work done in the **Main teaching activity**. Invite different children to say the amount of money in each bag and write the amount on the flip chart. Ask how they counted the money and how they checked the amount was right.

LESSON 6

RESOURCES

Sets of numbered cards 1–20 (enough for one card for each child); two plastic hoops; flip chart and pen; paper and pencils; for each group: a set of cards 10–50.

PREPARATION

Lay a shuffled set of cards 10–50 in four lines of ten cards in the centre of each table with sheets of paper and pencils.

LEARNING OUTCOMES

ORAL AND MENTAL STARTER and MAIN TEACHING ACTIVITY
● Partition additions into tens and units, then recombine.

ORAL AND MENTAL STARTER

ALL CHANGE: Use two hoops and 1–20 cards (see Lesson 1, Unit 2, Term 1, on page 30).

MAIN TEACHING ACTIVITY

ADDITION OF TWO TWO-DIGIT NUMBERS: Sit the children in front of the flip chart and tell them that they are going to add two two-digit numbers. Discuss what 'one-' and 'two-digit' numbers are, then demonstrate how to add two two-digit numbers (10–50) by partitioning them into tens and units and then recombining. For example: $1\underline{4} + \underline{2}4 = \underline{30} + 8 = 38$ or $1\underline{7} + \underline{3}4 = \underline{40} + 11 = 51$. Work through a few examples, inviting individual children to contribute their methods which you should scribe on to the chart.

Tell the children they are going to carry out an activity now with the 10–50 cards on each table. Explain that they have to choose two numbers and use them to write an addition sum. They should try to write 20 'sums' (or as many as they can) using two cards each time (double numbers can be included).

VOCABULARY

Number bonds; add; addition; more; plus; group/ partition into tens and units; find the total; equals; altogether; sum; make; one digit number; two-digit number; easiest; best way.

DIFFERENTIATION

More able: try writing addition sums with three numbers.
Less able: invite children to make the numbers with Cuisenaire rods (tens and units). They should group and add the tens and record the total, then group and add the units and record the total, finally adding tens and units together.

PLENARY

ADD BY GROUPING TENS AND UNITS: Remind the children of the process of partitioning two two-digit numbers into tens and units, then recombining them. Hold up two cards from a shuffled set of 10–50 cards and choose a child to say the total each time.

RESOURCES	A shuffled set of numeral cards 1–20 (one card for each child); three plastic hoops; photocopiable page 69 (Trios); pencils; flip chart and pen; Cuisenaire rods or interlocking cubes.
LEARNING OUTCOMES	**ORAL AND MENTAL STARTER** ● Add three small numbers by putting the largest number first and/or find a pair totalling 10. **MAIN TEACHING ACTIVITY** ● Solve mathematical problems or puzzles, recognise simple relationships, generalise or predict. Suggest extensions by asking 'What if...?' or 'What could I try next?' ● Repeat addition in a different order.
ORAL AND MENTAL STARTER	ALL CHANGE: Play this game (from Lesson 1 of Unit 4 in Term 1) with three hoops and cards 1–20.
MAIN TEACHING ACTIVITY	TRIOS: Show the children a copy of photocopiable page 69 (Trios) and tell them they are to find different ways to make 30 using three numbers. Remind them to write the numbers in the squares on each trio diagram and tell them to check that the total of each diagram adds up to 30 by adding the numbers in a different order before writing '30' in the centre. Write a few examples on the flip chart, choosing a child to say the numbers, and then how he or she checked the total each time. Then ask the children to return to their tables to carry out the activity.
DIFFERENTIATION	More able: encourage the children to include combinations of addition and subtraction, for example 25 + 9 − 4 = 30. Less able: provide Cuisenaire rods or interlocking cubes for children who may require additional support.
PLENARY	Review the work in the **Main teaching activity** using a flip chart. Invite individual children to say different ways to make 30 and explain their method of checking the total each time. Scribe responses and methods.

RESOURCES

A set of shuffled cards 10–30; a list of tens and units numbers for each child (see **Preparation**, below); 0–99 Number square teaching chart (photocopiable page 13); flip chart and pen; pencils and paper; Cuisenaire rods.

PREPARATION

0 tens	0 units
1 ten	1 unit
2 tens	2 units
to...	
9 tens	9 units

Prepare a Number square teaching chart by copying, and then enlarging, photocopiable page 13. Copy the list of tens and units numbers opposite on to the board, then on to a sheet of paper and make a copy of this for each child.

LEARNING OUTCOMES

ORAL AND MENTAL STARTER
● Put the larger number first and count on in tens and ones.

MAIN TEACHING ACTIVITY
● **Know what each digit in a two-digit number represents, including 0 as a place holder,** and partition two-digit numbers into a multiple of ten and ones (TU).

VOCABULARY

Add; count on; equal to; tens and units; ones; whole numbers; exchange; stands for; represents; place; place value; cross of the list.

ORAL AND MENTAL STARTER

ADD BY COUNTING ON TENS AND UNITS: Sit the children facing the flip chart. Tell them that you will hold up two cards (10–30) each time and choose a child to say the total of the two numbers. Remind them to add the numbers together by putting the larger number first, then add the second number by counting on the tens, before adding on the units. Demonstrate the method on the flip chart, for example: $26 + 13 = 26 \rightarrow 36 + 3 = 39$.

MAIN TEACHING ACTIVITY

CHANGING TENS AND UNITS INTO WHOLE NUMBERS: Tell the children that they are going to change tens and units into whole numbers. Ask them to look at the list on the board and demonstrate the method of recording on the flip chart. Tell the children to choose different 'tens' and 'units' numbers each time and record, for example: *2 tens and 4 units → 24*.

Each time they use a number they should cross it off the list. Be sure they choose different numbers each time and avoid using, for example, 1 ten and 1 unit. The activity ends when everyone has crossed all the numbers off their lists.

DIFFERENTIATION

More able: repeat the activity, using different numbers.
Less able: have Cuisenaire rods available for these children. Encourage them to build any numbers they are unsure of with tens and one rods (units), counting the tens, then the units.

PLENARY

NAME THE NUMBER: With the children facing the Number square teaching chart, ask: *What number is 6 tens and 5 units?* and so on. Choose a child to say and point to the answer.

LESSON 9

RESOURCES	A shuffled set of cards 1–10 (one card for each child); three plastic hoops; flip chart and pen; for each group: a set of dominoes spread out face down on each table; paper and pencils.
LEARNING OUTCOMES	**ORAL AND MENTAL STARTER** ● Add three small numbers by putting the largest number first and/or find a pair totalling 10; partition into '5 and a bit' when adding 6, 7, 8 or 9. **MAIN TEACHING ACTIVITY** ● Use the +, – and = signs to record mental additions and subtractions in a number sentence.
ORAL AND MENTAL STARTER	ALL CHANGE: Play this game (see Lesson 1, Unit 4, Term 1) with three hoops and sets of cards 1–10. Remind the children of ways of finding the total such as: $3 + 4 + 7 \rightarrow (7 + 3) = 10 \rightarrow 10 + 4 = 14$ (find a pair totalling 10); or $(3 + 4) \rightarrow 7$; $7 + 7 = 14$ (doubles) or $5 + 4 + 8 \rightarrow \underline{5} + 4 + \underline{5} + 3 \rightarrow \underline{10} + 7 = 17$ (partitioning into '5 and a bit'). Play the game, selecting some children to scribe their method on the flip chart during the game.
MAIN TEACHING ACTIVITY	TWO STEP OPERATIONS – ADDING AND SUBTRACTING DOMINOES: Tell the children they will be adding and subtracting with the spots on dominoes. They are to select two dominoes each time, add the spots on each domino in their heads to find out which has the larger total, then draw around both dominoes on a sheet of paper and mark in the spots, placing the domino with the larger total first and writing the total number of spots underneath each domino. Then they must subtract the second number from the first number, using the – and = signs to make the numbers into a subtraction sentence; for example: $6 – 4 = 2$. Draw outlines of two dominoes on the flip chart and hold up two dominoes. Ask the children to work through the method using the numbers on these dominoes. Scribe the method on the flip chart. Do this a few times before letting the children try 10 examples.
DIFFERENTIATION	More able: try completing another 10 examples. Less able: try five examples initially, then trying another five if possible.
PLENARY	Ask two-step questions about 'the bus' with numbers to 20: *10 people are on a bus. 2 more get on and 3 get off. How many on the bus now?*

LESSON 10

RESOURCES	A set of 20 plastic money bags (numbered 1–20) each containing different amounts of money from 50p to £3.00; self-adhesive address labels; flip chart and pen; paper and pencils.
LEARNING OUTCOMES	**ORAL AND MENTAL STARTER** and **MAIN TEACHING ACTIVITY** ● Recognise all coins and begin to use £.p notation for money (for example, know that £4.65 indicates £4 and 65p). ● Find totals, give change, and work out which coins to pay. ● Use mental addition and subtraction to solve simple word problems involving money.
ORAL AND MENTAL STARTER	SPEND AND CHANGE FROM £1.00: Ask oral questions, for example: *(Daniel) spent 80p. How much change will he have from £1.00?*
MAIN TEACHING ACTIVITY	MONEY BAGS TO £3.00: (See Lesson 5 on page 106).
DIFFERENTIATION	More able: try counting the total amount of money in pairs of bags. Less able: see Lesson 5 on page 106.
PLENARY	Review the work done in the **Main teaching activity.** Invite the children to say how much money was in each bag. Encourage them to refer to their sheet each time

LESSON 11

RESOURCES
A shuffled set of cards 1–20 (one card for each child) and a shuffled set of cards 10–50; three plastic hoops; flip chart and pen; a shuffled set of 10–29 cards for each group; elastic bands; Cuisenaire rods; paper and pencils.

PREPARATION
Sort out the cards required for each activity and secure each set with an elastic band. Lay a shuffled set of cards 10–29 face up in two lines of ten cards in the centre of each table with a box of Cuisenaire rods, paper and pencils.

LEARNING OUTCOMES

ORAL AND MENTAL STARTER
● Begin to add three single-digit numbers mentally.

MAIN TEACHING ACTIVITY
● Begin to add three two-digit numbers with the help of apparatus.

VOCABULARY

Addition; sum; add; total; makes; partition; group; tens and units; equals; two-digit numbers; re-arrange; best way; easiest way; number cards.

ORAL AND MENTAL STARTER
ALL CHANGE: Play this game with three hoops and cards 1–20 (see Lesson 1, Unit 4 of Term 1 on page 30).

MAIN TEACHING ACTIVITY
ADDITION OF THREE TWO-DIGIT NUMBERS: Use the flip chart to explain and demonstrate how to add three two-digit numbers between 10 and 29. Show the children how to use Cuisenaire rods to make each number in tens and units, how to group and add the tens and units separately, and then add them together to find the total, for example:

$$23 + \underline{1}2 + \underline{1}4 = \underline{4}0 + 9 = 49 \qquad \text{or} \qquad \underline{1}2 + \underline{1}2 + \underline{2}8 = \underline{4}0 + 12 = 52$$

(10)		
(10)		
(10)		
(10)		
40		

3	2	4
(9)		
+9		

or

(10)		
(10)		
(10)		
(10)		
40		

8	2	2
10		2
+12		

Repeat this with a few more examples, inviting the children to explain methods. Scribe the methods on the flip chart.

Now tell the children to return to their tables and look at the cards laid out there. Tell them to choose three cards and write down as many sums as they can using the chosen numbers. Remind them that they can use the rods if they need help and tell them they can use the number on one card twice as a double number in their sums. When they have exhausted all possibilities with the first three cards they should choose three more.

DIFFERENTIATION

More able: encourage the children to work without rods where they can.
Less able: ask the children to start by adding two numbers together. If they manage this easily, invite them to try adding three numbers.

PLENARY

ADD BY GROUPING TENS AND UNITS: Use a set of shuffled cards 10–50 and ask the children to add two numbers using the grouping into tens and units method. Hold up two cards each time and ask questions, such as: *What is the total of 23 and 35?*

LESSON 12

RESOURCES

Shuffled set of 1–20 numeral cards for each group; flip chart and pen; paper and pencils.

PREPARATION

Sort out the cards required for each activity and secure each set with an elastic band. Lay a set of cards 1–20 face up in two lines in the centre of each table with paper and pencils.

LEARNING OUTCOMES

ORAL AND MENTAL STARTER
● **Know by heart:** all pairs of numbers with a total of 20.

MAIN TEACHING ACTIVITY
● Recognise that addition can be done in any order, but not subtraction: for example, 3 + 21 = 21 + 3, but 21 – 3 does not equal 3 – 21.
● **Understand that subtraction is the inverse of addition.**
● **State the subtraction corresponding to a given addition and vice versa.**
● **Checking results of calculations:** Check with an equivalent calculation.
● **Choose and use appropriate operations and efficient calculation strategies.**

VOCABULARY

Calculate; calculations; addition; add; subtract; subtraction; total; check addition in a different order; tens and units; equals; does not equal; How many altogether?; How many are left?; answer; How did you work it out?; Show how you ...; explain your method.

ORAL AND MENTAL STARTER

Play the circle games 'Make 20' and 'Subtract from 20' with numbered cards 1–20 (see Unit 2, Lesson 1, on page 103).

MAIN TEACHING ACTIVITY

EQUIVALENT AND NON-EQUIVALENT CALCULATIONS: Start by writing an example of an addition on the flip chart, for example 5 + 6, and asking the children to give you the total. Then ask them how they know that this is correct – do they have a way to check if it is correct? Explain that you are going to show them some different ways to check whether they have found the right answer for additions and subtractions.
Explain that there are different ways to do this:
● Repeating single-digit addition in a different order, for example: 4 + 3 = 7; 3 + 4 = 7.
● Carrying out an equivalent calculation, for example, by grouping tens and units: 13 + 3 = 16: 10 + 6 = 16.
● Carrying out the inverse (addition or subtraction) calculation to check an addition or subtraction calculation, for example: 16 – 3 = 13; 13 + 3 = 16.

Show the children one example of each method on the flip chart. Then offer a few other examples, asking the children to say the method each time. Make sure that you include some examples to demonstrate that subtractions cannot be checked by putting the numbers in a different order, for example, 5 – 3 does not equal 3 – 5.

Tell the children that when they return to their tables they are to choose numbers from two different cards each time to make addition and/or subtraction sentences. They should then check whether each addition and subtraction sentence is correct by choosing and writing one of the checking methods they were shown on the flip chart underneath.

DIFFERENTIATION

More able: ask the children to choose one card over 10 each time and to use three different checking methods for each sum they write.
Less able: tell the children to only make addition sentences with the cards and to check each answer by repeating the addition in a different order.

PLENARY

Test the children with oral addition and subtraction problems with numbers to 20. Use a theme, such as making sandwiches: *(Jack) made 12 cheese and 8 jam sandwiches. How many sandwiches altogether? 20 sandwiches were made for tea, 16 were eaten, how many were left?*

LESSON 13

RESOURCES	A copy of photocopiable page 113 (Addition and subtraction) for each child; a shuffled set of numeral cards 10–30 (one card per child); flip chart and pen; pencils; Cuisenaire rods.
LEARNING OUTCOMES	**ORAL AND MENTAL STARTER** ● Put the larger number first and count on in tens or ones. **MAIN TEACHING ACTIVITY** ● Use the +, – and = signs to record mental additions and subtractions in a number sentence, and recognise the use of a symbol such as □ or △ to stand for an unknown number. ● Choose and use appropriate operations and efficient calculation strategies.
ORAL AND MENTAL STARTER	COUNT THE TENS THEN THE ONES: Use a shuffled set of cards 10–30. Hold up two cards and ask the children to add the numbers together. Remind them to put the larger number first, count on from the first number in tens then adding on the units, for example: 23 + 14 = 23 (add 1 ten) → 33 + 4 (add 4 units) = 27
MAIN TEACHING ACTIVITY	MISSING NUMBERS, SIGNS AND WORD PROBLEMS: Use the flip chart to demonstrate examples of additions and subtractions with □ or △ standing for an unknown or missing number, for example: 6 + □ = 10 or 10 – △ = 5. Ask the children to supply the missing numbers. Then give each child a copy of photocopiable page 113. Read through the first missing number and missing signs number sentences on the sheet with the children and ask them what they have to do. Then read together through all the written number sentences before the children return to their tables to complete the sheet.
DIFFERENTIATION	More able: encourage these children to work mentally where they can. Less able: provide Cuisenaire rods for children who need additional support.
PLENARY	Repeat 'Count the tens then the ones' with cards 10–30.

LESSON 14

RESOURCES	Sets of coin cards (photocopiable page 15) 1p, 2p, 5p, 10p, 20p, 50p, £1.00; photocopiable page 70 (Spend and change); sets of three dice (two marked 1p, 2p, 5p, 10p, 20p, 50p and one marked 50p, 50p, 50p, £1.00, £1.00, £1.00); coins; pencils and paper; dice marked 1p, 2p, 5p, 10p, 20p, 50p.
LEARNING OUTCOMES	**ORAL AND MENTAL STARTER** and **MAIN TEACHING ACTIVITY** ● Use mental addition and subtraction to solve simple word problems involving money. ● Recognise all coins and begin to use £.p notation for money (for example, know that £4.65 indicates £4 and 65p). ● Find totals, give change, and work out which coins to pay.
ORAL AND MENTAL STARTER	SPEND AND CHANGE FROM £1.00: Ask oral questions, such as: *(Fiona) spent 60p. How much change will she get from £1.00?*
MAIN TEACHING ACTIVITY	SPEND AND CHANGE FROM £2.00: Carry out this activity using photocopiable page 70 (See Lesson 5, Unit 9, Term 1 on page 68).
DIFFERENTIATION	More able: play 'Go for broke'. Each starting with a £2.00 coin, children take turns to throw the dice marked 1p, 2p, 5p, 10p, 20p, 50p and subtract the amount thrown from £2.00. The first child to run out of money is the winner. Less able: repeat 'Spend and change from £1.00' or play 'Go for broke' starting with a 50p coin.
PLENARY	SAVING UP £2.00 PROBLEMS: Ask oral questions, such as: *(Matt) has saved £1.20. How much more is needed to save up £2.00.*

LESSON 15

RESOURCES	A copy of photocopiable page 114 for each child; pencils and paper; flip chart and pen; sets of all coins to £1.00.
LEARNING OUTCOMES	**ORAL AND MENTAL STARTER** and **MAIN TEACHING ACTIVITY** ● Recognise all coins and begin to use £.p notation for money (for example, know that £4.65 indicates £4 and 65p). ● Find totals, give change, and work out which coins to pay. ● Use mental addition and subtraction to solve simple word problems involving money.
ORAL AND MENTAL STARTER	SPEND AND CHANGE FROM £2.00: Tell the children you are going to ask some questions about spending money and choose one of them to say the change from £2.00. For example, *(Sam) spends £1 20p. How much change will he have from £2.00?*
MAIN TEACHING ACTIVITY	BURGER BAR MEALS: Start by talking about going to eat out in a restaurant or café. Encourage the children to talk about their experiences and ask them how they choose their food. Would they know how much their food cost, or the total cost of the meal? Give each child a copy of photocopiable page 114 and read through the sheet together. Explain that they have £2.00 to spend each time. Ask what each item on the menu costs, and check that they understand what they have to do before they return to their tables to carry out the activity.
DIFFERENTIATION	More able: give these children a fresh sheet of paper and tell them they have £4 to buy a meal for themselves and a friend. They should choose food from the menu, work out how much they would have to pay and the change from £4. Less able: provide sets of coins for children who may require additional support.
PLENARY	Review the work done in the **Main teaching activity** on the flip chart. Go through each question on the sheet and invite individual children to say what they chose to buy, how much each item cost, the total cost and their change from £2.00. Scribe children's responses and their methods of doing the calculations on the flip chart.

Addition and subtraction

Missing numbers:

$6 + \boxed{} = 10$ $\qquad$ $13 + \boxed{} = 17$

$\boxed{} + 5 = 9$ $\qquad$ $\boxed{} + 2 = 16$

$7 - \triangle = 4$ $\qquad$ $20 - \triangle = 5$

$3 + \boxed{} = 12$ $\qquad$ $11 + \boxed{} = 20$

$\triangle + 7 = 14$ $\qquad$ $\triangle + 9 = 18$

Missing signs:

$3 \boxed{} 4 = 7$ $\qquad$ $16 \boxed{} 4 = 12$

$9 \boxed{} 3 = 6$ $\qquad$ $7 \boxed{} 7 = 14$

$6 \boxed{} 2 = 8$ $\qquad$ $19 \boxed{} 6 = 13$

$10 \boxed{} 5 = 5$ $\qquad$ $11 \boxed{} 5 = 16$

Write the answers to these number sentences.

Add 4 and 3. $\boxed{}$ $\qquad$ What is two more than six? $\boxed{}$

8 take away 2. $\boxed{}$ $\qquad$ Subtract 1 from 4. $\boxed{}$

Find the sum of 2 and 7. $\boxed{}$ $\qquad$ Nine minus three. $\boxed{}$

Two less than ten. $\boxed{}$ $\qquad$ What is the total of 4 and 8? $\boxed{}$

Burger bar meals

Can you find six ways to buy a hot snack, a sweet and a drink with £2.00? How much change each time?

Hot snacks		Sweets		Drinks	
Small burger	70p	Cake	25p	Small milk	20p
Large burger	£1.00	Biscuits	10p	Large milk	40p
Hot-dog	90p	Choc-ice	15p	Small cola	30p
Double burger	£1.50	Apple	20p	Large cola	50p
Chips	40p	Banana	20p	Orange juice	45p

UNITS 5-6

ORGANISATION (8 LESSONS)

	LEARNING OUTCOMES	ORAL AND MENTAL STARTER	MAIN TEACHING ACTIVITY	PLENARY
LESSON 1 +2 +3 +4	● Use and begin to read the vocabulary related to capacity. ● **Estimate, measure and compare capacities, using standard units** (litre)**; suggest suitable units for such measurements.** ● **Read a simple scale to the nearest labelled division,** recording estimates and measurements as 'a bit', 'about', 'nearly …'. ● Solve simple word problems involving capacity. ● **Explain how a problem was solved.**	ALL CHANGE: Playing games with two and three hoops and cards 1–20.	WET AND DRY GOODS: Comparing containers. WAYS TO FILL A LITRE MEASURE: Estimating, measuring and comparing. MAKING AND USING A ½ LITRE MEASURE: Comparing capacities. BUYING PAINT: Painting a house.	Reviewing work from the Main teaching activities.
LESSON 5 +6 +7 +8	● **Use the mathematical names for common 3-D and 2-D shapes.** ● **Sort shapes and describe some of their features.** ● Begin to recognise line symmetry. ● Make and describe shapes, pictures and patterns. ● **Explain how a problem was solved** orally.	QUICK DOUBLES and QUICK HALVES: Playing with numeral cards 1–20 or even-numbered cards 2–20. DOUBLES ADD 1: Doubling numbers, then playing a circle game with cards 1–10.	MAKING AND DRAWING 2-D SHAPES, AND SOLID SHAPES; MAKING SYMMETRICAL PATTERNS AND PICTURES WITH 2-D SHAPES; DRAWING AXES OF SYMMETRY.	Reviewing work from the Main teaching activities.

ORAL AND MENTAL SKILLS   Know by heart: all addition facts for each number to at least **10;** doubles of all numbers to 10 and the corresponding halves. Add three small numbers by putting the largest number first and/or find a pair totalling 10; partition additions into tens and units. Identify near doubles, using doubles already known.

Ideally, the lessons in Units 5 (Lessons 1–4) and 6 (Lessons 5–8) should be presented separately, but may also be organised as a 'circus' through which groups circulate.

RESOURCES

Flip chart and pen; a set of numeral cards 1–20 (one card for each child); three sorting hoops. WET AND DRY GOODS: a large, group recording sheet (see **Preparation**); a collection of everyday containers for goods bought in shops, such as a bottle, a can, a tub, a jar, a carton and a packet. WAYS TO FILL A LITRE MEASURE: for each group – a plastic litre bottle; a set of smaller containers of different capacities; a funnel; a washing-up bowl; waterproof aprons; pencils and photocopied charts (see **Preparation**, below). MAKING AND USING A ½ LITRE MEASURE: for each group – a clear plastic bottle (more than ½ litre); an elastic band; a clear plastic measuring jug calibrated to show ½ litre; a set of different small everyday containers; a funnel; a washing up bowl; waterproof aprons; paper and pencils. BUYING PAINT: photocopiable page 119; pencils; interlocking cubes.

PREPARATION

WET AND DRY GOODS: Make a large (preferably A2) recording chart as shown overleaf. WAYS TO FILL A LITRE MEASURE: Copy the chart below on to a flip chart sheet. Make a copy for each child on A4 paper. MAKING AND USING A ½ LITRE MEASURE: Place the equipment for each group on a table. Fill each washing-up bowl with two litres of water. Use one set of equipment for a demonstration. BUYING PAINT: Make a copy of photocopiable page 119 for each child.

LEARNING OUTCOMES

ORAL AND MENTAL STARTER
● **Know by heart: all addition facts for each number to at least 10.**
● Add three small numbers by putting the largest number first and/or find a pair totalling 10; partition additions into tens and units.

MAIN TEACHING ACTIVITIES
● Use and begin to read the vocabulary related to capacity.
● **Estimate, measure and compare capacities using standard units** (litre); **suggest suitable units for such measurements.**
● **Read a simple scale to the nearest labelled division,** recording estimates and measurements as 'a bit', 'about', 'nearly'.
● Solve simple word problems involving capacity.
● Explain how a problem was solved.

ORAL AND MENTAL STARTER

Choose a game to play on each day. ALL CHANGE: with two hoops and cards 1–20 or three hoops and cards 1–20 (see Unit 3, Lessons 6 and 7, pages 106 and 107). COUNT THE TENS, THEN THE ONES: See Unit 4, Lesson 13, page 111.

MAIN TEACHING ACTIVITY

bottles	cans
tubs	jars
cartons	packets

If you plan each of the activities that follow as separate, whole-class lessons, break up the teaching points over the days. If you decide to organise the activities on a circus basis, remind the children of the main teaching points at the start of each session.

WET AND DRY GOODS: Discuss your container collection. *How are wet and dry goods are sold in shops?* (In bottles, cans, tubs, jars, cartons and packets.) *What types of containers are used for wet items (also 'runny' or 'sticky' items) ...and dry items such as cereals and powders? Do you know what units are used to measure 'runny' goods? Does lemonade come in kg?* Introduce litres and ½ litres.

(If the children suggest 'cups' or 'spoons', you may wish to agree that there are standard measures in these units – the cup [8 fl. oz.] is particularly common in US recipes.) Give each group a recording sheet and tell them to work together to write a list of five different items that might be packaged in each type of container. They may need adult support for spelling or even the writing.

VOCABULARY

Containers; name; label; list; contains; capacity; bottle; can; tub; jar; carton; packet; wet; dry; litre; ½ litre; measure; fill; pour; count; more; less; holds the most/ least; nearly; exactly; full; half full; empty; a bit; more; less; not enough; just over; just under.

Ways to fill a litre measure		
Container	Estimate	Check by pouring and counting

WAYS TO FILL A LITRE MEASURE: Show the children a plastic litre bottle. Then invite two of them each to select a container and estimate how many of these will fill the bottle. Scribe the names of these containers and estimates on the enlarged chart. Ask the two children to work together, one holding the litre bottle and funnel in the bowl and the other filling the bottle with the container by scooping up water. Encourage the group to count. Scribe the result on the chart. Then ask the children to pour the water back into the bowl and repeat with the second container. Where a container does not fill the litre bottle exactly, discuss measures such as '5 and a bit'. Next, show the children a copy of the prepared 'Ways to fill...' sheet. Show them where to write down the name of each container (or draw it) in the first column on the sheet and record their estimates. (Supply a word list of relevant vocabulary.) Then they should take turns to fill the litre bottle with one of the containers while the rest of the group counts the number of times the container is poured into the bottle. When it is full, or nearly full, they must record the number on the sheet. Then the next pair repeats the process with another container, and so on.

MAKING AND USING A ½ LITRE MEASURE: Demonstrate how to make a ½ litre measure by measuring ½ litre water in the jug then, using the funnel, pour the water into the plastic bottle and mark the level of the water with an elastic band stretched around the bottle. Next, show the children how to compare the capacities of different containers using the prepared ½ litre measure, a funnel and one container. Choose a child to select a container to fill and pour repeatedly into the ½ litre measure (with the rest of the children keeping count) until the water reaches near to, or exactly, the water level mark. Ask, for example: *Do four cups nearly fill or do they exactly fill the ½ litre measure?* If the answer is 'nearly', ask: *How much more do you think you will need? Half a cup or less/more than half a cup?* Demonstrate the method of recording on the flip chart, for example:

4 cups hold nearly ½ litre.

5 yoghurt pots hold exactly ½ litre.

Now tell the children they are to work as a group to make their own ½ litre measure, like the one they were shown. Then, in pairs, they will take turns to carry out the measuring task with one of the containers. Tell the group to watch each pair, counting, then writing each result in a sentence, as they were shown on the flip chart, including when a number of containers nearly fill the litre measure, how much more they think they will need to fill the measure, as they were shown. Organise the children into pairs, within a group of four to six. Check that they know what they have to do before they return to their tables to carry out the activity.

BUYING PAINT: Give each child a copy of photocopiable page 119. Ask: *How much of each colour paint did Dad buy?* Read through the sheet together, concentrating on the table and questions. Tell the children to work out the answers mentally if they can, but to use interlocking cubes (one cube equals 1 litre of paint) if they need help. Ask the children to tell you what they have to do before they return to their tables to carry out the activity.

DIFFERENTIATION

Use mixed ability grouping for the practical capacity activities, pairing more with less able. More able: for 'Wet and dry goods' challenge the children to write a list of ten items under each heading. In 'Buying paint' give children a fresh sheet to work out how much paint Dad would buy to paint two houses and how much he would use.
Less able: in 'Wet and dry goods' ask children to draw two pictures of two items under each heading. For 'Buying paint' give out interlocking cubes from the start.

PLENARY

Select one of the Main teaching activities each day and review answers and methods. Discuss estimates and results in terms of comparison, using 'more/less/the same'.

LESSON 5

+6

+7

+8

RESOURCES

Shuffled set of even-numbered cards 2–20, shuffled sets of 1–10 and 1–20 cards (in both sets, one card for each child); flip chart and pen; Polydron or Clixie; 2-D and 3-D shapes; safety mirrors; rulers; photocopiable page 20 (Dotty paper); 9-pin geoboards; elastic bands (Beware children chewing or flicking these!); paper and pencils, crayons or pens.

PREPARATION

Make a teaching chart (an enlarged copy) of photocopiable page 20 and one A4 copy for each child. Place the relevant equipment for each group on the tables.

LEARNING OUTCOMES

ORAL AND MENTAL STARTER
- **Know by heart:** doubles of all numbers to 10 and the corresponding halves.
- Identify near doubles, using doubles already known.

MAIN TEACHING ACTIVITY
- **Use the mathematical names for common 3-D and 2-D shapes.**
- **Sort shapes and describe some of their features.**
- Begin to recognise line symmetry.
- Make and describe shapes, pictures and patterns.
- **Explain how a problem was solved** orally.

2-D and 3-D
shapes;
names; label;
description;
symmetrical;
line (axis) of
symmetry;
pattern;
picture;
vertical;
horizontal;
diagonal;
lines; ruler;
make; draw;
mirror line;
reflection;
pattern;
picture;
measure.

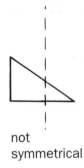

symmetrical

not
symmetrical

ORAL AND MENTAL STARTER

Choose one of these circle games to play on each day. All require a shuffled set of even-numbered cards 2–20 and a set of numeral cards 1–20 (one card for each child).
QUICK DOUBLES: Hold up cards for the children to say the double. QUICK HALVES: Hold up cards for the children to halve each time. DOUBLES ADD 1: Hold up a card. Choose a child to double the number on the card, then add 1, saying, for example, 'Double 4 is 8 and 1 is 9'. Change the rule to 'Double, then take one away'.

MAIN TEACHING ACTIVITIES

You may wish to present each of the activities below as a separate, whole-class lesson. Alternatively, you could organise them as a circus for different groups over four days. If so, you will need to remind the children of the main teaching points at the start of each day.

Start by holding up a selection of 2-D and 3-D shapes for the children to name. Can they suggest 'real-life' objects that are these shapes? Write the word 'symmetrical' on the flip chart. Draw a vertical line and then draw around one of the 2-D shapes so that you have two identical shapes either side of the line. Use this to explain the principle of symmetry in relation to building a matching pattern either side of a line. Then show how a symmetrical picture or pattern can be built up with 2-D shapes on either side of a horizontal or diagonal line. Next, draw around a square and explain the principle of line symmetry.

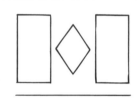

(Where a vertical, horizontal or diagonal line is drawn through the centre of a shape, cutting it in half, and the two halves are exactly the same, the shape is said to have 'line symmetry'.) Give examples of where a shape is and is not symmetrical. Demonstrate how to check whether a shape is symmetrical using a mirror.

MAKING AND DRAWING 2-D SHAPES USING 9-PIN GEOBOARDS: Give each child a copy of page 20, a 9-pin geoboard and some elastic bands. Tell the children to make four-sided shapes and copy them on to dotty paper. Able children can go on to five-sided shapes.
MAKING AND DESCRIBING SOLID SHAPES: Ask the children to make (at least) three different solid shapes with Polydron or Clixie, and write a sentence or sentences (with adult help, if necessary) about each shape, for example: 'My first shape has four triangle faces and one square face. It has 8 edges and 5 corners. It looks like a pyramid'.
MAKING SYMMETRICAL PATTERNS AND PICTURES WITH 2-D SHAPES: Tell the children they are going to make their own symmetrical patterns or pictures. Show them how to draw a vertical line down the centre of a sheet of paper with a ruler (or fold it). Then, using the line, they can build up a symmetrical design by drawing round 2-D shapes in position. Challenge more able children to start with a horizontal or diagonal line.
DRAWING AXES OF SYMMETRY ON 2-D SHAPES: Tell the children they are to draw around 2-D shapes on their sheets, then use the mirrors and rulers to draw dotted 'lines of symmetry' onto them. Tell them to write a sentence underneath each shape, for example: 'A square is symmetrical'. More able children might investigate whether each shape is symmetrical in all cases (vertically, horizontally and diagonally) and record the number of lines (axes) of symmetry, for example: 'A square has four lines (axes) of symmetry'.

DIFFERENTIATION

Suggestions for more able children are provided with the activities.
Less able: let these children work with a partner so that discussion can take place. Each child should still record separately for each activity.

PLENARY

Review one **Main teaching activity** each day. For 'Work with 2-D and 3-D shapes': Choose children to talk about their models. Ask them to count the shapes they have drawn on the dotty paper: *Who made more than five shapes? ...ten shapes?* Invite some children to draw their shapes on the teaching chart. For 'Work with symmetry': Talk about the types of lines and name the shapes used. Draw each one on the flip chart. Ask the children if it is symmetrical and to name the position(s) of the line(s) of symmetry. Add them to the flip chart drawing and point out any others the children do not mention.

House painting

Dad bought these cans of paint:

Complete this table.

	Dad bought	Dad used	How much left?
red	5 litres	4 litres	
white		7 litres	
green			1 litre
yellow		2 litres	
blue		$\frac{1}{2}$ litre	

How many litres of red and white paint did Dad use altogether? ☐

How many litres of green and yellow paint did Dad use altogether? ☐

How many litres of paint did Dad buy altogether? ☐

How many litres of paint did he have left? ☐

UNIT 7: Assess & Review

Choose from the following activities over the two lessons. During the group activities, some children can complete assessment worksheets 3a and 3b which assess their skills in adding and subtracting, and in naming and describing 2-D and 3-D shapes. The specific criteria for the assessment sheets can be found at the bottom of each sheet. The children will need dominoes, spread out face down, from which to choose to complete sheet 3a.

RESOURCES

Numeral cards 0–99, three plastic hoops, set of dominoes (at least to 'double 5'), rulers, sets of 2-D and 3-D shapes, ½l measure, a set of small plastic containers (each holding less than ½l), funnel and equipment for measuring capacity, pencils and paper; copies of Assessment worksheets 3a and 3b, photocopiable page 18 (Blank number square) and a capacity recording sheet (see **Preparation** below) for each child.

Ways to fill a ½ litre measure		
Container	Estimate	Check by pouring and counting

PREPARATION

Make a copy this recording chart on A4 paper for each child. Add as many rows as containers. Copy the other sheets as required.

ORAL AND MENTAL STARTER

ASSESSMENT

● Can the children: Describe and extend simple number sequences, counting in ones or tens? Recognise odd and even numbers? Use knowledge that addition can be done in any order to do mental calculations more efficiently?
● Do the children: Know by heart: all addition facts for each number to at least 10?

COUNTING: Count together, then round the circle, in ones, then tens. Start from numbers other than zero or 1. Move on to twos, counting from zero and 1. Ask which are the odd/even numbers. Play 'My number, your number' (see Lesson 3, Unit 1, on page 99) with the rules 'Count on/back 2'. Ask the children whether their number is odd or even each time.
ADDITION: Play 'All change' with two hoops and numeral cards 1–20. Extend to playing the game with three hoops (see Lesson 5, Unit 2, from Term 1 on page 34).

GROUP ACTIVITIES

ASSESSMENT

● Can the children: Count, read, write and order whole numbers to at least 100, knowing what each digit represents (including 0 as a place holder)? Estimate, measure and compare capacities, using standard units? Read a simple scale to the nearest labelled division?

KNOWING NUMBERS: Repeat 'Positioning numbers on a number square' with numeral cards 0–99 and copies of page 18 (see Lesson 4, Unit 2, on page 105.) Check numerals are written in correct place value order, i.e. not writing 'fifteen' as 51, and are not reversed: Ɛ .
MEASURES: Give out the prepared sheets and capacity resources for the children to use different containers to fill a ½ litre measure. Working in pairs or as a small group, they should select a container each time, estimate the number that will be needed to fill the measure, then pour and count, to find the actual number (see Lessons 1–4, Unit 5, on pages 115–117). Check whether they are making realistic estimates, whether their pouring and counting is reasonably accurate and whether they recognise and record that there is, for example, 'a bit more' than a whole container.

Assessment sheet 3a

Name_____ Date_____

Copy the dots on a domino. Write two sums.
Then write a matching subtraction.

Like this: 	Now you try: 
$3 + 1 = 4$ and $1 + 3 = 4$ $4 - 1 = 3$	
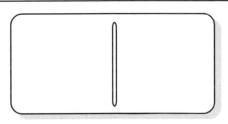	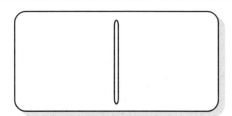
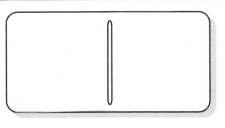	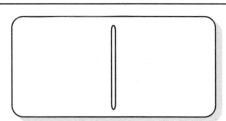
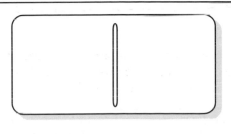	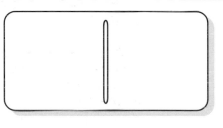

● Use knowledge that addition can be done in any order to do mental calculations more efficiently.
● Know by heart: all addition and subtraction facts for each number to at least 10.
● State the subtraction corresponding to a given addition and vice versa.

Assessment sheet 3b

Name_____   Date_____

Name these shapes.

Draw all the lines of symmetry on these shapes you can.

● Use the mathematical names for common 3-D and 2-D shapes. Describe some of the features of shapes.

UNIT 8

ORGANISATION (5 LESSONS)

	LEARNING OUTCOMES	ORAL AND MENTAL STARTER	MAIN TEACHING ACTIVITY	PLENARY
LESSON 1	● Use and begin to read the vocabulary of estimation and approximation; give a sensible estimate of at least 50 objects. ● Count reliably up to 100 objects by grouping them: for example, in tens, then in fives or twos.	2 AND 10 TIMES TABLES: Reciting the tables and quick-fire oral questions.	SCOOP TWO HANDFULS: Approximating, estimating and counting.	Reviewing the Main teaching activity, questioning the children's results.
LESSON 2	● **Describe and extend simple number sequences:** count on in twos from and back to zero or any small number and **recognise odd and even numbers** to at least 30.	COUNTING IN TWOS.	ODD AND EVEN NUMBERS: Making pairs/odd one and number patterns.	Identifying odd and even numbers less than 100 on a number square.
LESSON 3	● **Describe and extend simple number sequences:** count on in steps of 3 to at least 30, from and back to zero.	COUNTING ON IN TENS.	COUNTING ON IN STEPS OF 3: Identifying patterns of steps of three.	Reciting counting in threes.
LESSON 4	● **Describe and extend simple number sequences:** count on in steps of 3 to at least 30, from and back to zero, then from and back to any given small number.	COUNTING ON IN THREES.	COUNTING BACK/ON 3: Game using steps of 3.	Reciting counting in threes.
LESSON 5	● **Describe and extend simple number sequences: count on or back in tens, starting from any two-digit number.**	COUNTING BACK IN TENS: Counting from 90s numbers.	COUNTING BACK/ON 20: Game using steps of 20.	MY NUMBER/YOUR NUMBER: Adding or subtracting 20.

ORAL AND MENTAL SKILLS   Know by heart: multiplication facts for the 2 and 10 times tables. Describe and extend simple number sequences: count on or back in tens, starting from any two-digit number; count on in twos from and back to zero or any small number and **recognise odd and even numbers** to at least 30; count on in steps of 3 to at least 30, from and back to zero, then from and back to any given small number.

In Unit 8 Lessons 1, 2 and 3 are given in full with Lessons 4 and 5 as grids.

RESOURCES

For each group: a sorting hoop and a large tub or tray half filled with small countable objects, such as buttons, counters, centimetre cubes or pasta shapes; photocopiable page 128; flip chart and pen; paper and pencils.

PREPARATION

Make an enlarged teaching copy of photocopiable page 128 to use on the flip chart (or write it out onto a large sheet of paper). Make a copy of photocopiable page 128 for each group. Place the equipment for each group on their tables.

LEARNING OUTCOMES

ORAL AND MENTAL STARTER
● **Know by heart: multiplication facts for the 2 and 10 times tables.**

MAIN TEACHING ACTIVITY

● Use and begin to read the vocabulary of estimation and approximation; give a sensible estimate of at least 50 objects.
● Count reliably up to 100 objects by grouping them: for example, in tens, then in fives or twos.

VOCABULARY

Count; guess how many; approximate; estimate; exact; close; too many; too few; just over; just under; enough; not enough; objects.

ORAL AND MENTAL STARTER

2 AND 10 TIMES TABLES: Recite the 2 and 10 times tables together. Count around the circle in twos to 50 and back to 0, then in tens to 100 and back to 0. Follow with quick-fire questions to individual children, for example: *What are 5 twos?* or *What are 6 tens?*

MAIN TEACHING ACTIVITY

SCOOP TWO HANDFULS: approximating, estimating and counting. Sit the children facing the enlarged copy of photocopiable page 128 and show them a hoop and a tub of countable objects. Tell the children they will be working together in small groups to estimate, then use two hands together to scoop as many objects as they can hold from the tub. Ask the group to read the headings on the chart, then describe the difference between approximate and close estimates. Demonstrate the task by inviting two children to write their names on the chart. Then ask them to say and write their close estimate in the appropriate 'Approximate' column on the chart, for example:

Scoop two handfuls

	Approximately less than 40	Approximately more than 40 and less than 70	Approximately more than 70	
Name	Close estimate	Close estimate	Close estimate	Exact number
Jane		63		
Andrew			85	

Let each of the two children take a turn to scoop, then place the objects into the sorting hoop to count them. Remind them to group the objects into tens, grouping any objects left over into five or twos. Ask all the children to count the groups to find the total, then choose a child to write the number in the 'Exact number' column on the chart. The children replace the objects in the tub after each turn.

Divide the class into groups of four to six children and number the groups. Give each group a chart and tell them to:
● Write your names and estimated numbers in the appropriate column on the chart.
● Take turns to scoop two handfuls and count the number of objects in the hoop by grouping them in tens, with any left over in five or twos.
● The whole group watch to ensure that the number is counted correctly each time.
● Write the counted number in the 'Exact number' column on the chart by your name, then replace the objects in the tub before the next child takes a turn.

DIFFERENTIATION

More able: make a 'Scoop three handfuls' copy of the sheet with the headings: 'Less than 50; More than 50 and less than 100; More than 100'.
Less able: repeat the 'Scoop a cupful' activity from Lesson 1, Unit 1, Term 2 on page 97.

PLENARY

Review the **Main teaching activity**. Ask each group in turn to say which child or children:
● chose the correct approximation (e.g. more than 40 and less than 70)?
● chose an approximate number that was too few/too many?
● made the closest estimate to the exact number?
● estimated a number that was too few/too many?

RESOURCES

0–99 Number square teaching chart and individual 0–99 number squares (photocopiable page 13); small cubes; flip chart and pen; crayons or felt-tipped pens; pencils and paper; optional O/E card for each child (see **Plenary** session).

PREPARATION

Attach the enlarged Number square teaching chart to a flip chart. Make A4 copies of photocopiable page 13 for each child.

LEARNING OUTCOMES

ORAL AND MENTAL STARTER and MAIN TEACHING ACTIVITY

● **Describe and extend simple number sequences:** count on in twos from and back to zero or any small number, and **recognise odd and even numbers** to at least 30.

VOCABULARY
Odd and even numbers; pairs; every other; pattern; one left over; grouped in twos; describe the rule.

ORAL AND MENTAL STARTER

COUNTING IN TWOS: Sit the children in a circle and ask them to count around the circle in twos from zero, then 1. Repeat this, choosing a different child to start the count each time. Ask: *Which count gives the even/odd numbers?*

MAIN TEACHING ACTIVITY

ODD AND EVEN NUMBERS: Sit the children facing the Number square teaching chart. Tell them they are going to work with odd and even numbers. Ask: *What is an odd/even number?* Then remind the children that even numbers are 'pair' numbers or numbers belonging to the number sequence or pattern of 'count on in twos from zero'. Odd numbers are numbers that are not 'pair' numbers, have an odd one left over, or belong to the number sequence or pattern of 'count on in twos from 1'.

Demonstrate how to colour the pattern of odd numbers on the Number square chart, starting from 1 and recording the number sequence underneath the number square:

   1 → 3 → 5 etc.

Hand out the A4 copies of photocopiable page 13. Tell the children they are to copy the pattern and this number sequence on to their own sheet, then continue to colour the pattern and write the number sequence as far as they can.

DIFFERENTIATION

More able: play a number square and cube game. Give each child an individual 0–99 number square and a sheet of paper. Children throw the cube on to the square and record, on paper, whether the number is odd or even, for example: 41 → odd   36 → even
Less able: ask the children to complete the activity on a 0–49 number rectangle.

PLENARY

Sit the children facing the Number square teaching chart. Point to different numbers on the square and invite a child to say whether the number is odd or even each time. Alternatively, give all the children a piece of card with 'Odd' on one side and 'Even' on the other. They can then hold up the appropriate letter, all together, as you call out the numbers.

RESOURCES

A set of shuffled numeral cards 11–20; A4 copies of photocopiable page 13 (0–99 Number square) and an enlarged teaching chart copy; a coloured water-based pen; flip chart or easel; paper, pencils, crayons or felt-tipped pens.

PREPARATION

Make a copy of photocopiable page 13 for each child and enlarge one copy to use as a teaching chart.

LEARNING OUTCOMES

ORAL AND MENTAL STARTER
● **Count on or back in tens, starting from any two-digit number.**

MAIN TEACHING ACTIVITY
● **Describe and extend simple number sequences:** count on in steps of 3 to at least 30, from and back to zero.

VOCABULARY

Numbers to 100; count on ten; count on in threes; count back in threes; multiples of threes; pattern; number sequence; continue; predict; rule; colour; arrow; number square.

ORAL AND MENTAL STARTER

COUNTING ON IN TENS: Use a shuffled set of number cards 11–20. Sit the children in a circle and tell them they are going to play a game where they count around the circle in tens from the number you hold up on a card. If, for example, you hold up a card and say the number (14) the child chosen to continue the count will say 'Twenty-four', the next child will say 'Thirty-four', and so on until the count reaches 'Ninety-four'. Have a couple of practice rounds to get the children into the rhythm of the game, then ask them to count around the circle as quickly as they can. Once the children are familiar with the game, ask them to stand up then any child who says an incorrect number sits down and the count passes to the next child, and so on until a 'nineties' number is reached. At this point show another card and ask another child to start the count again. When all the cards have been used, ask the seated children to stand, then repeat the game.

MAIN TEACHING ACTIVITY

COUNTING ON IN STEPS OF 3: Place the Number square teaching chart on the flip chart or easel and seat the children facing it. Tell them they will be colouring the pattern of 'count on 3' and writing the number sequence. Use the number square to demonstrate how to start colouring the pattern of 3s (missing out two numbers each time) up to the number 6. Write the number sequence of 'count on 3' underneath the square at the same time, for example:

$0 \rightarrow 3 \rightarrow 6 \rightarrow$

Give out the individual number squares. Tell the children to copy the pattern and the number sequence onto their sheets and then to continue colouring the pattern and writing the sequence as far as possible.

DIFFERENTIATION

More able: children who have completed the activity can be given a fresh copy of the number square and asked to colour in the number 98. They should then colour and write the pattern of 'count back 3' as far as possible,
Less able: give children a 0–49 number rectangle to carry out the activity.

PLENARY

Recite counting in steps of 3 from 0 to 30, then back to 0. Finish by counting around the circle in steps of 3 to 30.

LESSON 4

RESOURCES	A shuffled set of cards 1–20 (one card for each child); a laminated 0–99 Number square (photocopiable page 13) and a small cube for each child; paper and pencils; photocopiable page 28 (Two-way counts).
LEARNING OUTCOMES	**ORAL AND MENTAL STARTER** and **MAIN TEACHING ACTIVITY** ● **Describe and extend simple number sequences:** count on in steps of 3 to at least 30, from and back to zero, then from and back to any given small number.
ORAL AND MENTAL STARTER	COUNTING ON IN THREES: Recite counting in steps of 3 from zero to 30, then back to zero. Give each child one of a shuffled set of 1–20 cards. Then ask them to take turns around the circle to count on 3 from the number on their card.
MAIN TEACHING ACTIVITY	COUNTING BACK/ON 3: Play a 'number square and cube game' with the rule 'count on 3' recording, for example, 24 → 27. When the children have completed 20 number statements they should repeat the game with the rule 'count back 3'.
DIFFERENTIATION	More able: give these children a copy of photocopiable page 28 (Two-way counts) and ask them to complete the sheet using the rule 'count on/count back 3'. Less able: ask these children to complete 10 number statements.
PLENARY	Repeat counting in steps of 3 from zero to 30, then back to zero. Then play a circle game 'Count on 3' with cards 1–20.

LESSON 5

RESOURCES	A set of shuffled numeral cards 90–99; flip chart or easel; Number square teaching chart (photocopiable page 13); a laminated 0–99 Number square (photocopiable page 13), a small cube, a copy of photocopiable page 28 (Two-way counts) and a pencil for each child.
LEARNING OUTCOMES	**ORAL AND MENTAL STARTER** and **MAIN TEACHING ACTIVITY** ● **Describe and extend simple number sequences:** count on or back in tens, starting from any two-digit number.
ORAL AND MENTAL STARTER	COUNTING BACK IN TENS: See the Oral and mental starter in Lesson 3, page 126.
MAIN TEACHING ACTIVITY	COUNTING BACK/ON 20: Sit the children facing the teaching chart and tell them they are going to play a two-way counting game with a number square and cube where they count on and count back 20 from each number. Use the teaching chart to demonstrate the method of counting on and back 20, then point to a few numbers and ask the children to say the count on and count back 20 numbers. Hand out copies of photocopiable page 28 (Two-way counts); remind the children to write the number the cube lands on in the centre box each time before they write in the count on and count back 20 numbers.
DIFFERENTIATION	More able: provide a fresh copy of photocopiable page 28 and ask the children to try 'count on/count back 30'. Less able: let the children work on plain paper. Ask them to complete 10 'count on 20' statements and 10 'count back 20 statements' (or five of each, according to ability).
PLENARY	MY NUMBER/YOUR NUMBER: Add 20 and subtract 20 (see Lesson 3, Unit 1, Term 2 on page 99).

Scoop two handfuls

Name	Approximately less than 40		Approximately more than 40 and less than 70		Approximately more than 70	
		Close estimate		Close estimate		Close estimate
						Exact number

UNIT 9

ORGANISATION (5 LESSONS)

	LEARNING OUTCOMES	ORAL AND MENTAL STARTER	MAIN TEACHING ACTIVITY	PLENARY
LESSON 1	● **Know by heart:** all pairs of multiples of 10 with a total of 100 (e.g. 30 + 70). ● Use patterns of similar calculations.	MAKE 10 and TAKE FROM 10: Counting in tens.	10 AND 100 ADDITION AND SUBTRACTION PATTERNS.	MAKE 100 TAKE FROM 100: Playing circle games.
LESSON 2	● **Order whole numbers to at least 100**, and position them on a 100 square.	ADDING BY GROUPING TENS AND UNITS: Playing a game with cards 10–50.	POSITIONING NUMBERS ON A NUMBER SQUARE.	Reviewing work from the Main teaching activity.
LESSON 3	● Begin to add three two-digit numbers with the help of apparatus (totals up to 100).	ALL CHANGE: Playing this game with three hoops and cards 1–30.	TRIOS: Making 100 using three numbers.	ALL CHANGE.
LESSON 4	● Add/subtract 9: add/subtract 10 and adjust by 1. ● Investigate a general statement about familiar numbers by finding examples that satisfy it.	NEAR DOUBLES: Asking oral questions.	ADDING AND SUBTRACTING 9 WITH A NUMBER SQUARE. Difference of 9 investigation.	MY NUMBER/ YOUR NUMBER: Adding and subtracting 9.
LESSON 5	● Recognise all coins and begin to use £.p notation for money (for example, know that £4.65 indicates £4 and 65p). ● Find totals, give change, and work out which coins to pay.	SPEND AND CHANGE FROM £2.00: Using coin cards.	WAYS TO MAKE £5.00: Using coins.	SPEND AND CHANGE FROM £2.00: Using coin cards.

ORAL AND MENTAL SKILLS Describe and extend simple number sequences: count on or back in tens, starting from any two-digit number. Know by heart: all addition and subtraction facts for each number to at least 10; all pairs of multiples of 10 with a total of 100. Partition additions into tens and units, then recombine. Add three small numbers by putting the largest number first and/or find a pair totalling 10. Identify near doubles, using doubles already known.

In Unit 9 Lessons 1, 2 and 4 are given in full, while Lessons 3 and 5 are provided as grids.

RESOURCES

A shuffled set of cards numbered in tens 10–100 (one card for each child); flip chart and pen; paper and pencils; Cuisenaire rods.

LESSON 1

LEARNING OUTCOMES

ORAL AND MENTAL STARTER
● **Describe and extend simple number sequences: count on or back in tens, starting from any two-digit number.**
● **Know by heart: all addition and subtraction facts for each number to at least 10.**

MAIN TEACHING ACTIVITY
● **Know by heart:** all pairs of multiples of 10 with a total of 100 (e.g. 30 + 70).
● Use patterns of similar calculations.

ORAL AND MENTAL STARTER

MAKE 10/TAKE FROM 10: Count on in tens together from several two-digit starting numbers, carry on through 100 if the children are confident. Then play 'Make 10' and 'Take from 10' (see Lesson 5, Unit 2, in Term 1, on page 33).

MAIN TEACHING ACTIVITY

10 AND 100 ADDITION AND SUBTRACTION PATTERNS: Tell the children that they are going to build addition and subtraction patterns for 10 and 100. First use the flip chart to demonstrate how to start building addition patterns of 10 and 100 together:

$1 + 9 = 10$ $10 + 90 = 100$
$2 + ? = 10$ $20 + ? = 100$

Ask the children to tell you what number comes next in each pattern. Then demonstrate how to start building subtraction patterns of 10 and 100:

$10 - 1 = 9$ $100 - 10 = 90$
$10 - 2 = ?$ $100 - 20 = ?$

Encourage the children to tell you what number comes next in each pattern.

Tell the children to start by copying the addition patterns on to their sheet of paper and then to continue writing the patterns as far as they can. When they finish this they should copy the subtraction patterns and then continue with these patterns as far as they can.

DIFFERENTIATION

More able: include $100 + 900 =$ and $1000 - 100 =$ in the pattern.
Less able: provide Cuisenaire rods for any child who may require additional support.

PLENARY

MAKE 100/TAKE FROM 100: Play circle games with cards in tens to 100 in the same way as 'Make 10/Take from 10' in the **Oral and mental starter**.

RESOURCES

A set of shuffled numeral cards 10–50 in ones (one card for each child); flip chart or small easel, water-based pen and cleaning cloth; photocopiable page 18 (Blank 0–99 number square) A4 copies and a laminated and enlarged teaching chart; a few completed 0–99 number squares; crayons or felt tipped pens and pencils.

PREPARATION

Make two copies of photocopiable page 18 (Blank 0–99 number square) for each child. Enlarge one copy as a teaching chart and laminate it. Colour 10 random squares on the laminated chart with a water-based marker pen and attach it to a flip chart or small easel.

LEARNING OUTCOMES

ORAL AND MENTAL STARTER
● Partition additions into tens and units, then recombine.

MAIN TEACHING ACTIVITY
● **Order whole numbers to at least 100,** and position them on a 100 square.

ORAL AND MENTAL STARTER

ADDING BY GROUPING TENS AND UNITS: Hold up two numeral cards between 10 and 50. Tell the children you want them to add the numbers together. Encourage them to group the tens first, then add on the units. Tell them to put up their hands when they have found the total. Choose a child to say the answer each time and explain what he or she did.

MAIN TEACHING ACTIVITY

POSITIONING NUMBERS ON A NUMBER SQUARE: Sit the children facing the blank number square teaching chart. Tell them that the coloured squares on the chart have to be changed for correct numbers on a number square. Point to one of the coloured squares and choose a child to try to say the correct number. Wipe the coloured square clean and ask the child to write in the correct number with a water-based pen. Do this with each coloured square. Clean the chart after use.

VOCABULARY

Numbers 0–10 and 0–100 in tens; add; make; subtract from; equals; leaves.

VOCABULARY

Partition; additions; recombine; add; equals; sum; make; total; altogether; order; size; position; place; place value; first; second; last; before; after; in-between; next; bigger; biggest; smaller; smallest; largest; greatest; explain your method.

Now tell the children that they are to work with a partner with two copies of the blank number square each. Tell them each to colour ten squares on one of their sheets and exchange it with their partner. Then, on their second sheet, write in the correct numbers to match the positions of the coloured squares on their partner's sheet. When they have both finished, they can check together whether the numbers on both sheets are all correct.

DIFFERENTIATION

More able: ask children to colour 20 separate squares.
Less able: let the children refer to completed 0–99 number squares.

PLENARY

Sit the children facing the blank 0–99 Number square chart. Review the work done in the Main teaching activity by pointing to different squares on the chart and inviting individual children to write the correct number in the square on the chart each time with a water-based pen. Ask if the children can tell you about any patterns that help them (such as the 0s column, then 1s column or adding on in tens down each column).

RESOURCES	Numeral cards 1–30; three sorting hoops; flip chart and pen; photocopiable page 69 (Trios) for each child; pencils; Cuisenaire 'tens' rods.
LEARNING OUTCOMES	**ORAL AND MENTAL STARTER** ● Add three small numbers by putting the largest number first, and/or find a pair totalling 10. **MAIN TEACHING ACTIVITY** ● Begin to add three two-digit numbers with the help of apparatus (totals up to 100).
ORAL AND MENTAL STARTER	ALL CHANGE: Play this game with three hoops and cards 1–30 (as in Lesson 5 in Unit 2 of Term 1, on page 34).
MAIN TEACHING ACTIVITY	TRIOS: Sit the children facing the flip chart while you copy one of the 'trio' diagrams from photocopiable page 69 onto it. Ask the children to tell you three numbers that have a total of 100. Scribe in their numbers and write 100 in the centre. Then tell them to complete each diagram on their own sheets, using three different numbers to add up to 100 each time.
DIFFERENTIATION	More able: encourage the children to include two-digit numbers ending in 5. Less able: provide sets of Cuisenaire 'tens' rods as support.
PLENARY	Repeat the 'All change' game with three hoops and cards 1–30.

RESOURCES

0–99 Number square chart (photocopiable page 13); small cubes; photocopiable page 28 (Two-way counts); flip chart and pen; pencils and paper, including some prepared sheets (see **Preparation**, below).

PREPARATION

Enlarge a copy of photocopiable page 13 and laminate it for use as a teaching chart. Attach the number square chart to a flip chart. Before or during the activity write 'Difference of 9' at the top of a sheet of paper for each of the more able children.

LEARNING OUTCOMES

ORAL AND MENTAL STARTER
● Identify near doubles, using doubles already known (e.g. 8 + 9, 40 + 41).

MAIN TEACHING ACTIVITY
● Add/subtract 9: add/subtract 10 and adjust by 1.
● Investigate a general statement about familiar numbers by finding examples that satisfy it.

VOCABULARY

Doubles; near doubles; total; add; equals; addition; minus; subtraction; subtract; less; leaves; altogether; number square; rule; arrow; difference between; difference of; predict; describe the pattern.

ORAL AND MENTAL STARTER

NEAR DOUBLES: Begin by reminding the children about 'near doubles'. (They should have learned in Year 1 that two numbers positioned next to each other can be added together by using simple doubles.) Remind them how to use doubles they know by doubling the lower number and adding 1, for example: $7 + 8 \rightarrow 14 + 1 = 15$. Try questions such as: *What is the total of 5 + 6? ...6 + 7? ...40 + 41?* Repeat this with examples where children double the higher number and subtract 1, for example: $29 + 30 \rightarrow 60 - 1 = 59$.

MAIN TEACHING ACTIVITY

ADDING AND SUBTRACTING 9 WITH A NUMBER SQUARE: Sit the children facing the number square teaching chart, then use it to demonstrate the pattern of add/subtract 9. Point to different numbers on the square and choose a child to say the 'add 9' number. Repeat this, choosing a child to say the 'subtract 9' number a few times. Show the children a copy of photocopiable page 28 (Two-way counts) and explain that they are going to play a number square and cube game. Tell them to write 'Add and subtract 9' in the rule box on the sheet before they start the game. Then remind them how to complete the sheet:

● Write the number the cube lands on in the middle box on the sheet each time.
● Write the 'subtract 9' and the 'add 9' numbers in the two side boxes, for example:
  $33 \leftarrow 42 \rightarrow 51$

Check that the children know what they have to do before they return to their tables to carry out the activity.

DIFFERENTIATION

More able: when they have completed the sheet, give them each a plain sheet of paper with 'Difference of 9' written at the top. Tell them to use the number square teaching chart to find and write down as many pairs of numbers as they can with a 'difference of 9'. Demonstrate the recording:
$13 < \text{———} > 4$ or $25 < \text{———} > 34$
Less able: let the children carry out the activity on paper. Ask them to write 10 'add 9' statements, then 10 'subtract 9' statements (or five of each, according to ability).

PLENARY

With the number square chart displayed to help them, play 'My number, your number' with the rule 'add 9', saying, for example: *My number is 24. (Alex) your number is?* Change the rule to 'subtract 9'. Can more able children see a pattern/rule for adding 9? (+ 10 − 1)?

RESOURCES	A set of coin cards: 5p, 10p, 20p, 50p, £1.00 (photocopiable page 15); a set of coins: 1p, 2p, 5p, 10p, 20p, 50p, £1.00, £2.00 for each group; flip chart and pen; paper and pencils.
LEARNING OUTCOMES	**ORAL AND MENTAL STARTER** and **MAIN TEACHING ACTIVITY** ● Recognise all coins and begin to use £.p notation for money (for example, know that £4.65 indicates £4 and 65p). ● Find totals, give change, and work out which coins to pay.
ORAL AND MENTAL STARTER	SPEND AND CHANGE FROM £2.00: Sit the children in a semicircle. Give each child a coin card from 5p to £1.00. Ask two children to stand facing the group and hold up their cards. Choose a child sitting down to say the total. Scribe this total on the flip chart, then ask the group to work out the change from £2.00. Choose a child to give the answer. Repeat by asking two more children to stand facing the group.
MAIN TEACHING ACTIVITY	WAYS TO MAKE £5.00: Tell the children they are to use the sets of coins on their tables to find different ways to make £5.00. They should record each way by drawing around the coins and labelling them on their sheet. Challenge them to find at least five different ways.
DIFFERENTIATION	More able: can they find 10 different ways to make £5.00? Less able: change the activity to ways to make £2.00 or even £1.00.
PLENARY	Repeat the 'Spend and change from £2.00' game with coin cards from the **Oral and mental starter**.

UNIT 10

ORGANISATION (5 LESSONS)

	LEARNING OUTCOMES	ORAL AND MENTAL STARTER	MAIN TEACHING ACTIVITY	PLENARY
LESSON 1	● **Understand the operation of multiplication as repeated addition or as describing an array.** ● Use the × and = signs to record mental calculations in a number sentence.	10 TIMES TABLE: Reciting the 10 times table and asking oral questions.	BUILDING THE 10 TIMES TABLE: Colouring the pattern of multiples of 10.	Reciting the 10 times table. Playing a 'Times 10' circle game with cards 1–10.
LESSON 2	● **Understand the operation of multiplication as repeated addition or as describing an array.** ● Use the × and = signs to record mental calculations in a number sentence.	2 TIMES TABLE: Reciting the 2 times table and asking oral questions.	BUILDING THE 2 TIMES TABLE: Colouring the pattern of multiples of 2.	Reciting the 2 times table. Playing a 'Times 2' circle game with cards 1–20.
LESSON 3	● Use known number facts to carry out mentally simple multiplications. ● Use the × and = signs to record mental calculations in a number sentence. ● Check with an equivalent calculation.	DOUBLE AND HALF: Playing a game with even-numbered cards 2–20.	DOMINO ADDITION AND MULTIPLICATION. Shop for sweets with £2.00.	DOMINO TIMES. Reviewing work from the Main teaching activity.
LESSON 4	● Use mental addition, subtraction and simple multiplication to solve simple word problems involving numbers in 'real life' or money, using one or two steps. ● Explain how the problem was solved.	MULTIPLE BUYING: Asking oral questions.	SHOP FOR SWEETS WITH £2.00.	Reviewing work from the Main teaching activity.
LESSON 5	● Begin to recognise and find one half of shapes. ● Solve mathematical problems or puzzles. Suggest extensions by asking 'What if ...?' or 'What could I try next?'	DOUBLE AND HALF: Playing a game with even-numbered cards 2–20.	SHAPE PUZZLE: a colouring half investigation.	Reviewing work from the Main teaching activity.

ORAL AND MENTAL SKILLS **Know by heart: multiplication facts for the 2 and 10 times tables;** doubles of all numbers to 10 and the corresponding halves. Derive quickly: division facts corresponding to the 2 and 10 times tables. Use mental addition, subtraction and simple multiplication to solve simple word problems involving numbers in 'real life' or money, using one or two steps. **Explain how a problem was solved.**

In Unit 10, Lessons 1, 2 and 5 are provided as grids, while Lessons 3 and 4 are given in full.

UNIT 10

LESSON 1

RESOURCES	A set of shuffled cards 1–10 (one card for each child); sets of cards in multiples of 10 (a set for each pair); the number square teaching chart (photocopiable page 13) and coloured water-based marker; a copy of photocopiable page 13 for each child; paper, pencils, crayons or felt-tipped pens; Cuisenaire rods.
LEARNING OUTCOMES	**ORAL AND MENTAL STARTER** ● **Know by heart: multiplication facts for the 10 times table.** ● Derive quickly: division facts corresponding to the 2 and 10 times tables. **MAIN TEACHING ACTIVITY** ● **Understand the operation of multiplication as repeated addition or as describing an array.** ● Use the × and = signs to record mental calculations in a number sentence.
ORAL AND MENTAL STARTER	10 TIMES TABLE: Sit the children in a circle and recite the 10 times table. Give pairs of children a set of cards in multiples of 10 to lay in front of them. Tell them they should hold up a card to give an answer to the question each time. Then ask quick-fire multiplication and division questions such as: *What are 5 tens? How many tens in 60?*

MAIN TEACHING ACTIVITY	BUILDING THE 10 TIMES TABLE: Sit the children facing the teaching chart and tell them they are to colour the pattern of tens on their number squares (photocopiable page 13) and write the 10 times table on a separate sheet of paper as far as possible. Demonstrate how to start colouring the pattern of tens to 20 on the teaching chart and explain that multiplication statements can be written with the numbers in a different order. Tell the children that when they write the ten times table they should write both versions. Demonstrate this as:
	   $0 \times 10 = 0$ $10 \times 0 = 0$
	   $1 \times 10 = 10$ $10 \times 1 = 10$
	Ask the children how to write the two multiplication statements for 10×2, then tell them to copy the pattern on the chart on to their number square and copy the multiplication statements on to their sheet. Encourage them to continue colouring the pattern and writing the multiplication statements as far as they can.

DIFFERENTIATION	More able: encourage these children to try to extend the table beyond 100, for example 11×10, and so on. Less able: provide Cuisenaire rods for children who require support.
PLENARY	Recite the 10 times table. Then give each child a numeral card between 1 and 10 and ask them, in turn, to multiply the number on their card by 10 saying, for example, '10 times 6 equals 60'.

LESSON 2

RESOURCES	A set of shuffled cards 1–20 (one card for each child); a copy of photocopiable page 13 for each child; paper, pencils, crayons or felt-tipped pens; Cuisenaire rods or interlocking cubes.
LEARNING OUTCOMES	**ORAL AND MENTAL STARTER** ● **Know by heart: multiplication facts for the 2 times table.** ● Derive quickly: division facts corresponding to the 2 and 10 times tables. **MAIN TEACHING ACTIVITY** ● **Understand the operation of multiplication as repeated addition or as describing an array.** ● Use the × and = signs to record mental calculations in a number sentence.
ORAL AND MENTAL STARTER	2 TIMES TABLE: As for Lesson 1, above, but with the 2 times table.
MAIN TEACHING ACTIVITY	BUILDING THE 2 TIMES TABLE: As for Lesson 1, above, but with the 2 times table.
DIFFERENTIATION	More able: encourage the children to extend the table as far as possible – to 50, to 100, above 100? Less able: provide Cuisenaire rods or interlocking cubes for children who require support.
PLENARY	As for Lesson 1, above, but with the 2 times table.

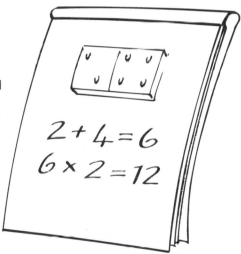

LESSON 3

RESOURCES

A shuffled set of even-numbered cards 2–20 (one card for each child); a box of dominoes for each group; paper and pencils; Cuisenaire rods.

PREPARATION

Place paper, pencils and a box of dominoes on each table.

LEARNING OUTCOMES

ORAL AND MENTAL STARTER

● KNOW BY HEART: doubles of all numbers to 10 and the corresponding halves.

MAIN TEACHING ACTIVITY

● Use known number facts to carry out mentally simple multiplications.
● Use the × and = signs to record mental calculations in a number sentence.
● Check with an equivalent calculation.

ORAL AND MENTAL STARTER

DOUBLE AND HALF: Play with even-numbered cards 2–20 only, as in Lesson 5, Unit 6, page 117.

MAIN TEACHING ACTIVITY

DOMINO ADDITION AND MULTIPLICATION: Sit the children facing the flip chart. Tell them they are going to do addition and multiplication with dominoes. Explain that they have to select one domino each time, add the spots, multiply the total by 2 and record the answer as a number sentence on paper. Demonstrate the method of recording on the flip chart. See the example on the right:

As the children become familiar with the activity, encourage them to carry out the addition step of the calculation mentally recording, for example: $6 \times 2 = 12$ only. When they have finished writing the number sentence, they replace the domino and take another.

DIFFERENTIATION

More able: encourage these children to repeat the activity, only this time multiplying the total number of spots on each domino by 10 and recording, for example:
    $2 + 4 = 6 \times 10 = 60$
or just
    $6 \times 10 = 60$.
Less able: remove the double six and six/five dominoes from the set. Have Cuisenaire rods available for children to use if they require help.

PLENARY

DOMINO TIMES: Sit the children in a circle and give each child a domino. Ask them to take turns to show their domino, say the total number of spots on it, and multiply the number by two, for example: 'Six spots; six times two equals twelve'. Repeat this, changing the rule to multiply by 10'.

VOCABULARY

Double; half; halve; multiply; lots of; groups of; times two; multiplication; twice; add; addition; equals; total; makes; sum; times ten.

RESOURCES

Photocopiable page 138 (Shop for sweets); spotted or numbered six-sided dice; dice marked 1, 2, 3, 1, 2, 3 and 0–5; sets of all coins to £2.00; pencils.

PREPARATION

Make sufficient copies of photocopiable page 138 for each child to have a shopping list. Cut the sheets in half. Make one enlarged copy on a sheet of card and laminate this for use as a teaching chart. While the children are playing the game, copy the following Winners charts on to the class board (adding further rows if you have more groups).

Winner of the most sweets bought		
Group number	Most sweets bought	Method of addition
Group 1		
Group 2		
Group 3		
Group 4		

Winner with most change from £2.00			
Group number	Money spent	Change from £2.00	Method of addition
Group 1			
Group 2			
Group 3			
Group 4			

VOCABULARY

Multiply; add; subtract; price; buy; spend; total; cost; price; change; pay; bought; money spent; how much?; how many?; cheap; costs; dear; less; cheaper; method; how did you work it out?; calculate; calculation; mental calculation; most; least.

LEARNING OUTCOMES

ORAL AND MENTAL STARTER and MAIN TEACHING ACTIVITY

● Use mental addition, subtraction and simple multiplication to solve simple word problems involving numbers in 'real life' or money, using one or two steps.
● Explain how the problem was solved.

ORAL AND MENTAL STARTER

MULTIPLE BUYING: Ask oral questions using 2s and 10s, for example: *A marble costs 2p. How much will five marbles, three marbles, seven marbles cost? A super bouncy ball costs 10p. How much will three balls cost? Eight balls...? Five balls...?* etc.

MAIN TEACHING ACTIVITY

SHOP FOR SWEETS WITH £2.00: Sit the children facing the teaching chart and tell them they are going to play a game where they shop for sweets. They have £2.00 to spend. Use the teaching chart and two children to demonstrate the rules of the game:
● Work together in pairs, starting with the first on the sheet (Mini lollies).
● One child throws the dice to see how many you are to buy and you both write the number in the 'Number to buy' column on the sheet.

● Work out the total cost for the sweets and write this amount in the 'Total cost' column.
● Repeat the activity with the next sweet, taking turns to throw the dice each time.
● When you have worked with all six sweets, add the numbers, then the money, in the easiest order, to find the totals. Then work out how much change you would get from £2.00 using the total cost of all the sweets bought in the game.
● When all the children in the group have completed the sheet, discuss results together as a group and find the two winners – the pair who bought the most sweets; and the pair with most change from £2.00.

Organise the children to work with partners in groups of six to eight children and number each group. Check that they know what they have to do, then hand out the copies of photocopiable page 138 and ask them to return to their tables to carry out the activity.

DIFFERENTIATION

More able: give these children dice marked 0–5 so they work with multiples up to 10.
Less able: provide sets of coins to support any children who are unsure. You could also allow them to work with a dice marked 1, 2, 3, 1, 2, 3.

PLENARY

Review the work done in the **Main teaching activity** by inviting the pairs of children who are winners in each group to give their results. Scribe the results and methods on the Winners charts on the class board and ask which group is the overall winner. Ask the children to explain their calculation methods.

This activity is not intended to encourage written, vertical calculation methods, but careful recording and 'agility' with mental addition and multiplication strategies. Do not be tempted to teach the children to 'add up' the columns, units first, for example.

RESOURCES	A shuffled set of even-numbered cards 2–20, (one card for each child); a copy of photocopiable page 139 for each child and a teaching chart made from an enlarged copy; coloured pens; pencils, crayons or felt-tipped pens.
LEARNING OUTCOMES	**ORAL AND MENTAL STARTER** ● **Know by heart:** doubles of all numbers to 10 and the corresponding halves. **MAIN TEACHING ACTIVITY** ● Begin to recognise and find one half of shapes. ● Solve mathematical problems or puzzles. Suggest extensions by asking 'What if …?' or 'What could I try next?'
ORAL AND MENTAL STARTER	DOUBLE AND HALF: Play with even-numbered cards 2–20 as in Lesson 3 on page 135.
MAIN TEACHING ACTIVITY	SHAPE PUZZLE: Sit the children facing the teaching chart and tell them they are going to try a shape puzzle where they have to find different ways to colour half of 16 squares. First ask: *What is half of 16?* Then demonstrate the activity on the teaching chart by inviting two children to colour half the squares (8) in two of the grids in a different way with a coloured pen. Show the children a copy of photocopiable page 139. Tell them to try to find a different way to colour half the squares in each grid.
DIFFERENTIATION	More able: Encourage to include diagonally cut 'half squares' in some of their arrangements such as 7 squares with two half squares or 6 whole squares with four half squares. Less able: Encourage them to create different designs by doing 8 squares on the grid each time. Ask them to check to check that they have coloured eight squares each time.
PLENARY	Review the work done in the **Main teaching activity** by inviting individual children to colour one half of each grid on the teaching chart. Challenge them to use a different configuration each time.

Name

Shop for sweets

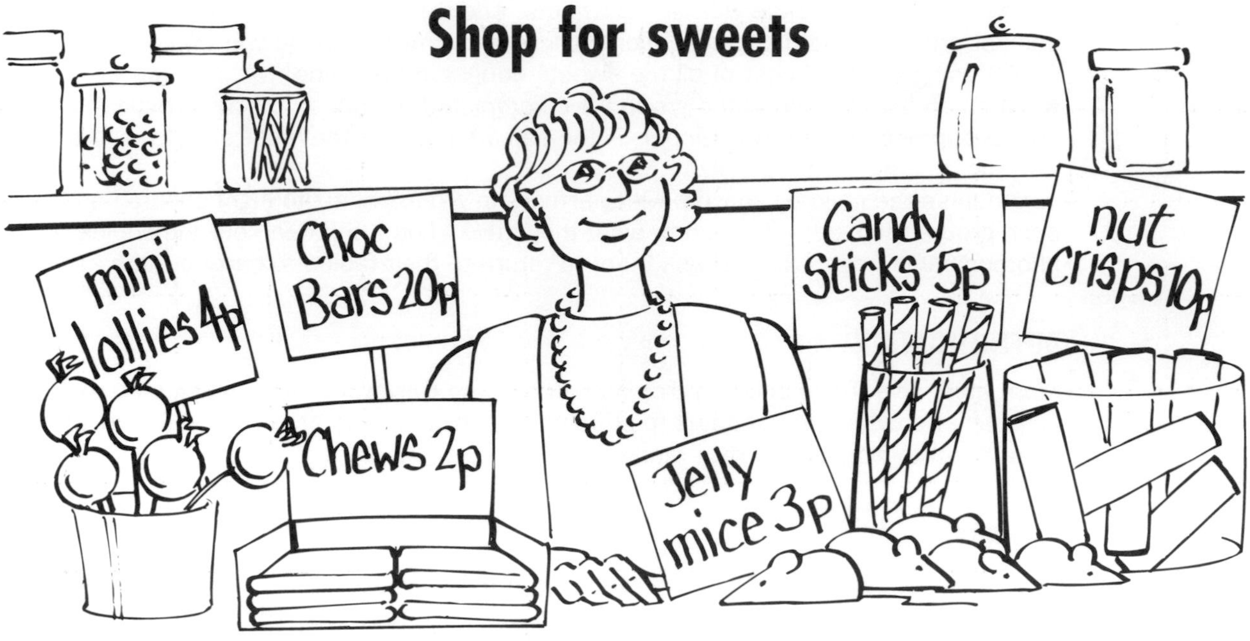
mini lollies 4p
Choc Bars 20p
Chews 2p
Candy Sticks 5p
nut crisps 10p
Jelly mice 3p

Sweets	Price	Number to buy	Total cost

Total money spent [ ] Change from £2.00 [ ]

Name

Shape puzzle

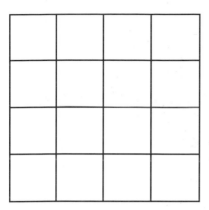
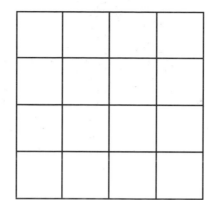
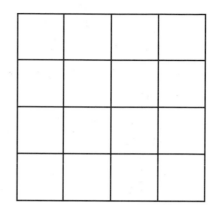

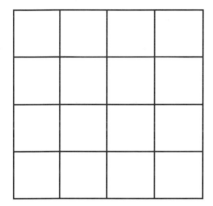
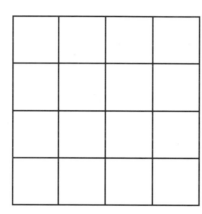
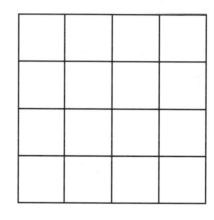

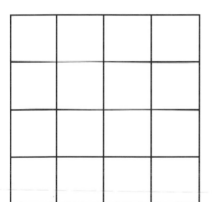
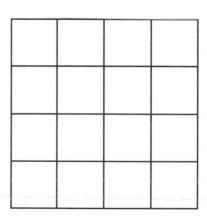
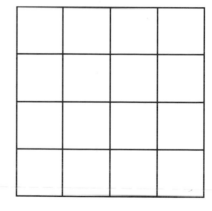

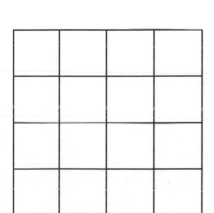
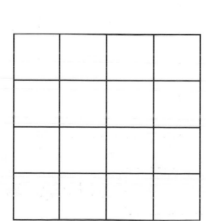
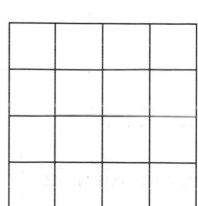

UNITS 11-12

ORGANISATION (10 LESSONS)

	LEARNING OUTCOMES	ORAL & MENTAL STARTER	MAIN TEACHING ACTIVITY	PLENARY
LESSON 1 +2 +3	• Use and begin to read the vocabulary related to length, mass and capacity. • **Estimate, measure and compare lengths, masses and capacities, using standard units** (m, cm, kg, litre); **suggest suitable units and equipment for such measurements.** • **Use a ruler to draw and measure lines to the nearest centimetre.**	RECITE THE 2 AND 10 TIMES TABLES: asking oral questions.. Circle games: TIMES TWO/DIVIDE BY TWO with even-numbered cards 2–20. DOMINO TIMES.	SORTING OBJECTS BY MASS: Working with objects that weigh: less than ½ kg/between ½ kg and 1 kg/more than 1 kg. MAKING AND USING A ¼ LITRE MEASURE. ESTIMATING A WALK OF THREE METRES: Measuring and comparing the actual length walked. DRAWING PATTERNS WITH A RULER AND MEASURING LINES.	Reviewing work from the Main teaching activities.
LESSON 4 +5	• Solve a given problem by sorting, classifying and organising information in simple ways, such as: in a list or simple table; in a pictogram; in a block graph. Discuss and explain results.	ADDING TWO-DIGIT NUMBERS: Adding by counting on or partitioning into tens and units. Playing a game with cards 10–30.	FAVOURITE ALLSORT. SORTING LIQUORICE ALLSORTS & MAKING A GRAPH.	Reviewing work from the Main teaching activities.
LESSON 6 +7 +8 +9	• Order the months of the year. • Read the time to the quarter hour on an analogue clock. • Use mental addition and subtraction to solve simple word problems.	ONE HOUR LATER AND EARLIER: Playing games with a teaching clock. Times to the hour, half hour and quarter hour .	NEXT MONTH/LAST MONTH: Playing with cards January to December. TIMES TO THE QUARTER HOUR: Quarter past, quarter to the hour in analogue form. TWO HOURS LATER AND EARLIER: Playing with time cards to the half hour.	ONE HOUR LATER AND EARLIER: Playing games with a teaching clock. Times to the hour, half hour and quarter hour .
LESSON 10	• Use mental addition and subtraction to solve simple word problems.	THREE HOURS LATER AND EARLIER.	PLANE JOURNEYS IN HOURS.	Reviewing work from the Main teaching activities.

ORAL AND MENTAL STARTER **Know by heart multiplication facts for the 2 and 10 times tables.** Derive quickly: division facts corresponding to the 2 times table. Put the larger number first and counting on in tens or ones; partition additions into tens and units. **Choose and use efficient calculation strategies.** Use mental addition and subtraction to solve simple word problems involving numbers in 'real life'.

In Unit 11 Lessons 1–3 can be presented as separate lessons or on a circus basis. Lessons 4 and 5 offer two different variations of a similar activity. In Unit 12, Lessons 6–9 can again be presented on a circus basis or as individual lessons. Lesson 10 is given in full.

LESSON 1 +2 +3

RESOURCES

A set of even-numbered cards 2–20; a set of dominoes (one domino for each child); a flip chart or small easel; three metre sticks; a beanbag; a rope or cane to be used as a starting line; centimetre rulers; photocopiable pages 147 and 148; paper and pencils; a pan balance, 1kg and ½kg weights; a ¼ litre measure; a washing-up bowl holding approximately 1 litre of water; a clear plastic bottle (larger than ¼ litre); an elastic band; a funnel; a set of different small containers, such as an eggcup, spray can top, yoghurt pot, coffee jar lid or doll's cup.

PREPARATION

Make a copy of photocopiable pages 147 and 148 for each child plus one enlarged copy to use as a teaching chart. On page 148 you will need to fill in the names of the small containers you will be using before you make the copies. Collect all the equipment together and place the appropriate equipment for each group or activity on tables. For 'Estimating a walk of 3 metres', draw the following chart on a flip chart or a large sheet of paper.

Estimating a walk of 3 metres		
Less than 3 m	About 3 m	More than 3 m

Clear a large floor space in the classroom (or use the school hall if it is available). Sit the children in two lines facing each other. Place the starting line and the teaching chart at one end of the lines.

LEARNING OUTCOMES

ORAL AND MENTAL STARTER
● **Know by heart multiplication facts for the 2 and 10 times tables.**
● Derive quickly: division facts corresponding to the 2 times table.

MAIN TEACHING ACTIVITY
● Use and begin to read the vocabulary related to length, mass and capacity.
● **Estimate, measure and compare lengths, masses and capacities, using** standard units (m, cm, kg, litre); **suggest suitable units and equipment for such measurements.**
● **Use a ruler to draw and measure lines to the nearest centimetre.**

VOCABULARY

Estimate; guess; measure; count; metres; distance; more; less; about; further; furthest; between; nearly; longer; shorter; balance; 1 and ½kg; weight; weighs; mass; heavy; heavier; heaviest; light; lighter; lightest; empty; full; nearly full; pour; till; count; holds; mark; ¼ litre; container; contains; exact; exactly; drawing; measuring; draw; label.

ORAL AND MENTAL STARTER

Select one 2 and 10 times tables game to play each day:
● RECITE THE 2 AND 10 TIMES TABLES: Follow this with quick-fire questions, such as: *6 twos?* or *5 tens?*
● TIMES 2/DIVIDE BY 2: see Lesson 5 in Unit 6 on page 117.
● DOMINO TIMES: see Lesson 3 in Unit 10 on page 135.

MAIN TEACHING ACTIVITY

You may wish to plan the activities below as separate, whole-class lessons or organise them as a range of activities for different groups over three days on a circus basis. You will need to introduce (or revise) the main teaching points of the relevant activities each day.

Explain that these activities are all about measuring. Talk about different units of measurement the children have met before, such as metres and ½l.

SORTING OBJECTS BY MASS: Sit the children in front of the displayed teaching chart version of photocopiable page 147. Pass ½kg and 1kg weights round for the children to handle. Invite a child to choose an object in the classroom which he or she thinks will weigh about ½kg, then establish a result with a balance. Ask the children in the group to judge whether the pans look balanced (or nearly balanced) or whether the object clearly weighs more or less than ½kg. If the object clearly weighs more, balance it against the 1kg weight to see whether it weighs more or less than 1kg. Discuss the result and ask the children which is the right column on the chart to write the object's name. Sketch a small picture of the object and write its name underneath in the appropriate column on the teaching chart. Repeat the demonstration with another child's chosen object.

Give each child a copy of photocopiable page 147 and tell them they will be working together in small groups. Explain what they have to do:

● Everybody chooses an object in the classroom they think weighs about ½kg.
● Take turns to balance your object against the ½kg weight, then the 1kg weight.
● Discuss each result as a group, then draw and label the objects in the appropriate column on your own sheet.

MAKING AND USING A ¼l MEASURE: Sit the children in front of the teaching chart version of photocopiable page 148 and the appropriate equipment. Demonstrate how to make a ¼l measure by filling the ¼l measure, pouring the water into the plastic bottle and marking the water level with an elastic band. Then tell the children that they are to find out how many of each small container it takes to fill the ¼l measure. Demonstrate the activity by inviting two children to estimate how many eggcups will fill the ¼l measure, then ask them to work together (one to hold the plastic ¼l measure and the funnel in the bowl, the other to do the pouring) to establish the result. The rest of the group keeps count. As the water level rises towards the elastic band, ask the children if they think there is room for one more each time. Ask the group to tell the child to stop pouring as soon as the water touches the ¼l measure mark. Scribe the results in the column on the teaching chart while the children pour the water carefully back into the bowl.

Hand out copies of photocopiable page 148 and tell the children what to do.

● Work together as a group to make the ¼l measure.
● Write your estimates individually for each container in the column on the sheet.
● Choose a partner to work with, and together select one container from the sheet.
● Take turns (in pairs) to use one container to fill the ¼l measure.
● Everyone in the group should count, telling the child to stop pouring when the water reaches the ¼l mark.
● Everyone then records the result on their own sheet.
● Pour the water back into the bowl and let the next pair repeat the process with another container, and so on.

Check that the children know what they have to do before they return to their tables to carry out the activity.

ESTIMATING A WALK OF 3 METRES: Sit the children in the prepared space, preferably with a helper to adjudicate and scribe. Discuss what is measured in metres and what in centimetres. Tell the children they are going to take turns to judge a walk of three metres, then choose a child to walk three metres from the starting line, stopping when he or she thinks the distance is right. Mark the walk by placing a beanbag on the floor in front of the child's feet. Then choose two children to measure the distance to the beanbag with metre sticks. (Where the measurement is judged as about or nearly 3m, allow approximately 10cm more or less.) The child who walked, writes his or her first name in the appropriate column on the chart. When everyone has had a go, discuss the results with the children.

DRAWING PATTERNS WITH A RULER AND MEASURING LINES: This activity would be useful if you wish to have a paper-and-pencil activity running alongside one of the practical tasks, particularly if you need to be able to focus on a less able group of children. Tell the children they are going to draw a pattern using a ruler to draw lines on a sheet of paper. Demonstrate on a flip chart how to draw a pattern with a ruler, recording the length of each line at its end to the nearest centimetre. Tell the children to colour their finished patterns.

DIFFERENTIATION

Organise children to work in mixed ability groups for these activities to encourage children of all abilities to share their perceptions of each task.

More able: put children into mixed ability groups for these activities to encourage children of all abilities to share perceptions of each task.

Less able: try writing a list of measurements on a flip chart for children to draw and label on the sheet, e.g. _____ 5 cm.

PLENARY

Review the work from one **Main teaching activity** each day. Discuss the results in terms of comparisons: more/less; longer/ shorter; heavier/lighter etc. *Did anyone's estimates match the actual number? Did anyone walk exactly 3 metres?*

LESSON
4
+5

RESOURCES

A shuffled set of numeral cards 10–40 (one card for each child); teaching chart and marker (see Preparation, below); photocopiable page 149; for each group: a packet of liquorice allsorts (young children are less likely to try to eat liquorice during the activities!) and a large clean piece of paper (for sorting the sweets); paper, pencils, crayons or pens.

PREPARATION

Make two copies of photocopiable page 149 for each child. For 'Favourite allsort', make a teaching chart by copying the tally chart on photocopiable page 149 on to a large sheet of paper or card. For 'Sorting allsorts', place on each table a packet of liquorice allsorts, a large sheet of clean paper, copies of photocopiable page 149 and paper, pencils, crayons or felt-tipped pens. Write the following on the board:
    Draw pictures and write numbers to show:
● The allsort with the largest number.
● The allsort with the smallest number.
● Allsorts with equal numbers.
● Your favourite type of allsort and the number.
    Write numbers for these questions:
● How many different types of allsorts in your packet?
● What is the total number of allsorts in your packet?
● What is the difference between the largest and smallest number of allsorts?
● Your favourite type of allsort. How many would be in two packets?

LEARNING OUTCOMES

ORAL AND MENTAL STARTER
● Put the larger number first and counting on in tens or ones; partition additions into tens and units.
● **Choose and use efficient calculation strategies.**

MAIN TEACHING ACTIVITY
● Solve a given problem by sorting, classifying and organising information in simple ways, such as: in a list or simple table; in a pictogram; in a block graph.
Discuss and explain results.

VOCABULARY

Sort; count; tally; vote; numbers; group; set; types; largest/ smallest/ equal numbers; difference; how many?; favourite; block graph; list; table; pictogram; present; represent; most/least; popular; common; discuss.

ORAL AND MENTAL STARTER

ADDING TWO-DIGIT NUMBERS: Sit the children in a semicircle and give each child a numeral card between 10 and 40. Choose two children to stand up and show their cards and say their numbers. Ask the seated children to add the numbers shown, but tell them they have to decide whether to put the larger number first and then count on in tens or ones, or to split the two numbers into tens and units, add the tens and then add on the units. When they have found the answer, they are to put up their hands and you will choose someone to say the total, and the method they used. Repeat this several times, using the child who answers correctly, plus one other to replace those standing up.

MAIN TEACHING ACTIVITY

You may wish to plan the activities below as separate, whole-class lessons or organise them for different groups over two (or more) days on a circus basis. You will need to introduce (or revise) the main teaching points of the relevant activities each day.
FAVOURITE LIQUORICE ALLSORT: Sit the children facing the prepared teaching chart and tell them they are going to find out which liquorice allsort children in the class like best. Ask each child in turn to draw a 'tally mark' by their 'favourite' allsort on the chart. Write 'Dislike all' on the last row on the chart for children who do not like any liquorice sweet. Then choose a child to count the number in each row and write in the total. Ask questions about the results, for example: *How many tally marks did the most/least favourite allsort get?* Next give each child a copy of photocopiable page 149. Tell them to copy the results of the group tally chart on to the sheet. They will need to copy 'Dislike all' into the last box on the graph. They should then complete the block graph by colouring one square for each tally mark. Alternatively, you could make the block graph together as a teaching activity.

SORTING LIQUORICE ALLSORTS AND MAKING A GRAPH: Explain that, working together in small groups, the children should sort their packet of allsorts into different types. Show examples, such as a 'double sandwich'. Tell the children to place allsorts of the same type together, even though they may be different colours. Then give them these instructions:
● In your group, sort the allsorts, setting out each type in a line on the sheet of paper.
● Use your own copy of photocopiable page 149 to make a tally chart of the types. (If you find types other than the ones drawn on the sheet write 'Other types' in the last row of the chart and sort and count all other allsorts as 'Other types'.)
● Use your tally chart to draw a graph underneath. Colour one square for each tally mark.
● Use a sheet of plain paper to copy and complete the written statements on the board.

DIFFERENTIATION

More able: give the children a sheet of paper to work out how many of each sweet there would be in two packets, or ten packets?
Less able: make a copy of the questions on the board on A4 paper with answer spaces for each child to complete.

PLENARY

Review the work done in the **Main teaching activity**, asking questions about comparisons between different types of allsorts. For 'Sorting allsorts', read through each statement on the board with the children. Invite a child from each group to give a response to each statement. Ask why the numbers of types of allsorts may not be the same in different packets. Include questions about two packets and ten packets for more able children.

LESSON

6
+7
+8
+9

RESOURCES

NEXT MONTH/LAST MONTH: a set of 12 cards in a tray showing the name of each month; flip chart and pen; paper and pencils.
TIMES TO THE QUARTER HOUR: a teaching clock; sets of 12 time cards showing different times ¼ past the hour and ¼ to the hour; photocopiable page 16 (Clocks); cardboard clocks; pencils.
TWO HOURS LATER AND EARLIER: teaching clock; photocopiable page 90 (Later and earlier), sets of 12 time cards showing different o'clock times; cardboard clocks; pencils.

PREPARATION

Put out the resources for each activity on tables. Make two copies of pages 16 (Clocks) and 90 (Later and earlier) for each child. Make three sets of 12 cards showing:
● Names of the months of the year.
● Times quarter past the hour around the clock.
● Times quarter to the hour around the clock.

VOCABULARY

Names of the months of the year; next/last month; times; o'clock; half-past; quarter past; quarter to; earlier; later; morning; afternoon; evening; night; midnight; how long ago?; how long will it be?; before; after; between; analogue clock hands.

LEARNING OUTCOMES

ORAL AND MENTAL STARTER
● Use mental addition and subtraction to solve simple word problems.

MAIN TEACHING ACTIVITY
● Order the months of the year.
● Read the time to the quarter hour on an analogue clock.
● Use mental addition and subtraction to solve simple word problems.

ORAL AND MENTAL STARTER

ONE HOUR LATER AND EARLIER: Sit the children facing the teaching clock. Set the hands on the clock to different times on the hour and choose a child to say the time one hour later each time, then try 'one hour earlier'. In another session, change the rule to 'two hours earlier/later', or set the hands to show times to the half-hour and ask the children to say the time one hour later. Try a different version of this game each lesson.

MAIN TEACHING ACTIVITY

You may wish to plan each of these activities as separate, whole-class lessons or organise them for different groups over four days on a circus basis. You will need to introduce (or revise) the main teaching points of the relevant activities at the beginning of each session.

Start by explaining that these activities are all about time passing and telling the time. NEXT MONTH/LAST MONTH: Sit the children in front of the flip chart. Show them a tray of month name cards. Tell them they are going to carry out an activity where they select a card from the tray, copy it on to their sheet and then write the name of 'next' month, for example: May → June. Demonstrate this on the flip chart, holding up a different card each time and asking the children to say the name on the card, then the name of the next month. Tell the children that before they start the activity they should write the title 'Next month' on their sheet. Explain that when they have completed all 12 month cards they will repeat the activity. This time they should put the title 'Last month' and write the name of the month, followed by the name of the 'last' month, for example: September → October. TIMES TO THE QUARTER HOUR: Sit the children facing the teaching clock. Tell them they are going to carry out an activity with times 'quarter past' the hour. Demonstrate the position of the clock hands for 'quarter past' and choose a child to say the time for each one. Show the children a copy of page 16. Tell them they will be using this sheet with their cardboard clocks and the tray of time cards. They should select a different card each time and complete the sheet by writing the time underneath a clock and drawing in the hands. TWO HOURS LATER AND EARLIER: Sit the children facing the teaching chart. Tell them they are going to carry out an activity where they have to write times 'two hours earlier and two hours later'. Use the teaching chart and the teaching clock to demonstrate. Set the hands on the teaching clock to a time on the hour and ask a child to draw hands which show the same time on the first 'middle' clock on the chart. Then ask a child to say the time two hours earlier and draw these hands on the clock on the left. Ask another child to say the time two hours later and draw these hands on the clock on the right. Repeat this with another example, asking the children which clock you should draw the hands on each time.

Next, show the children a copy of photocopiable page 90 and a set of time cards showing times to the hour. Tell them they should choose a card, write the time on the card underneath the middle clock on their sheet, draw in the hands and then, on the two clocks either side, draw in the hands to show the times 'two hours earlier and later', writing the times underneath each clock. Check the children know what they have to do.

DIFFERENTIATION

More able: extend the activity by challenging these children to take the tasks a step further – 'two months later and earlier' or 'three hours later and earlier'.
Less able: provide a chart of the 12 months in order to help with the order and spelling. For children who are still unsure of reading and writing times to the half-hour, carry out the reading and writing times activity with a set of time cards to the half-hour. Move on to using the quarter-hour time cards if the children seem confident. For 'Two hours later and earlier' suggest they might use a cardboard clock to help them if they are unsure.

PLENARY

Play variations of the game 'One hour later and earlier' as in the Oral and mental starter.

RESOURCES

Teaching chart and worksheets (see below); teaching clock; cardboard clocks; sets of time cards marked with different times to the hour; sets of two 'spotty' 1–6 dice; flip chart and pen; pencils.

Plane journeys		
Take-off time	Flight time	Arrival time

PREPARATION

Copy this teaching chart on to the flip chart, and then make an A4 copy for each child. Place copies of this worksheet, a set of time cards, cardboard clocks, dice and pencils on each table.

LEARNING OUTCOMES
ORAL AND MENTAL STARTER and MAIN TEACHING ACTIVITY
● Use mental addition and subtraction to solve simple word problems involving numbers in 'real life'.

VOCABULARY

Plane journeys; flight time; times; o'clock; arrival time; longest/ shortest/ same time; holiday; quicker; quickest; takes longer; takes less time; how long will it take?.

ORAL AND MENTAL STARTER

THREE HOURS LATER AND EARLIER: Sit the children in a semicircle facing the teaching clock. Set the hands on the clock to different times to the hour. Choose a child to say the time three hours later each time. Change the rule to 'three hours earlier'.

MAIN TEACHING ACTIVITY

PLANE JOURNEYS IN HOURS: Sit the children facing the teaching chart. Tell them they are going to carry out an activity about plane journeys. Talk briefly about how long it takes to get to holiday destinations (expect their timing suggestions to be somewhat wild! Encourage them to think about 'all day', 'by lunch time' and so on). Explain to the children that they are going to find out when a plane will arrive by writing down the time the plane takes off and adding on how long the flight takes. First they will throw a dice to see how long the flight will take. Demonstrate the activity with the time cards in hours and the teaching clock. Select a time card and write the time shown on the card in the 'Take-off time' column. Then choose a child to throw the two dice and say the total. Tell the children that the total number thrown is the flight time in hours. Write the number as hours in the 'Flight time' column. Then set the hands on the teaching clock to the 'Take-off time', tell the children to add or count on the flight time and ask: *When will the plane arrive?* Choose a child to write this time in the 'Arrival time' column on the chart, for example:

Take-off time	Flight time	Arrival time
3 o'clock	5 hours	8 o'clock

Repeat with a few more examples, talking about strategies for doing the additions. Then tell the children they are to carry out the activity with the time cards and sheets on their tables. Tell them to:
● Select a time card and write the number as the 'Take-off time' on your sheet.
● Throw the two dice and write the total number as the 'Flight time' on your sheet.
● Find out the 'Arrival time' by adding on the 'Flight time' to the 'Take-off time'. Fill in the 'Arrival time' on your sheet.
● Try to repeat the activity ten times.
  Encourage the children to work out the 'Arrival times' mentally where they can and to write an 'H' beside each arrival time they have worked out entirely in their heads. Check that they know what they have to do before they return to their tables to carry out the activity.

DIFFERENTIATION

More able: hand out another copy of the sheet and tell the children to write the time on the time card as the arrival time, throw the two dice to find the flight time, then subtract the flight time from the arrival time to find the take-off time.
Less able: provide a cardboard clock which the children can count round in ones if they need help.

PLENARY

Review the work done in the **Main teaching activity** on the teaching chart. Invite individual children to give different examples of a plane journey ('Take-off' and 'Flight time') from their sheet. Scribe each journey on the chart and ask the class to say when each plane will arrive. Invite the children to look at the chart and say which was the longest/shortest journey and whether any plane journeys took the same time.

Name

Sorting objects by mass

Less than $\frac{1}{2}$ kg	Between $\frac{1}{2}$ kg and 1 kg	More than 1 kg

Estimating and filling $\frac{1}{4}$ litre

Name of container	Estimated number	Actual number
eggcup		

Name

Liquorice allsorts

Tally chart

Block graph

10								
9								
8								
7								
6								
5								
4								
3								
2								
1								

UNIT 13: Assess & Review

Choose from the following activities over the two lessons. During the group activities, some children can complete Assessment worksheets 4a and 4b which assess their skills in addition, halving and doubling, and reading a simple scale, including using a ruler. The specific criteria for the assessment sheets can be found at the bottom of each sheet.

RESOURCES

Numeral cards 0–99; three different-coloured hoops; sets of dominoes; ½kg weights, pan balances and sets of objects for balancing; centimetre rulers; pencils, coloured crayons or felt-tipped pens and paper; copies of Assessment worksheets 4a and 4b and photocopiable pages 18 and 147 for each child.

PREPARATION

Copy the required photocopiable sheets for each child. Put out the resources on tables.

ORAL AND MENTAL STARTER

ASSESSMENT

● Can the children: Describe and extend simple number sequences: counting in tens, twos and threes? Recognise odd and even numbers? Use and choose appropriate operations and efficient strategies to solve problems?
● Do the children: Know by heart: multiplication facts for the 2 and 10 times tables?

NUMBER SEQUENCES: Count on/back in tens from any two-digit number. Use numeral cards 11–20 and 90–99 to repeat Lessons 3 and 5, Unit 8, on pages 126 and 127. Count on in twos and threes from zero, and in twos from 1. Play 'My number, your number' with the rules 'Count on/back 3': *My number is 5. So, (Luke) your number is?* (8).
ODD OR EVEN CALCULATION? Repeat 'All change' with three hoops and numeral cards 1–20. (See Lesson 5, Unit 2, Term 1, on page 34.) Ask the children to tell you each time they change places whether the answer number is odd or even. Hold up some numeral cards at the end and ask individuals if the cards show odd or even numbers.
2 AND 10 TIMES TABLES: Recite these times tables together. Use quick-fire questions such as: *Six twos? Five tens? How many twos in 14? How many tens in 60?* Give each child in the circle a numeral card 1–10. Select children to multiply the number on their card by 2, then others to multiply the number by 10. Pitch your questions to the abilities of the children and challenge their methods if they cannot recall the answers immediately.

GROUP ACTIVITIES

ASSESSMENT

● Can the children: Order whole numbers to at least 100? Use and choose appropriate operations and efficient strategies to solve problems? Estimate, measure and compare masses, using standard units?
● Do the children know: Addition facts for all numbers to 10? Multiplication facts for the 2 times table?

NUMBERS TO 100: Repeat the group activity in Lesson 3, Unit 2, on page 104. Give each child a copy of page 18, ten cards 1–98 and two different-coloured pens: one to write in these ten numbers and the other to fill in the rest. Check for order and number formation.
ADDITION AND MULTIPLICATION: Use a set of dominoes for the children to repeat 'Adding and multiplying dominoes' in Lesson 3, Unit 10 on page 135. Check whether the children are able to record the number sentences correctly, for example $4 + 2 = 8$, $8 \times 2 = 16$, and whether they count the spots on the domino or work the calculation out mentally.
MEASURES: Using page 147 and the balancing equipment, ask the children to repeat Lesson 1, Unit 11 on page 142. Check the children are able to use the balance and make reasonably accurate judgements about the mass of each object in relation to the weights.

Assessment sheet 4a

Complete:

$2 + 25 = \boxed{}$ $4 + 57 = \boxed{}$

$5 + 36 = \boxed{}$ $6 + 83 = \boxed{}$

$2 + 7 + 4 = \boxed{}$ $3 + 8 + 2 = \boxed{}$

$1 + \boxed{} + 5 = 7$ $\boxed{} + 8 + 5 = 15$

$6 + 3 + \boxed{} = 18$ $7 + 3 + 7 = \boxed{}$

$9 + 8 = \boxed{}$ $7 + 8 = \boxed{}$

$6 + 7 = \boxed{}$ $6 + 9 = \boxed{}$

$12 + 23 = \boxed{}$ $15 + 22 = \boxed{}$

$14 + 15 = \boxed{}$ $11 + 37 = \boxed{}$

$17 + 22 = \boxed{}$ $22 + 35 = \boxed{}$

$19 + 31 = \boxed{}$ $26 + 41 = \boxed{}$

Double 4 $= \boxed{}$ $\frac{1}{2} \times 4 = \boxed{}$

Double 6 $= \boxed{}$ $\frac{1}{2} \times 6 = \boxed{}$

Double 10 $= \boxed{}$ $\frac{1}{2} \times 10 = \boxed{}$

Double 8 $= \boxed{}$ $\frac{1}{2} \times 8 = \boxed{}$

● Choose and use efficient calculation strategies.
● Know by heart: all addition and subtraction facts for each number to at least 10;
multiplication facts for the 2 times table.

Name

Assessment sheet 4b

How much water in the jugs?

_____   _____   _____

What are the heights of these tables?

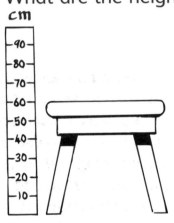   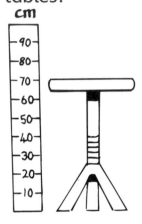   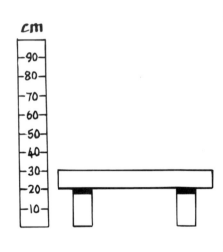

_____   _____   _____

Measure these lines in centimetres (cm).

Draw these lines:

14cm

5cm

9cm

● Measure and compare lengths, masses and capacities using standard units (m, cm, kg, l); suggest suitable units for such measurements. Use a ruler to draw and measure lines to the nearest cm.

Term 3 extends children's knowledge
of number sequences to include
counting on and back in hundreds
and in steps of 3, 4 and 5.
Understanding addition,
subtraction, multiplication and
division is further developed
through mental strategies, solving
related numerical and practical
'real-life' problems including the
use of money up to £5.00.
Doubling multiples of 5, halving
multiples of 10 and multiplication
facts for the 5 times table are
taught and practised.
Position, direction and movement
includes turn and right angles.
Children are taught to find quarters
of shapes and small numbers.
Their skills of estimating and
measuring using standard units are
extended. They are taught
relationships between units of time,
to read the time to the quarter hour
on a digital clock, and to draw
graphs in data-handling activities.

ENLARGE THIS SHEET TO A3 AND USE IT AS YOUR MEDIUM-TERM PLANNING GRID.

Oral and mental skills: Say the number names in order to at least 100, from and back to zero. Use and begin to read the vocabulary of comparing and ordering numbers. **Describe and extend simple number sequences: count on or back in tens starting from any two-digit number;** count in hundreds from and back to zero; count on in steps of 5 to at least 30, from and back to zero; count in twos from and back to 0. Begin to recognise two digit multiples of 2, 5 or 10. Round numbers less than 100 to the nearest 10. **Know by heart: multiplication facts for the 2 and 10 times tables;** doubles of all numbers to 10 and the corresponding halves; all pairs of multiples of 10 with a total of 100. Derive quickly: doubles of all numbers to at least 15; division facts corresponding to the 2 and 10 times table. **Use knowledge that addition can be done in any order to do mental calculations more efficiently.** Partition additions into tens and units, then recombine. Add/subtract 9 or 11: add/subtract 10 and adjust by 1. Begin to add/subtract 19 or 21: add/subtract 20 and adjust by 1. Identify near doubles, using doubles already known. Begin to add three single-digit numbers mentally (totals up to about 20). Count in hundreds from and back to zero. Count on in twos from and back to zero or any small number. Begin to recognise two-digit multiples of 2, 5, or 10. Count on in steps of 3, 4 or 5 to at least 30,

Unit	Topic	Objectives: Children will be taught to...
1	Counting and properties of numbers	● **Describe and extend simple number sequences: count on or back in ones or tens, starting from any two-digit number;** count on in steps of 4 or 5 to at least 30, from and back to zero, then from and back to any given small number. **Recognise odd and even numbers** to at least 30. Begin to recognise two-digit multiples of 2, 5 or 10.
2–4	Place value, ordering, estimating and rounding Understanding + and – Mental calculations (+ and –) Money and 'real life' problems Making decisions and checking results	● **Order whole numbers to at least 100,** and position them on a number line and a 100 square. ● Use the +, – and = signs to record mental additions and subtractions in a number sentence, and recognise the use of a symbol such as ☐ or △ to stand for an unknown number. Begin to add three two-digit numbers with the help of apparatus (totals up to 100). ● **Use knowledge that addition can be done in any order to do calculations more efficiently.** Add three small numbers by putting the largest number first and/or find a pair totalling 10. Add/subtract 9 or 11: add/subtract 10 and adjust by 1. Begin to add/subtract 19 or 21: add/subtract 20 and adjust by 1. Use patterns of similar calculations. Find a small difference by counting up from the smaller to the larger number. **State the subtraction corresponding to a given addition, and vice versa.** Use known number facts and place value to add/subtract mentally. Bridge through 10 or 20, then adjust. ● Use mental addition and subtraction or simple multiplication to solve simple word problems involving numbers in 'real life' or money, using one or two steps. Explain how the problem was solved. Recognise all coins and begin to use £.p notation for money (for example, know that £4.65 indicates £4 and 65p). Find totals, give change, and work out which coins to pay. **Choose and use appropriate operations and efficient calculation strategies to solve problems.** ● Repeat addition in a different order. Check with an equivalent calculation.
5–6	Measures including problems Shape and space Reasoning about shapes	● **Estimate, measure and compare masses, using standard units.** Solve simple word problems involving numbers in 'real life' and measures. ● **Use mathematical vocabulary to describe direction and movement.** Recognise whole, half and quarter turns, to the left or right, clockwise or anti-clockwise. Know that a right angle is a measure of a quarter turn, and recognise right angles in squares and rectangles. Give instructions for moving along a route in straight lines and round right-angled corners: for example, to pass through a simple maze. Begin to recognise line symmetry. ● Solve mathematical problems or puzzles. Suggest extensions by asking 'What if' or 'What could I try next?' **Explain how a problem was solved** orally.
7	Assess and review	● **Describe and extend simple number sequences: count on or back in ones or tens, starting from any two-digit number. Know by heart: multiplication facts for the 2 and 10 times tables. Recognise odd and even numbers. Use knowledge that addition can be done in any order to do mental calculations more efficiently. State the subtraction corresponding to a given addition, and vice versa. Choose and use appropriate operations and efficient calculation strategies to solve problems, explaining orally how the problem was solved. Estimate, measure and compare masses, using standard units. Use mathematical vocabulary to describe position, direction and movement.**

Oral and mental skills: Describe and extend simple number sequences: count in hundreds from and back to zero; count on in twos from and back to zero or any small number; count on in steps of 3, 4 or 5 to at least 30, from and back to zero, then from and back to any given small number. Begin to recognise two-digit multiples of 2, 5, or 10. **Know by heart: multiplication facts for the 2 and 10 times tables;** doubles of all numbers to 10 and the corresponding halves. Begin to know: multiplication facts for the 5 times table. Derive quickly: division facts corresponding to the 2 and 10 times tables; doubles of multiples of 5 to 50 (e.g. 20 × 2 or 35 × 2); halves of multiples of 10 to 100 (e.g. half of 70). **Know and use halving as the inverse of doubling.** Partition additions into tens and units, then recombine. Begin to add three numbers mentally. Use known number facts and place value to subtract mentally. Add/subtract 11 or 21. Use patterns of similar calculations. Use known number facts and place value to carry out mentally simple multiplications and divisions. Use simple multiplication and division to solve simple word problems involving money.

Unit	Topic	Objectives: Children will be taught to...
8	Counting and properties of numbers Reasoning about numbers	● **Describe and extend simple number sequences:** count on in hundreds from and back to zero; count on in twos from and back to zero or any small number; count on in steps of 3, 4 or 5 to at least 30, from and back to zero, then from and back to any given small number. Derive quickly: doubles of multiples of 5 to 50 (e.g. 20 × 2 or 35 × 2); halves of multiples of 10 to 100 (e.g. half of 70).
9	Place value and ordering estimating and rounding Understanding + and – Mental calculation strategies (+ and –) Money and 'real life' problems Making decisions and checking results	(See **Oral and mental skills**.) ● Use the +, – and = signs to record mental additions and subtractions in a number sentence, and recognise the use of a symbol such as ☐ or △ to stand for an unknown number. **Understand that subtraction is the inverse of addition** (subtraction reverses addition). Begin to add three single-digit numbers mentally (totals up to about 20) or three two-digit numbers with the help of apparatus (totals up to 100). ● **Use knowledge that addition can be done in any order to do calculations more efficiently.** For example: Partition additions into tens and units, then recombine. Use patterns of similar calculations. Use known number facts and place value to subtract mentally. ● Recognise all coins and begin to use £.p notation for money (for example, know that £4.65 indicates £4 and 65p). Find totals, give change, and work out which coins to pay. ● **Choose and use appropriate operations and efficient calculation strategies to solve problems**
10–11	Understanding × and ÷ Mental calculation strategies (× and ÷) Money and 'real life' problems Making decisions and checking results Fractions	● Use the × and = signs to record mental calculations in a number sentence. **Know and use halving as the inverse of doubling.** Use the +; –; ×, ÷ and = signs to record mental calculations in a number sentence, and recognise the use of a symbol such as ☐ or △ to stand for an unknown number. ● **Know by heart: multiplication facts for the 10 times tables.** Begin to know: multiplication facts for the 5 times table. Derive quickly: division facts corresponding to the 10 times table; doubles of multiples of 5 to 50; halves of multiples of 10 to 100. Use known number facts and place value to add and to carry out mentally simple multiplications. ● Recognise all coins and begin to use £.p notation for money (for example, know that £4.65 indicates £4 and 65p). Find totals, give change, and work out which coins to pay. Explain how the problem was solved. ● Begin to recognise and find one quarter of shapes and small numbers of objects. Begin to recognise that four quarters make one whole and that two quarters and one half are equivalent. Solve mathematical problems or puzzles. Suggest extensions by asking 'What if …?' or 'What could I try next?'
12–13	Measures, and time including problems Handling data	● Use and begin to read the vocabulary related to time. Suggest suitable units to estimate or measure time. Use units of time and know the relationships between them. Solve simple word problems. Use mental addition and subtraction to solve simple word problems. Read the time to the hour, half hour or quarter hour on an analogue clock and a 12-hour digital clock, and understand the notation 7:30. **Estimate, measure and compare capacities using standard units. Read a simple scale to the nearest labelled division, including using a ruler to draw and measure lines to the nearest centimetre.** ● Solve a given problem by sorting, classifying and organising information in simple ways. Discuss and explain results
14	Assess and review	● **Describe and extend simple number sequences. Understand that subtraction is the inverse of addition. Use knowledge that addition can be done in any order to do mental calculations more efficiently. Choose and use appropriate operations and efficient calculation strategies to solve problems. Know and use halving as the inverse of doubling. Know by heart: multiplication facts for the 2 and 10 times tables. Estimate, measure and compare capacities using standard units. Read a simple scale to the nearest labelled division, including using a ruler to draw and measure lines to the nearest centimetre.**

UNIT 1

ORGANISATION (3 LESSONS)

LEARNING OUTCOMES STARTER	ORAL AND MENTAL ACTIVITY	MAIN TEACHING	PLENARY
LESSON 1 ● **Describe and extend simple number sequences:** count on in steps of 4 to at least 30, from and back to zero, then from and back to any given small number.	COUNTING: Counting in tens to 100; in hundreds to 1000. Recognising multiples of tens to 100.	PATTERN OF 4s: Colouring a number square and writing the pattern of 'count on 4'.	Counting. Review work on Main teaching activity.
LESSON 2 ● **Describe and extend simple number sequences:** count on in steps of 5 to at least 30, from and back to zero; then from and back to any given small number. ● Begin to recognise two-digit multiples of 5.	2s, 5s AND 10s: Reciting the 2 and 10 times tables. Counting in fives and twos.	PATTERN OF 5s: Colouring a number square and writing the pattern of count on 5.	Reciting the 2 and 10 times tables. Counting in fives to 100. Counting in twos from and back to zero.
LESSON 3 ● **Describe and extend simple number sequences: count on or back in ones or tens, starting from any two-digit number.** ● Begin to recognise two-digit multiples of 2, 5 and 10. ● **Recognise odd and even numbers** to at least 30.	QUICK DOUBLES: with cards 1–20.	NUMBER SEQUENCES.	Reviewing work from the Main teaching activity.

ORAL AND MENTAL SKILLS   Say the number names in order to at least 100, from and back to zero. Begin to recognise two-digit multiples of 5 and 10. **Describe and extend simple number sequences:** count on or back in tens; count in hundreds from and back to zero; count on in steps of 5 to at least 30, from and back to zero; count on in twos from and back to zero. **Know by heart: multiplication facts for the 2 and 10 times tables.** Derive quickly: doubles of all numbers to at least 15.

Lesson 1 is presented in full. Lessons 2 and 3 are given as follow-on grids, outlining the continuing work on number sequences linked to the times tables patterns of multiples.

RESOURCES

Photocopiable page 13; a small easel and coloured water-based marker; individual number squares; small cubes; a three-minute timer; paper and pencils, crayons or felt-tipped pens.

PREPARATION

Make two copies of photocopiable page 13 for each child and enlarge and laminate one copy for use as a teaching chart. Attach the teaching chart to a small easel.

LEARNING OUTCOMES

ORAL AND MENTAL STARTER
● Say the number names in order to at least 100, from and back to zero.
● **Describe and extend simple number sequences: count on or back in tens;** count in hundreds from and back to zero; count on in steps of 5 to at least 30.
● Begin to recognise two-digit multiples of 10.

MAIN TEACHING ACTIVITY
● **Describe and extend simple number sequences:** count on in steps of 4 to at least 30, from and back to zero, then from and back to any given small number.

VOCABULARY

Numbers 0–100, 100–1000; count on; count up; count down; count back; tens; hundreds; fives; fours; more; less; multiples; sequence; pattern; rule; arrow; describe the rule; describe the pattern.

ORAL AND MENTAL STARTER

COUNTING: Ask the children to recite counting in tens to 100 from and back to 0. Then ask oral questions such as: *Give me the number that is 4 tens. How many tens in 60?*

MAIN TEACHING ACTIVITY

PATTERN OF 4s: Sit the children facing the teaching chart. Tell them they are going to colour the pattern of 'count on 4' on a number square and write the number sequence. Demonstrate how to start colouring the pattern of 4 up to the number 8 (missing out three numbers) on the teaching chart, writing the corresponding number sequence underneath the square at the same time, for example 0 → 4 → 8 → ? Ask: *What number has to be coloured next?* Colour the 12 square and write 12 as the next number in the sequence. Then tell the children, using one of the number square sheets on their table, to copy the pattern and the number sequence, then continue to colour the pattern and write the sequence as far as they can.

DIFFERENTIATION

More able: encourage these children to play a number square and cube game with a 3-minute timer. Give each player a laminated number square, a sheet of paper and a small cube. Tell the children the game is played like other number square and cube games with the rule 'count on 4'. All players start the game when the timer is turned over. The child who writes down the most 'count on 4' statements (for example: 42 → 46) in three minutes is the winner. Repeat the game with the rule 'count back 4'.
Less able: give children a 0–49 number rectangle to carry out the activity.

PLENARY

Use the teaching chart (wiped clean), colour in the zero (0) with a coloured marker, then tell the children you will choose different children to colour numbers on the chart in the 'count on 4' pattern. Ask: *What number is coloured next?* each time before choosing a child to colour the number on the chart.

LESSON 2

RESOURCES	Number square teaching chart (photocopiable page 13); a small easel and coloured water-based marker; copies of photocopiable page 13 and individual number squares; small cubes; a three-minute timer; paper, pencils, crayons or felt-tipped pens.
LEARNING OUTCOMES	**ORAL AND MENTAL STARTER** ● **Know by heart: multiplication facts for the 2 and 10 times tables.** ● **Describe and extend simple number sequences:** count on in steps of 5 from and back to zero; count in twos from and back to zero. **MAIN TEACHING ACTIVITY** ● **Describe and extend simple number sequences:** count on in steps of 5 to at least 30, from and back to zero, then from and back to any given small number. ● Begin to recognise two-digit multiples of 5.
ORAL AND MENTAL STARTER	2s, 5s AND 10s: Recite the 2 and 10 times tables, then count in fives to 100. Next, count in twos from zero all the way around the circle once, then reverse the count back the other way in twos to zero so that each child says the same number, but in reverse order. Start the game slowly, but quicken the pace as you repeat it to encourage rapid recall.
MAIN TEACHING ACTIVITY	PATTERN OF 5s: Talk about the pattern of fives: say the numbers together, then around the class. Think about number endings (0 or 5). Point to different numbers on the teaching chart. Ask: *Is this a pattern of 5 number?* Then ask them to colour the pattern of 5s on a number square and write the number sequence of 'count on 5' (as for the pattern of 4s in Lesson 1).
DIFFERENTIATION	More able: play a number square and cube game with the rule 'count on 5' with a three-minute timer. Repeat the game changing the rule to 'count back 5' (see Lesson 1). Less able: give children a 0–49 number rectangle to carry out the activity.
PLENARY	Refresh children about the rule for pattern of 5 numbers (ending in 0 or 5). Use the teaching chart to point to different numbers. Ask: *Is this a pattern of 5 number?*

LESSON 3

RESOURCES	Numeral cards 1–20 (one card for each child) photocopiable page 158, one copy for each child; pencils; individual number squares.
LEARNING OUTCOMES	**ORAL AND MENTAL STARTER** ● Derive quickly: doubles of all numbers to at least 15. **MAIN TEACHING ACTIVITY** ● **Describe and extend simple number sequences: count on or back in ones or tens, starting from any two-digit number.** ● Begin to recognise two-digit multiples of 2, 5 or 10. ● **Recognise odd and even numbers to at least 30.**
ORAL AND MENTAL STARTER	QUICK DOUBLES: Sit the children in a circle. Give each child a 1–20 card and choose children randomly around the circle to double the number on their card saying, for example: 'double four is eight'. Collect in the cards, shuffle and give them out again. Tell the children that they have to take turns around the circle to double the number on their card following on from each other as quickly as possible.
MAIN TEACHING ACTIVITY	NUMBER SEQUENCES: Give each child a copy of photocopiable page 158. Ask them to look at each line on the sheet in turn and complete each number sequence. Check that they know what to do before they return to their tables.
DIFFERENTIATION	More able: provide children who finish quickly with an individual number square and a sheet of paper and challenge them to make up some more difficult sequences between 0 and 14 – for example, count on in 6s, 7s, 8s, or 12s, 13s, 14s, and so on. Less able: provide number squares for children who may require support.
PLENARY	Review the work done in the **Main teaching activity**. Go through each number sequence on the sheet on the class board and invite the children to say the missing numbers in the sequences. Ask children to say if they have written different numbers for any sequence. Write their numbers on the board and discuss with the children where the sequence has gone wrong and why.

UNIT 1

Number sequences

Continue and complete.

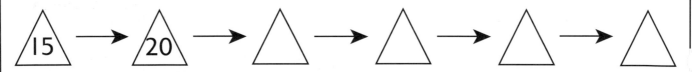

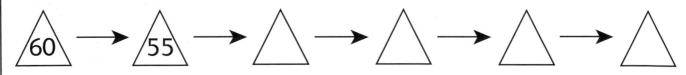

Write down the sequence of even numbers between 21 and 41.

Write down the sequence of odd numbers between 26 and 46.

ORGANISATION (15 LESSONS)

	LEARNING OUTCOMES	ORAL AND MENTAL STARTER	MAIN TEACHING ACTIVITY	PLENARY
LESSON 1	● Add/subtract 11: add/subtract 10 and adjust by 1.	MY NUMBER/YOUR NUMBER: Adding 9 and subtracting 9.	Adding and subtracting 11 with a number square.	MY NUMBER/ YOUR NUMBER.
LESSON 2	● **Use knowledge that addition can be done in any order to do calculations more efficiently.** ● Add three small numbers by putting the largest number first and/or find a pair totalling 10.	ADDING BY COUNTING ON TENS THEN UNITS: Playing a game with cards 10–30.	LOTS OF SPOTS: Adding numbers of spots on three dominoes.	ADDING BY COUNTING ON TENS THEN UNITS.
LESSON 3	● **State the subtraction corresponding to a given addition, and vice versa.**	Reciting the two and ten times tables. Asking quick-fire questions.	CORRESPONDING ADDITION AND SUBTRACTION STATEMENTS: Working with dominoes.	Reviewing work from the Main teaching activity.
LESSON 4	● Find a small difference by counting up from the smaller to the larger number.	DOUBLE AND HALF: Playing a game with even-numbered cards 2–20.	DOMINO DIFFERENCES.	DOUBLE AND HALF. Reviewing work from the Main teaching activity.
LESSON 5	● **Order whole numbers to at least 100** and position them on a number line and 100 square.	Reciting the 2 and 10 times tables. Counting in fives from and back to 0. GIVE ME A NUMBER.	POSITIONING NUMBERS ON A NUMBER SQUARE.	Reviewing work from the Main teaching activity.
LESSON 6	● Begin to add/subtract 19: add/subtract 20 and adjust by 1. ● Use patterns of similar calculations.	MY NUMBER/YOUR NUMBER: Adding and subtracting 9.	ADDING 19 PATTERNS: Adding 19 and subtracting 19. Playing a number square and cube game.	MY NUMBER/ YOUR NUMBER: Adding and subtracting 19.
LESSON 7	● Begin to add/subtract 21; add/subtract 20 and adjust by 1. ● Use patterns of similar calculations.	MY NUMBER/YOUR NUMBER: Adding and subtracting 11.	ADDING 21 PATTERNS: Adding 21 and subtracting 21. Playing a number square and cube game.	Reviewing work from the Main teaching activity. MY NUMBER/ YOUR NUMBER: Adding and subtracting 21.
LESSON 8	● **Choose and use appropriate operations and efficient calculation strategies.** ● Repeat addition in a different order. Check with an equivalent calculation. ● Use the +, – and = signs to record mental additions and subtractions in a number sentence, and recognise the use of a symbol such as ☐ or △ to stand for an unknown number.	MAKE 100/TAKE FROM 100: Using cards numbered in tens to 100.	ADDITION AND SUBTRACTION PROBLEMS.	Reviewing work from the Main teaching activity.
LESSON 9	● Add 11; begin to add 21. ● Use patterns of similar calculations.	NEAR DOUBLES.	ADD 11/ADD 21 FOR TWO-STEP ADDITION: Using numeral cards 40–60.	NEAR DOUBLES.

LEARNING OUTCOMES	ORAL & MENTAL STARTER	MAIN TEACHING ACTIVITY	PLENARY
LESSON 10 • Use mental addition and subtraction or simple multiplication to solve simple word problems involving numbers in 'real life' or money, using one or two steps. • **Explain how a problem was solved.**	MY NUMBER/YOUR NUMBER: Adding and subtracting 19.	SHOPPING FOR SWEETS.	Reviewing work from the Main teaching activity.
LESSON 11 • Begin to add three two-digit numbers with the help of apparatus (totals up to 100).	ADDING BY GROUPING TENS AND UNITS: Playing with cards 10–50.	TRIOS: Adding three two-digit numbers with cards 10–30.	ALL CHANGE: Playing with three hoops and cards 10–30.
LESSON 12 • Use known number facts and place value to add/subtract mentally. • Use patterns of similar calculations.	ALL CHANGE: Playing with three hoops and cards 10–30.	SUBTRACTING 'TEENS' NUMBERS WITHOUT BRIDGING THROUGH TEN.	Reviewing work from the Main teaching activity.
LESSON 13 • Use known number facts and place value to add/subtract mentally. • Bridge through 10 or 20, then adjust. • Use patterns of similar calculations.	ADDING BY GROUPING TENS AND UNITS: Playing with cards 10–50.	Subtracting 'teens' numbers by bridging through ten.	Reviewing work from the Main teaching activity. Adding by grouping tens and units with cards 10–50.
LESSON 14 • Use known number facts and place value to add/subtract mentally. • **Choose and use appropriate operations and efficient calculation strategies to solve problems.**	Reciting the 2 and 10 times tables, counting in fives from and back to 0. NEAREST 10: Playing a game with a number square.	Addition and subtraction: ADDING AND SUBTRACTING TWO-DIGIT NUMBERS.	CHANGING PLACES.
LESSON 15 • Recognise all coins and begin to use £.p notation for money (for example, know that £4.65 indicates £4 and 65p). • Find totals, give change, and work out which coins to pay. • Use mental addition and subtraction or simple multiplication to solve simple word problems involving numbers in 'real life' or money, using one or two steps. • **Explain how a problem was solved.**	MY NUMBER/YOUR NUMBER: Adding and subtracting 21.	MONEY PROBLEMS: Spending a £5.00 gift voucher with change.	Reviewing work from the Main teaching activity.

ORAL AND MENTAL SKILLS **Know by heart: multiplication facts for the 2 and 10 times tables.** Begin to recognise two-digit multiples of 2, 5 or 10. Use and begin to read the vocabulary of comparing and ordering numbers. Round numbers less than 100 to the nearest 10. **Know by heart:** doubles of all numbers to 10 and the corresponding halves; all pairs of multiples of 10 with a total of 100. Derive quickly: division facts corresponding to the 2 and 10 times tables. **Use knowledge that addition can be done in any order to do mental calculations more efficiently.** For example: partition additions into tens and units, then recombine. Begin to add three single-digit numbers mentally (totals up to about 20). Add/subtract 9 or 11: add/subtract 10 and adjust by 1. Begin to add/subtract 19 or 21: add/subtract 20 and adjust by 1. Identify near doubles, using doubles already known.

In Unit 2 Lesson 3 is given in full with the other four lessons (1, 2, 4 and 5) provided in grid form. In Unit 3 Lessons 7 and 10 are in grid form, while Lessons 6, 8 and 9 are provided in full detail. In Unit 4 Lessons 11, 12 and 13 are provided in full, with the last two lessons (14 and 15) again as grids.

LESSON 1

RESOURCES	Photocopiable page 13 (0–99 number square) A4 copies and an enlarged version for use as a teaching chart and photocopiable page 28 (Two-way counts); small cubes; paper and pencils.
LEARNING OUTCOMES	**ORAL AND MENTAL STARTER** ● Add/subtract 9: add/subtract 10 and adjust by 1. **MAIN TEACHING ACTIVITY** ● Add/subtract 11: add/subtract 10 and adjust by 1.
ORAL AND MENTAL STARTER	MY NUMBER/YOUR NUMBER: as in Lesson 3, Unit 1 of Term 2 on page 99, but with the rule 'add 9'. Discuss strategies for adding 9 such as 'add 10 and adjust by 1' (see Lesson 4, Unit 9, Term 2, on page 132). Change the rule to 'subtract 9'. Play the game at a fast pace to encourage rapid recall.
MAIN TEACHING ACTIVITY	ADD/SUBTRACT 11: Now think together about adding 11: *In what way is it a bit like adding 9?* (Add 10 and adjust by 1.) Introduce the 'Number square and cube' activity 'Two-way counts' using photocopiable page 28 with the rule 'add 11' (see Lesson 4, Unit 9, Term 2, on page 132).
DIFFERENTIATION	More able: give these children a number square with a sheet of paper to find and write down as many pairs of numbers as they can with a difference of 11, recording, for example: 16 → —— → 27 or 49 › —— › 38. Less able: give these children a sheet of paper instead of the 'Two-way counts' sheet. Ask them to complete ten 'add 11' examples instead. Children who finish quickly can go on to try ten 'subtract 11' examples.
PLENARY	Play 'My number/your number' as in the **Oral and mental starter**, but with the rule 'add 11'. Change the rule to 'subtract 11'.

LESSON 2

RESOURCES	A shuffled set of numeral cards 10–30 (one card for each child); flip chart and pen; a set of dominoes for each group; paper and pencils.
LEARNING OUTCOMES	**ORAL AND MENTAL STARTER** ● **Use knowledge that addition can be done in any order to do mental calculations more efficiently.** ● Partition additions into tens and units, then recombine. **MAIN TEACHING ACTIVITY** ● **Use knowledge that addition can be done in any order to do mental calculations more efficiently.** ● Add three small numbers by putting the largest number first and/or find a pair totalling 10.
ORAL AND MENTAL STARTER	ADDING BY COUNTING ON TENS THEN UNITS: Give each child one of a shuffled set of 10–30 cards. Invite two children to stand facing the group and show their cards. Tell the seated children to add the numbers shown, starting from the larger number and adding on the other number mentally by counting on the tens then the units. Choose a seated child to answer.
MAIN TEACHING ACTIVITY	LOTS OF SPOTS: Sit the children facing the flip chart. Explain that they are going to be finding totals of spots on three dominoes. Spread a set of dominoes face down. Explain that the children will select three dominoes each time, draw them and write the total number of spots underneath each domino. They will then write an addition 'sum' using the three numbers arranged to show the easiest calculation method, before replacing the dominoes and taking three more. Demonstrate the method of recording.
DIFFERENTIATION	More able: ask the children to select four dominoes each time. Less able: ask the children to select two dominoes each time.
PLENARY	Repeat 'Adding by counting on tens then units' from the **Oral and mental starter**.

LESSON 3

RESOURCES

Flip chart and pen, a shuffled set of even-numbered cards 2–20 (one card for each child); a box of dominoes for each group; paper and pencils; Cuisenaire rods.

PREPARATION

Spread out a set of dominoes face down on each table. Place sheets of paper and pencils on each table.

LEARNING OUTCOMES
ORAL AND MENTAL STARTER
● **Know by heart: multiplication facts for the 2 and 10 times tables.**
● Derive quickly: division facts corresponding to the 2 and 10 times tables.

MAIN TEACHING ACTIVITY
● **State the subtraction corresponding to a given addition, and vice versa.**

ORAL AND MENTAL STARTER

Recite the 2 and 10 times tables, then follow this with quick-fire questions, for example: *What are: 3 twos? 3 tens?; How many: twos in 30? tens in 60?*

MAIN TEACHING ACTIVITY

CORRESPONDING ADDITION AND SUBTRACTION STATEMENTS:
Sit the children facing the flip chart to demonstrate this activity. Spread out a set of dominoes face down. Select a domino, sketch its outline on the flip chart and mark in the spots. Choose children to make two addition sentences for the spots on the domino. Scribe the sentences on the chart. Then ask the group how they could change the numbers around to make two subtraction sentences. Scribe the subtraction sentences underneath. Repeat with another example. Tell the children to go back to their tables and carry out the activity as shown. They should replace each domino they use face down and select another until they have used ten dominoes altogether.

$$6 + 4 = 10$$
$$4 + 6 = 10$$
$$10 - 4 = 6$$
$$10 - 6 = 4$$

VOCABULARY

add; addition; more; plus; make; sum; total; equals; altogether; subtract; subtraction; less; take away; minus; leave; how many left?; how many left over?; explain your method; give me an example of ...; show how ....

DIFFERENTIATION

More able: give children who finish quickly a fresh sheet of paper and two sets of playing cards ace to 10 (A–10). Tell them to lay the cards face up in two lines in the centre of the table and repeat the activity by selecting the numbers from two different cards each time.
Less able: provide Cuisenaire rods for children who may require additional support.

PLENARY

Review the **Main teaching activity**. Choose children to say their domino numbers and the two addition and two subtraction sentences. Write all the sentences on the flip chart.

RESOURCES	A shuffled set of even-numbered cards 2–20 (one card for each child); flip chart and pen; sets of dominoes (one per group); paper and pencils.
LEARNING OUTCOMES	**ORAL AND MENTAL STARTER** ● **Know by heart**: doubles of all numbers to 10 and corresponding halves. **MAIN TEACHING ACTIVITY** ● Find a small difference by counting up from the smaller to the larger number.
ORAL AND MENTAL STARTER	DOUBLE AND HALF: Sit the children in a circle. Give each child one of a shuffled set of even-numbered cards 2–20. Children take turns around the circle to double the number on the card saying, for example: 'Double six is twelve'. Change the rule to halving the number on the card, for example: 'Half of twelve is six'. Encourage a fast pace to support rapid recall.
MAIN TEACHING ACTIVITY	DOMINO DIFFERENCES: Sit the children facing the flip chart to demonstrate the activity: select a domino and draw around it, mark in the spots and then write a difference sentence for the domino underneath, for example: for a 6/2 spot domino: 6 ← 4 → 2. Replace that domino face down and select another. Tell the children to select 10 dominoes altogether.
DIFFERENTIATION	More able: spread a pack of cards A–10 face down on the table. Children select two cards each time and write a difference sentence. Less able: provide Cuisenaire rods to help with finding the differences.
PLENARY	Repeat the 'Double and half' activities from the **Oral and mental starter**.

LESSON 5

RESOURCES	A copy of photocopiable page 18 with some squares shaded plus a blank copy for each child (see 'Main teaching activity'); a laminated blank Number square teaching chart, (photocopiable page 18, see Term 2, Unit 2, Lesson 3); a coloured water-based marker; 0–99 number squares.
LEARNING OUTCOMES	**ORAL AND MENTAL STARTER** ● **Know by heart: multiplication facts for the 2 and 10 times tables.** ● Begin to recognise two-digit multiples of 2, 5 or 10. ● Use and begin to read the vocabulary of comparing and ordering numbers. **MAIN TEACHING ACTIVITY** ● **Order whole numbers to at least 100,** and position them on a number line and 100 square.
ORAL AND MENTAL STARTER	GIVE ME A NUMBER: Recite the 2 and 10 times tables, count in fives from and back to 0. Then play 'Give me a number' by asking questions such as: *Give me a number more than 20 and less than 35; …less than 40 and more than 25; …between 39 and 45… .*
MAIN TEACHING ACTIVITY	POSITIONING NUMBERS ON A NUMBER SQUARE: You will need to shade in some of the squares on a master copy of page 18 (as shown below) before making a copy for each child (or pair). Sit the children facing the blank Number square teaching chart. Show them a copy of the partially shaded grid. Tell them they must look at the position of each shaded square and try to write the correct number for each one in the same position on the blank grid. Tell them to cross out each shaded square after they have written a number for that position on the blank grid. Demonstrate a few examples on the teaching chart. Colour in some squares, then invite different children to wipe a square clean and write in the correct number for that position.
DIFFERENTIATION	The number of shaded squares could be altered for more/less able. More able: give these children a set of numeral cards 0–99 and a copy of photocopiable page 13 (Blank number square). Children take ten or twenty cards each and write the numbers on the cards in the correct position on the number square. Less able: provide some 0–99 number squares for children who may require additional support.
PLENARY	Review the work done in the **Main teaching activity** with a Blank Number square teaching chart. Copy the shaded numbers on the sheet on to the chart, using a coloured water-based marker. Invite a child to wipe a square clean and write in a number each time. Notice, talk about and correct any common mistakes such as 15 written as 51 and vice versa, or any numerals written in reversed form such as: 2Γ for 27.

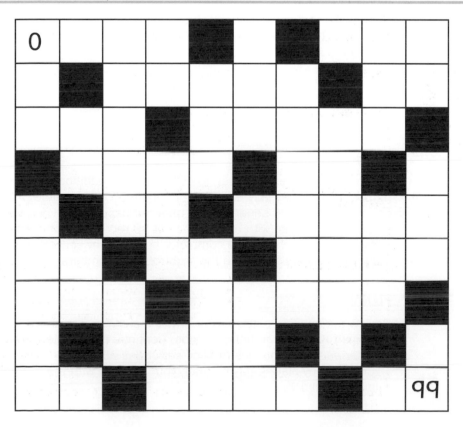

RESOURCES

Individual number squares and a 0–99 Number square teaching chart (photocopiable page 13); photocopiable page 28 (Two-way counts); small cubes; paper and pencils.

PREPARATION

Make a copy of photocopiable page 28 for each child. Write the following addition patterns on the board:

3 + 19	5 + 19	7 + 19	9 + 19
13 + 19	15 + 19	17 + 19	19 + 19
23 + 19	25 + 19	27 + 19	29 + 19
33 + 19	35 + 19	37 + 19	39 + 19
43 + 19	45 + 19	47 + 19	49 + 19

LEARNING OUTCOMES

ORAL AND MENTAL STARTER

● Add/subtract 9: add/subtract 10 and adjust by 1.

MAIN TEACHING ACTIVITY

● Begin to add/subtract 19: add/subtract 20 and adjust by 1.
● Use patterns of similar calculations.

ORAL AND MENTAL STARTER

MY NUMBER/YOUR NUMBER: Play this with the rule 'add 9'. Then repeat with the rule 'subtract 9'. Play the game at a fast pace to encourage rapid recall.

MAIN TEACHING ACTIVITY

ADDING 19 PATTERNS: Sit the children facing the Number square teaching chart. Tell them they are going to carry out an activity where they add and subtract 19 using a number square. Use the teaching chart to remind children of the method of adding and subtracting 9. Then demonstrate the principle of 'add 19' and 'subtract 19' (add or subtract 20 and adjust by one). Point to a few different numbers on the chart for children to say the 'add 19' number, then repeat with 'subtract 19'.

Tell the children to use a sheet of paper to copy and complete the addition statements on the board using a number square if they require help. When they have done this, they will use a 'Two-way counts' sheet to play a number square and cube game with the rule 'add and subtract 19'. Use a copy of photocopiable page 28 to remind children how to complete the sheet (write the number the cube lands on in the middle box, then the 'subtract 19' number in the left-hand circle and the 'add 19' number in the right-hand circle each time). Check that the children know what they have to do before they return to their tables to carry out the activity.

DIFFERENTIATION

More able: ask these children to continue each addition pattern on the board to a 90s number before they play the number square and cube game. After playing the game they can use the number square with a sheet of paper to find and write down as many pairs of number as they can with a difference of 19 recording, for example: 16 → 35 or 64 → 45. Less able: invite children to complete the 'Two way counts' sheet by working out all the 'add 19' numbers first, then the 'subtract 19' numbers.

PLENARY

Review the addition pattern work. Invite the children to give answers to the statements on the board and explain their methods. Continue each pattern to a 90s number. *What is the number pattern/sequence in each set of answers?*

Conclude by playing 'My number/your number' with the rule 'add 19'. Repeat with the rule 'subtract 19'.

VOCABULARY

Numbers 0–100; add; adding; addition; subtract; subtracting; subtraction; count back 1–9; count on; difference; how many more?; how many less?; equals; arrow; symbol.

LESSON 7

RESOURCES	A copy of photocopiable page 28 (Two-way counts) for each child; individual number squares; small cubes; paper and pencils.
LEARNING OUTCOMES	**ORAL AND MENTAL STARTER** ● Add/subtract 11: add/subtract 10 and adjust by 1. **MAIN TEACHING ACTIVITY** ● Begin to add/subtract 21: add/subtract 20 and adjust by 1. ● Use patterns of similar calculations.
ORAL AND MENTAL STARTER	MY NUMBER/YOUR NUMBER: Play this with the rule 'add 11'. Repeat with the rule 'subtract 11'. Play at a fast pace to encourage rapid recall.
MAIN TEACHING ACTIVITY	ADDING 21 PATTERNS: Carry this out in the same way as Lesson 6 (Adding 19 patterns). Write the following addition patterns on the board for the children to copy and complete: 3 + 21 5 + 21 7 + 21 9 + 21 and so on 13 + 21 15 + 21 23 + 21 33 + 21 43 + 21 When the children have finished they should play a number square and cube game using photocopiable page 28 (Two-way counts) with the rule 'add/subtract 21'.
DIFFERENTIATION	More able: continue each addition pattern to a 90s number. Then, after playing the number square and cube game, they can use the number square with a sheet of paper to find and write down as many pairs of numbers as they can with a difference of 21 recording, for example: 26 → 47 or 66 → 45. Less able: invite the children to complete the 'Two-way counts' sheet by working out all the 'add 21' numbers first, then the 'subtract 21' numbers.
PLENARY	Review the addition patterns (see the **Plenary session** of Lesson 6). Then play a 'My number/your number' game with the rule 'add 21'. Repeat with the rule 'subtract 21'.

LESSON 8

RESOURCES

A set of shuffled cards numbered in tens 10–100 (one card for each child); photocopiable page 171 (Addition and subtraction problems); paper and pencils; Cuisenaire rods.

PREPARATION

Make a copy of photocopiable page 171 for each child.

LEARNING OUTCOMES

ORAL AND MENTAL STARTER
● **Know by heart:** all pairs of multiples of 10 with a total of 100.

MAIN TEACHING ACTIVITY
● **Choose and use appropriate operations and efficient calculation strategies**.
● Repeat addition in a different order. Check with an equivalent calculation.
● Use the +, − and = signs to record mental additions and subtractions in a number sentence, and recognise the use of a symbol such as □ or △ to stand for an unknown number.

ORAL AND MENTAL STARTER

MAKE 100/TAKE FROM 100: Sit the children in a circle and give each child one of a shuffled set of cards numbered in tens 10–100. Tell them to take turns around the circle to say the number on their card and the number needed to make 100, for example: 'Seventy and thirty make a hundred'. Repeat this, changing the rule to 'take from 100' where the children say, for example: 'One hundred take forty leaves sixty'. Play the game at a fast pace to encourage rapid recall.

VOCABULARY

one hundred; multiples; multiples of; add; addition; more, plus, makes; equals; total; altogether; subtract; subtraction; take away; minus; leave; less; left; problems; calculate; calculations; mental; jottings; workings; answer; right; correct; wrong; signs; symbols.

MAIN TEACHING ACTIVITY

ADDITION AND SUBTRACTION PROBLEMS: Give each child a copy of photocopiable page 171 and a separate sheet for 'workings'. Read each question on the sheet with the children and ask them to say whether they have to use addition or subtraction to solve the problem. Encourage all children to work mentally where they can and tell them to record 'workings' on the separate sheet where they are unsure.

Ask the children to tell you what they have to do before they return to their tables to carry out the activity.

DIFFERENTIATION

More able: give these children a fresh sheet of paper and ask them to work with a partner to make up some number problems as 'stories' of their own.

Less able: encourage children to try drawing a 'number' picture of any problem they are having difficulty with, and provide Cuisenaire rods for children who may require additional support.

PLENARY

Review the work done in the **Main teaching activity** by going through each question from the sheet on the board. Invite the children to contribute solutions and methods.

LESSON 9

RESOURCES	Flip chart and pen; a copy of photocopiable page 172 (Two-step addition and subtraction) for each child; individual number squares; pencils; for each group: a shuffled set of numeral cards 40–60 spread out face up in a random order in the centre of each table.
LEARNING OUTCOMES	**ORAL AND MENTAL STARTER** ● Identify near doubles, using doubles already known. **MAIN TEACHING ACTIVITY** ● Add 11; begin to add 21. ● Use patterns of similar calculations.
ORAL AND MENTAL STARTER	NEAR DOUBLES: ask questions such as: *Add 6 and 7; ...21 and 22;* etc. Discuss strategies to ensure the children spot and use 'near doubles' whenever possible.
MAIN TEACHING ACTIVITY	ADD 11/ADD 21 – TWO-STEP ADDITION: Sit the children facing the flip chart. Tell them they are going to carry out an activity where they add 11 and then add 21 to a number. Write a number between 40 and 60 on the chart, for example 42. Ask the children to add 11 to the number then to add 21, recording 42 → 53 → 74 on the chart. Repeat this a few times. Show the children a copy of photocopiable page 172 and explain that they will work with a set of numeral cards 40–60, then tell them what to do. ● Look at the cards on the table, select a number and write it in the first square on the sheet. ● Add 11 to the number and write the answer in the triangle. ● Then add 21 to the number in the triangle and write the total in the circle. ● The activity finishes when you have completed 20 different numbers. Ask the children to tell you what they have to do before they return to their tables to carry out the activity.
DIFFERENTIATION	More able: give these children a fresh copy of the sheet to complete using the rule 'add 9, then add 19' to a number. Less able: modify the rule to 'add 11 and then another 11' to each number. Provide individual number squares for children who require additional support.
PLENARY	Repeat 'Near doubles' from the **Oral and mental starter**.

LESSON 10

RESOURCES	Photocopiable page 138 (Shop for sweets); paper and pencils; Cuisenaire rods and/or coins.
LEARNING OUTCOMES	**ORAL AND MENTAL STARTER** ● Add/subtract 19. **MAIN TEACHING ACTIVITY** ● Use mental addition and subtraction or simple multiplication to solve simple word problems involving numbers in 'real life' or money, using one or two steps. ● Explain how the problem was solved.
ORAL AND MENTAL STARTER	MY NUMBER/YOUR NUMBER: Adding and subtracting 19. Play the game at a fast pace to encourage rapid recall.
MAIN TEACHING ACTIVITY	SHOPPING FOR SWEETS: Repeat the activity from Lesson 4 in Unit 10 of Term 2 (see page 136). Tell the children they are going to play the shopping for sweets game again and tell them that this time they should try to work out the answers out in their heads.
DIFFERENTIATION	More able: children who finish quickly can be given a fresh copy of the sheet to replay the game. Less able: provide Cuisenaire rods and sets of coins for children who may require additional support.
PLENARY	See Lesson 4, Unit 10 in Term 2, on pages 136–137, for details of results charts and plenary discussion.

LESSON 11

RESOURCES

A shuffled set of numeral cards 10–50 (one card for each child); a flip chart and pen; copies of photocopiable page 69 (Trios); a shuffled set of numeral cards 10–40 for each group; paper and pencils; three hoops; cards 10–30; Cuisenaire rods.

PREPARATION

Make a copy of photocopiable page 69 (Trios) for each child. Place a set of numbered cards 10–30 face up in random order in three rows in the centre of each table.

LEARNING OUTCOMES

ORAL AND MENTAL STARTER
● Partition additions into tens and units, then recombine.

MAIN TEACHING ACTIVITY
● Begin to add three two-digit numbers with the help of apparatus (totals up to 100).

ORAL AND MENTAL STARTER

ADDING BY GROUPING TENS AND UNITS: Playing with cards 10–50 (see Term 2, Unit 8, Lesson 3 on page 126).

MAIN TEACHING ACTIVITY

TRIOS: Sit the children facing a flip chart and tell them they are going to add three numbers that each have two digits. Ask: *What is a two-digit number?*

Write an example of a three two-digit addition sentence on the flip chart. Demonstrate how to add the numbers together by grouping and adding the

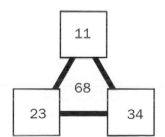

tens first, then the units, then adding the numbers together to find the total, for example: $23 + 34 + 11 \rightarrow 60 + 8 = 68$

Repeat this with a few more examples, inviting the children to work through the steps orally.

Next, show the children a copy of photocopiable page 69 (Trios). Explain that they have to look at the number cards on the tables and choose three different numbers. Write the numbers in a diagram on the sheet. Then add the numbers by grouping the tens together, adding on the units and writing the total in the centre of each diagram.

VOCABULARY

Numbers to 100; add; addition; equals; total; sum; add tens; add units; add together; grow; how much; altogether; two-digit number; trio diagrams; number cards.

Encourage the children to work the totals out mentally where they can, but tell them they can use the separate sheet to carry out 'workings' if required. Ask them to tell you what they have to do before they return to their tables to carry out the activity.

DIFFERENTIATION

More able: give children who finish quickly a fresh copy of the sheet to repeat the activity, but challenge them to choose three two-digit numbers ending in 5–9 in some examples. Less able: provide Cuisenaire rods for children who may require additional support.

PLENARY

Play 'All change' with three hoops and cards 10–30.

RESOURCES

A set of shuffled numeral cards 1–30; three different coloured sorting hoops; a flip chart and pen; paper and pencils; individual 0–99 number squares.

PREPARATION

Place paper and pencils on each table. Write the following subtractions on the board:

26 – 13 =	27 – 14 =	28 – 15 =	29 – 16 =
36 – 13 =	37 – 14 =	38 – 15 =	39 – 16 =
46 – 13 =	47 – 14 =	48 – 15 =	49 – 16 =
56 – 13 =	57 – 14 =	58 – 15 =	59 – 16 =
66 – 13 =	67 – 14 =	68 – 15 =	69 – 16 =

LEARNING OUTCOMES

ORAL AND MENTAL STARTER
● Begin to add three single-digit numbers mentally (totals up to about 20).

MAIN TEACHING ACTIVITY
● Use known number facts and place value to add/subtract mentally.
● Use patterns of similar calculations.

ORAL AND MENTAL STARTER

ALL CHANGE: Use three hoops and 1–30 cards (see Lesson 5, Unit 2, Term 1 on page 34).

MAIN TEACHING ACTIVITY

SUBTRACTING 'TEENS' NUMBERS WITHOUT BRIDGING THROUGH TEN: Tell the children they are going to be subtracting 'teens' numbers from two-digit numbers. Use the flip chart to demonstrate how to subtract by counting back ten from the larger number then counting back the units, for example: $35 - 12 \rightarrow 35 - 10 - 2 = 25 - 2 = 23$
Carry out a few more examples. Ask children to contribute the method while you scribe it on the flip chart. Then tell the children to return to their tables and copy and complete the subtractions on the board, using this method. Encourage them to work mentally, but to write 'method workings' where they are unsure. Check they know what they have to do.

DIFFERENTIATION

More able: challenge these children to continue each subtraction pattern to a 90s number. Less able: provide 0–99 number squares for children who may require additional support.

PLENARY

Ask children to complete the statements on the board, explaining their methods. Continue each pattern to a 90s number. Can they spot the number pattern in each set of answers?

VOCABULARY

Subtract; subtraction; minus; take away; leaves; equals; teens numbers; counting back tens and units method; mental calculation; jottings; workings; answer; correct.

RESOURCES

Flip chart and pen; a shuffled set of numeral cards 10–50 (one card for each child); paper and pencils; individual 0–99 number squares.

PREPARATION

Write the following subtraction patterns on the class board.

24 – 16 =	25 – 17 =	26 – 18 =	27 – 19 =
34 – 16 =	35 – 17 =	36 – 18 =	37 – 19 =
44 – 16 =	45 – 17 =	46 – 18 =	47 – 19 =
54 – 16 =	55 – 17 =	56 – 18 =	57 – 19 =
64 – 16 =	65 – 17 =	66 – 18 =	67 – 19 =

LEARNING OUTCOMES

ORAL AND MENTAL STARTER
● Partition additions into tens and units, then recombine.

MAIN TEACHING ACTIVITY
● Use known number facts and place value to add/subtract mentally.
● Bridge through 10 or 20, then adjust.
● Use patterns of similar calculations.

VOCABULARY

Numbers 0–100; add; group; addition; subtract; subtraction; count back; tens; units; bridging ten; tens boundary; method; workings; jotting; mental calculation; check; correct; right; wrong.

ORAL AND MENTAL STARTER

ADDING BY GROUPING TENS AND UNITS: Sit the children in a semicircle. Give each child one of a shuffled set of cards 10–50. Invite two children to stand facing the group and show their cards each time. Remind the seated children to add the numbers on the cards by mentally grouping and adding the tens, followed by grouping and adding the units. Choose a seated child to say the answer each time.

MAIN TEACHING ACTIVITY

SUBTRACTING 'TEENS' NUMBERS BY BRIDGING THROUGH TEN: Sit the children facing the flip chart and tell them they are going to subtract high 'teens' numbers from two-digit numbers. Use the flip chart to demonstrate and explain the method of subtracting the tens from the first (larger) number, then subtracting or counting back the units through the 'tens' number, for example: $35 - 16 \rightarrow 35 - 10 - 6 \rightarrow 25 - 5 - 1 = 19$
Work through a few examples, asking children to contribute the method while you scribe it on the flip chart. Then ask them to copy and complete the subtractions on the board, using the counting back ten, then ones method. Encourage the children to work mentally where they can, but to write the 'method workings' where they are unsure. Ask the children to tell you what they have to do before they return to their tables to carry out the activity.

DIFFERENTIATION

More able: challenge these children to continue each subtraction pattern through to a 90s number.
Less able: provide 0–99 number squares for children who require additional support.

PLENARY

Review the work done in the **Main teaching activity** by inviting different children to give responses to each statement while you scribe the answers on the board. Can the children say what the number pattern is in each set of answers? Conclude by repeating 'Adding by grouping tens and units' with cards 10–50, as in the **Oral and mental starter**.

LESSON 14

RESOURCES	A copy of photocopiable page 173 (Addition and subtraction) for each child; pencils and paper; 0–99 Number square teaching chart; individual 0–99 number squares and/or Cuisenaire rods.
LEARNING OUTCOMES	**ORAL AND MENTAL STARTER** ● **Know by heart: multiplication facts for the 2 and 10 times tables.** ● Begin to recognise two-digit multiples of 2, 5 or 10. ● Round numbers less than 100 to the nearest 10. **MAIN TEACHING ACTIVITY** ● Use known number facts and place value to add/subtract mentally. ● **Choose and use appropriate operations and efficient calculation strategies to solve problems.**
ORAL AND MENTAL STARTER	Recite the 2 and 10 times tables, then count in fives from and back to 0. Say that you are going to concentrate on tens numbers and play 'Nearest 10' with a number square (see Lesson 4, Unit 2, Term 2, on page 105).
MAIN TEACHING ACTIVITY	ADDITION AND SUBTRACTION: Give each child a copy of photocopiable page 173. Read each section with them to check that they understand what they have to do. Remind them to choose the easiest methods they can to complete the questions.
DIFFERENTIATION	More able: encourage children to work mentally where possible but to write down 'workings' where they are unsure. Less able: supply 0–99 number squares and/or Cuisenaire rods for children who may require the support of using apparatus.
PLENARY	Review work done in the **Main teaching activity** by going through each section from the sheet on the board. Invite children to contribute solutions and describe their methods. Highlight particular effective methods by scribing the child's methods on the board and working through the method orally with the children.

LESSON 15

RESOURCES	A copy of photocopiable page 174 (Spending a £5 gift voucher) for each child; pencils and paper; sets of all coins; OHP. For more able children: a toy or gift catalogue (if available).
LEARNING OUTCOMES	**ORAL AND MENTAL STARTER** ● Begin to add/subtract 21. **MAIN TEACHING ACTIVITY** ● Recognise all coins and begin to use £.p notation for money (for example, know that £4.65 indicates £4 and 65p). ● Find totals, give change, and work out which coins to pay. ● Use mental addition and subtraction or simple multiplication to solve simple word problems involving numbers in 'real life' or money, using one or two steps. ● Explain how the problem was solved.
ORAL AND MENTAL STARTER	MY NUMBER/YOUR NUMBER: with the rule 'add 21'. Then repeat with the rule 'subtract 21'. Play the game at a fast pace to encourage rapid recall.
MAIN TEACHING ACTIVITY	MONEY PROBLEMS: Start by discussing money given as a gift: 'pocket' money or 'birthday' money (being sensitive to the children's financial circumstances). Have the children ever had a 'gift voucher'? Discuss receiving a gift voucher as a present and making decisions on how to spend it. Put some sets of coins on the OHP (£1, £1, 50p; £1 × 4, 20p, 10p; £1, 50p, 10p, 10p, 5p etc.) asking each time: *How much money? I was given a £5 voucher. If this was my change, how much did I spend?* Give each child a copy of photocopiable page 174. Read through the sheet with the children and make sure they understand what they have to do before completing the sheet. Encourage them to use mental calculation strategies.
DIFFERENTIATION	More able: these children, working in pairs, can make up their own gift list with prices using a printed catalogue (if available) within a given amount of money – for example, £20, and to work out the total cost, checking it with a calculator. Less able: have sets of cans available for children who may require additional support. Let children work in pairs to carry out this activity.
PLENARY	Review the work done in the **Main teaching activity** by inviting different children to give responses to the tasks on the sheet and explain their methods. This activity does not expect any vertical/column addition methods to be used, so you should encourage the children's own methods, with 'workings' if necessary.

Name

Addition and subtraction problems

In a class there are 12 boys and 15 girls. How many children altogether?	In a box there were 31 pencils. 21 are given out. How many are left?
What number is 19 less than 48?	Find the total of 24 and 15.
In a box of toy cars there are 5 red cars, 4 blue cars and 6 green cars. How many cars altogether?	24 people got on a bus. 10 people got on and 3 got off. How many on the bus?

Write these number sentences another way.

12 + 14 = 26   70 + 30 = 100

18 – 5 = 13   39 – 10 = 29

100 – 20 = 80   17 + 6 = 23

Write the missing numbers and signs.

90 + ☐ = 100   100 – ☐ = 40

20 – ☐ = 8   ☐ + 16 = 20

12 ☐ 6 = 18   19 ☐ 6 = 13

Name

Two-step addition and subtraction

Rule _____

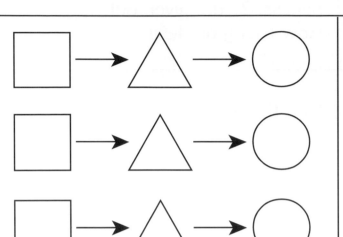
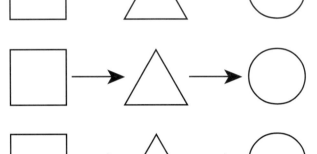
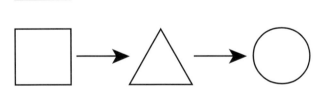
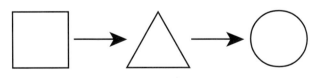
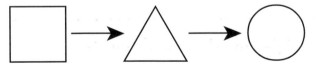
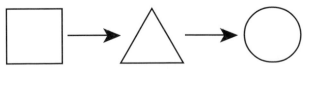
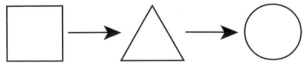

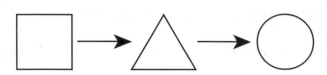

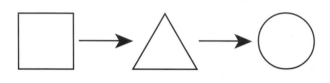
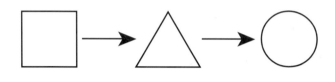
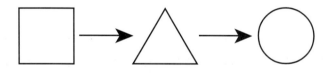
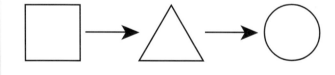
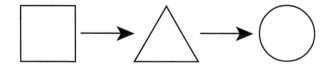
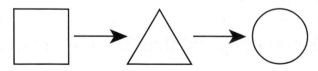
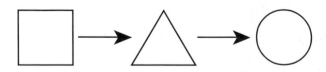
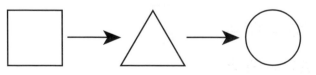

Addition and subtraction

Add by grouping tens and units.

36 + 22 =

52 + 26 =

13 + 34 =

61 + 23 =

27 + 31 =

11 + 15 + 22 =

13 + 23 + 12 =

14 + 21 + 10 =

20 + 12 + 19 =

16 + 24 + 18 =

Subtract by counting back 10, then ones.

39 – 14 =

28 – 13 =

47 – 16 =

29 – 11 =

45 – 15 =

Subtract by counting back 10, then ones, through the 'tens' number.

24 – 16 =

45 – 17 =

56 – 18 =

36 – 17 =

67 – 19 =

UNITS 2–4

Spending a £5.00 gift voucher

book
£1.25

watch £3.50

pen £1.00

jigsaw 50p

CD
£4.00

camera £4.50

Find four different ways to spend the gift voucher. Make four shopping lists.

List 1	Item	Cost

List 1: Total [ ]   Change [ ]

List 3	Item	Cost

List 3: Total [ ]   Change [ ]

List 2	Item	Cost

List 2: Total [ ]   Change [ ]

List 4	Item	Cost

List 4: Total [ ]   Change [ ]

Work out the total cost for List 1.
Work out your change from £5.00.
Now try for Lists 2, 3 and 4.

UNITS 5-6

ORGANISATION (8 LESSONS)

LEARNING OUTCOMES	ORAL AND MENTAL STARTER	MAIN TEACHING ACTIVITY	PLENARY
LESSON 1 +2 +3 +4 +5 ● **Use mathematical vocabulary to describe direction and movement**. ● Recognise whole, half and quarter turns, to the left or right, clockwise or anti-clockwise. ● Know that a right angle is a measure of a quarter turn and recognise right angles in squares and rectangles. ● Give instructions for moving along a route in straight lines and round right angled corners: for example, to pass through a simple maze. ● Solve mathematical problems or puzzles. Suggest extensions by asking 'What if...?' or 'What could I try next?'	MAKE 100/TAKE FROM 100: Playing with cards 10–100 in tens. MY NUMBER/YOUR NUMBER: Using the rules add/subtract 9; add/subtract 19; add/subtract 11; add/subtract 21.	IN POSITION: Activities to develop positional language and giving directions. TAKE A TURN: Activities to develop understanding of whole, half and quarter turns, and right angles as quarter turns.	Reviewing work from the Main teaching activities.
LESSON 6 ● **Estimate, measure and compare using standard units.** ● Solve simple word problems involving numbers in 'real life' or measures.	COUNTING IN 5S: Counting around the circle in fives from and back to zero. QUICK DOUBLES.	SPICY SHOPPING: Estimating and balancing 100g.	Reviewing work from the Main teaching activity.
LESSON 7 +8 ● Begin to recognise line symmetry. ● **Explain how a problem was solved** orally.	MAKE 100/TAKE FROM 100. NEAR DOUBLES.	SYMMETRICAL? Sorting upper case letters of the alphabet as 'symmetrical or not symmetrical'. Completing and making symmetrical patterns.	Reviewing work from the Main teaching activity.

ORAL AND MENTAL SKILLS   Describe and extend simple number sequences: count on in steps of 5.
Know by heart: all pairs of multiples of 10 with a total of 100. Derive quickly: doubles of all numbers to at least 15. Add/subtract 9 or 11. Begin to add/subtract 19 or 21. Identify near doubles using doubles already known.

In Unit 5 the lessons can be presented separately or can be used, on a circus basis, to provide work for different groups for a full week. In Unit 6, Lesson 6 is given in grid form. Lesson 7 is laid out in full, with Lesson 8 extending the work of Lesson 7.

RESOURCES

A shuffled set of cards numbered 10–100 (one card for each child).
IN POSITION:
Making a class/group picture: A1 sheet of white card or paper (or several smaller sheets taped together); a set of jumbo crayons or coloured felt-tipped pens.
Treasure hunt: photocopiable page 180 (Treasure hunt); Treasure map teaching chart (see Preparation); flip chart or easel; pencils.
Mouse and cheese investigation: photocopiable page 181 (Mouse and cheese); pencils.
Robot maze: a floor robot (Roamer, Pip or Pixie); centimetre rulers to mark out the route; flip chart and pen.
(*Note: The Robot maze activity is optional, depending on availability of equipment.*)

LESSON 1 +2 +3 +4 +5

TAKE A TURN:

Whole, half and quarter turns: a teaching clock; Direction and movement teaching chart (see Preparation); red and blue water-based pens; photocopiable page 182; cardboard clocks; pencils.

Right angles and quarter turns: photocopiable page 183; newspaper; pencils.

PREPARATION

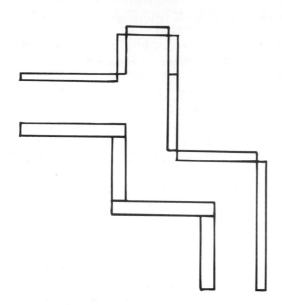

Copy one of the diagrams on photocopiable page 182 on to A3 card. Laminate the resulting teaching chart. Also make an A3 laminated copy of the Treasure map on photocopiable page 180. Make copies of pages 180, 181, 182 and 183 for each child. Tear up sheets of newspaper to approximately A5 in size (one for each child).

For the 'Robot maze' activity, clear a space in the classroom and use centimetre rulers to set out a route with right-angled, left and right turns, and a dead end (perhaps a garage) as shown. Place the resources for each activity on different tables.

LEARNING OUTCOMES

ORAL AND MENTAL
● **Know by heart:** all pairs of multiples of 10 with a total of 100.
● Add/subtract 9 or 11. Begin to add/subtract 19 or 21.

MAIN TEACHING ACTIVITY
● **Use mathematical vocabulary to describe direction and movement.**
● Recognise whole, half and quarter turns, to the left or right, clockwise or anti-clockwise.
● Know that a right angle is a measure of a quarter turn, and recognise right angles in squares and rectangles.
● Give instructions for moving along a route in straight lines and round right-angled corners: for example, to pass through a simple maze.
● Solve mathematical problems or puzzles. Suggest extensions by asking 'What if...?' or 'What could I try next?'

VOCABULARY

Describe position; top; bottom; side; in; on; beside; inside; outside; next to; between; apart; higher; lower; opposite; in front; under; over; above; behind; whole turn; half turn; quarter turn; left; right; clockwise; anti-clockwise; right angle; square; rectangle; direction; movement; straight line; fold; bend; forwards; backwards; up; down; along; through; reverse; turn; corner; around; centre; middle; edge; start from; across; journey; route; same way; different way.

ORAL AND MENTAL STARTER

Choose from the following games each day: 'Make 100/Take from 100' (see Lesson 8, Unit 3, on page 165) or 'My number/your number' with the rules: 'Add/subtract 9, 19, 11, 21 (see Units 2–4, Lessons 1, 6, 7 and 10 on pages 161, 164, 165 and 167 respectively). Play the games at a fast pace to encourage rapid recall.

MAIN TEACHING ACTIVITIES

You may wish to plan the following activities as separate, whole-class lessons or organise them as work for different groups on a circus basis. The lessons have been grouped into two linked sets. You will need to introduce or reinforce the main teaching points of the relevant activities each day.

IN POSITION: Use these activities to introduce positional language.

1. Making a class picture: Place an A1-sized sheet of paper on the floor with jumbo crayons or felt-tipped pens. Sit the children around it and tell them they are going to make a picture of a house by following instructions. Start by drawing the basic outline of the house yourself, then choose different children to draw in details on the picture by following instructions, for example: *(Charlotte) draw two chimneys on the roof; ...a door in the middle; ...a tree beside the house; ...a pond in front of the house; ...curtains in the windows* and so on. Ask the children to suggest further items that can be added to the picture and where they should be placed. When the picture is complete, ask the children questions about the positions of the items in the picture, for example: *Where is the tree?*

2. Treasure hunt: Sit the children facing the Treasure map teaching chart. Demonstrate a route from one site to another, for example from the church to the pond, by counting squares left or right, up or down. Scribe the route on the chart, for example 3 squares left, 1 square down. Use another example and ask the children to say the route. This time draw the directional arrows shown on photocopiable page 180 and demonstrate how the children are to follow the directions to find the treasure (at the pond).

Next show the children a copy of photocopiable page 180 and tell them to carry out the activity as they have been shown. Challenge any children who finish quickly to make up another hiding place for the treasure on the grid, using arrow diagrams to record this on a fresh sheet of paper. Tell them to start at the beach square and plot their own secret route to the treasure.

3. Mouse and cheese investigation: Show the children a copy of photocopiable page 181 and explain that they have to draw the different route the mouse takes on each maze drawing to avoid the cat and get to the cheese.

4. Robot maze: Use a flip chart and the floor robot to demonstrate the commands for the robot to move forwards, backwards, take a quarter turn to the right and left. Ask the children to sit around the maze and give each child a trial run to drive the robot through the maze. During each turn try to improve the accuracy of each command in relation to the distance to travel. Ask: *How can we get the robot to move to where we want on the route? What command should we try for this part of the route? Is the command correct? What should we try next?* Scribe estimates on the flip chart until the correct commands are found for each part of the route. Write the correct commands in sequence on the chart and ask each child to drive the robot through the maze using the correct commands.

TAKE A TURN: Use the teaching clock to explain and demonstrate clockwise turns (to the right) and anticlockwise turns (to the left), full turns, half turns and quarter turns clockwise and anti-clockwise. Then use the teaching chart and red water-based pen to draw an arrow at the '12 o'clock' position. Invite different children to draw another arrow on the chart in blue to show the position after a quarter turn clockwise. Wipe the blue arrow from the board and choose a child to draw an arrow showing a quarter turn anti-clockwise, then a half turn clockwise, and so on.

1. Whole, half and quarter turns: Show the children a copy of photocopiable page 182 and tell them they have to draw an arrow on each diagram to show the amount of turn written underneath as they have been shown on the teaching chart. Tell them to use a cardboard clock if they need help .

2. Right angles and quarter turns: Demonstrate how to make a paper right angle by folding a small torn sheet of newspaper in half to made a straight edge, then fold along the straight edge to make a right angled corner. Demonstrate, by holding the paper right angle against different objects, that square and rectangular objects have right angles. Then use the teaching chart to demonstrate how to line up one side of the paper right angle on the arrow and use the other side to draw the position of a clockwise right angle or quarter turn. Next, show the children a copy of photocopiable page 183 and tell them to work in pairs, using their paper right angle, to find and write a list of 20 objects in the classroom which have right-angled corners. They should then, individually, use paper right angles to complete the bottom half of the sheet as they have been shown.

DIFFERENTIATION

More able: for 'Making a class picture', children can be encouraged to make up pictures of their own and write sentences on a sheet of paper to describe where each item is. Extend 'Treasure hunt' by giving these children a blank Number square grid (page 18) to make their own 'Treasure map' and plan a route to the hidden treasure.

Less able: let children work with a partner to make up a picture or design a treasure map, and to carry out the 'Take a turn' activities with a partner, but recording results individually.

PLENARY

Select one of the **Main teaching activities** to review each day, choosing individual children to contribute answers, results and methods. Highlight the point that left-hand and right-hand turns depend upon which way you are facing – that the turn is always made to the front of a person. Ask: *Is a right-hand/left-hand turn a clockwise/anti-clockwise turn?* Ask: *If a visitor came to the school, what directions would you give at the entrance door for the visitor to find this classroom?* (or other places in the school).

LESSON 6

RESOURCES	A copy of photocopiable page 184 (Spicy shopping) and a recording sheet for the balancing activity for each child (see illustration opposite); pencils; flip chart and pen; Cuisenaire rods. For each group: a pan balance; 100g weight; six sets of small objects for balancing.

Balancing 100g		
Objects	Estimate	Actual

LEARNING OUTCOMES	**ORAL AND MENTAL STARTER** ● **Describe and extend simple number sequences:** count on in steps of 5. ● Derive quickly: doubles of all numbers to at least 15. **MAIN TEACHING ACTIVITY** ● **Estimate, measure and compare using standard units.** ● Solve simple word problems involving numbers in 'real life' or measures.
ORAL AND MENTAL STARTER	COUNTING IN 5s: Sit the children in a circle. Recite counting in fives to 100, from and back to zero, then count around the circle in fives, from and back to zero. Ask the children to count round the circle as quickly as they can to encourage rapid recall. QUICK DOUBLES: Ask, for example: *What is double 5? ...10? ...12?* Choose different children to answer each time. Include doubles of multiples of 10 up to 50 such as: *What is double 20?*
MAIN TEACHING ACTIVITY	SPICY SHOPPING: Talk about buying some goods by weight: *Why are spices weighed in grams?* Tell the children they are going to carry out some spicy shopping addition sums in grams, and do an estimating and balancing activity with 100g, working together in small groups. (These activities could be carried out on a circus basis with groups rotating between them, or, when they have finished the balancing activity, they can work on their own to do the 'Spicy shopping' sums.) Give each child a copy of photocopiable page 184. Read through the problems together, asking different children to say the mass of each spice and which spices each customer buys. Check that they know what to do. Then give them a recording sheet each for the balancing activity and tell them to: ● Write down the names of each set of objects on the table in the first column of the sheet and record your estimates of the number of objects to balance 100g individually. ● Take turns, in pairs, to balance one set of objects against 100g and count the objects. ● Everyone in the group records the actual number of objects that balance 100g on their sheets. The next pair then repeats the process with another set of objects, and so on. Ask the children to tell you what they have to do before you organise them into groups, with partners, to carry out the activity.
DIFFERENTIATION	More able: encourage the children to do the 'Spicy shopping' sums mentally where possible but to write down 'workings' where they are unsure. Less able: provide Cuisenaire rods for children who may require additional support. Carry out the 'Spicy shopping' activity as a teacher-directed activity, where you direct each step and discuss results throughout the activity.
PLENARY	Review the 'Spicy shopping' sums by going through each question on the sheet on a flip chart and inviting children to give answers and explain methods. Review results from the balancing activity. Select children from each group to give results for one object and scribe results on a chart on the board. Ask: *Which estimate number was more than/less than/the same as the actual number of objects that balanced 100g?* Can they predict how many of each object could balance 200g?

LESSON 7 +8

RESOURCES
A shuffled set of cards numbered in tens to 100; flip chart and marker pens; a set of wooden or plastic upper case letters of the alphabet; small trays; plastic safety mirrors; rulers; squared paper; paper, pencils, colouring pencils and/or felt-tipped pens; photocopiable page 185.

PREPARATION
For Lesson 7 sort the letters of the alphabet into equal numbers for each group and place each set in a small tray (containing at least one letter for each child in the group). Ensure that each set contains both symmetrical and non-symmetrical letters. Place a tray of letters, a mirror, sheets of paper, pencils and rulers on each table. Make a copy of photocopiable page 185 for each child.

LEARNING OUTCOMES

ORAL AND MENTAL
- **Know by heart**: all pairs of multiples of 10 with a total of 100.

MAIN TEACHING ACTIVITY
- Begin to recognise line symmetry.
- **Explain how a problem was solved** orally.

VOCABULARY

Symmetrical; non-symmetrical; vertical; horizontal; diagonal; lines (axes) of symmetry; fold; mirror line; reflection; match; label.

ORAL AND MENTAL STARTER

MAKE 100/TAKE FROM 100: Play these circle game with cards 10–100 in tens. Play the games at a fast pace to encourage rapid recall.

MAIN TEACHING ACTIVITY

SYMMETRICAL?: Sit the children facing the flip chart. Start by writing the words 'symmetrical' and 'non-symmetrical' on the flip chart and asking the children to read the words with you. Then use large drawings of a few letters of the alphabet on the chart to demonstrate and explain the principle of line symmetry. (When a vertical, horizontal or diagonal line is drawn through the centre of a letter to 'cut' the letter in half, if the two halves are exactly the same, the letter is said to be symmetrical. If the two halves are not exactly the same, the letter is said to be non-symmetrical). Show the children how to check whether a letter is symmetrical by using a mirror.

Tell the children they are going to sort the letters of the alphabet into symmetrical/non-symmetrical by drawing around letter templates, using a ruler to draw a line to 'cut' each letter in half, checking whether the letter is symmetrical or not by using a mirror, then writing a label underneath each letter, for example:

A

symmetrical

R

non-symmetrical

If children finish quickly, they can take a fresh sheet of paper and move to another table to try other letters.

DIFFERENTIATION

More able: ask the children to investigate whether any letters have more than one line (axis) of symmetry, for example the letter X.

Less able: encourage children to work with a partner to carry out this activity but where each child carries out its own recording.

PLENARY

Review the work done in the **Main teaching activity**. Use a table with two columns on a flip chart headed 'Symmetrical' and 'Non-symmetrical'. Invite children to name letters that are symmetrical or non-symmetrical and scribe the letters on the table in the appropriate column. *Did you find any letters with more than one line of symmetry?*

LESSON 8

In the **Oral and mental starter**, play 'Near doubles' (see Lesson 9 in Unit 3, on page 166). In the **Main teaching activity**, give each child a copy of page 185. Tell them that they should start by colouring in the squares on the grids that have letters in using red for R, blue for B, green for G and yellow for Y. They should then colour the other half of the grid to make a symmetrical shape or pattern. Advise them to use a mirror if they need help with sorting out which colour a square should be. Tell less able children to colour one square and its match at a time. At the bottom of the sheet there are four grids for the children to design their own symmetrical shapes or patterns. Provide squared paper for more able children to use to make symmetrical 6 × 6 grid patterns. Suggest they try creating the pattern with a diagonal line of symmetry. Use the **Plenary** session to review the work done in the **Main teaching activity**.

Treasure hunt

			school		
	pond			tower	
			house		
	church				
shop				tree	
		gate			

Start at the gate square. Follow these directions.

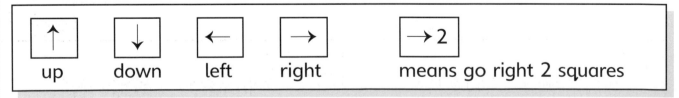

↑ up	↓ down	← left	→ right	→2 means go right 2 squares

1. ↑ 1   2. →2   3. ↑ 3   4. ↑ 1   5. ← 2   6. ↓ 3

7. ←   8. ↓ 1   9. ← 2   10. ↑ 2   11. →1   12. ↑ 1

The treasure is buried at _____

Name

Mouse and cheese

Draw different routes from the mouse to the cheese. Watch out for cats!
Compare your routes with your friends'. Are all your routes the same?

Name

Whole, half and quarter turns

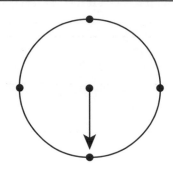

clockwise

anti-clockwise

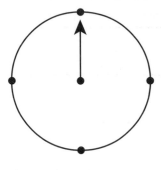

whole turn

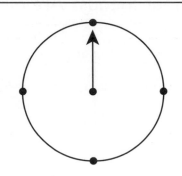

half turn

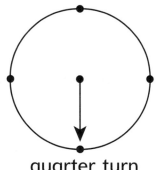

whole turn

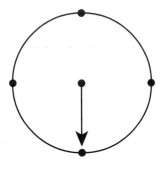

half turn

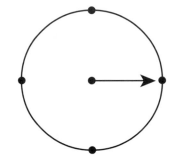

whole turn

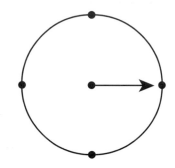

half turn

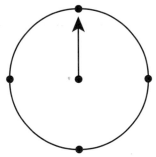

quarter turn
clockwise

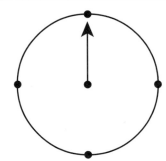

quarter turn
anti-clockwise

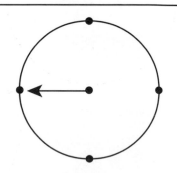

quarter turn
clockwise

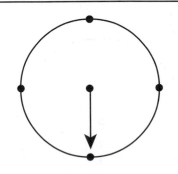

quarter turn
anti-clockwise

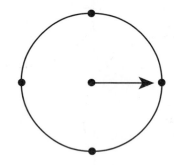

quarter turn
clockwise

quarter turn
clockwise

Right angles

Make a list of 20 objects with right angles.

1. _____

2. _____

3. _____

4. _____

5. _____

6. _____

7. _____

8. _____

9. _____

10. _____

11. _____

12. _____

13. _____

14. _____

15. _____

16. _____

17. _____

18. _____

19. _____

20. _____

Draw lines on these circles to make right angles.

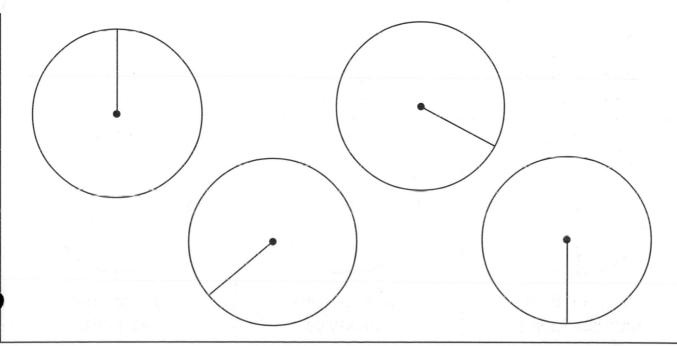

Name

Spicy shopping

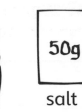 curry
25g

50g
salt

 25g
ginger
cinnamon

30g

 50g
mustard

pepper

25g

 20g
all spice

How much do these customers buy? Fill in their shopping lists.
Work out the total weight for each list.

List 1

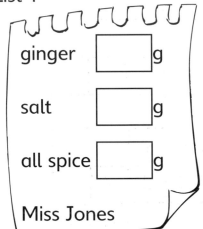

ginger [ ] g

salt [ ] g

all spice [ ] g

Miss Jones

List 1: Total weight [ ]

List 3

mustard [ ] g

all spice [ ] g

cinnamon [ ] g

Mr Wu

List 3: Total weight [ ]

List 2

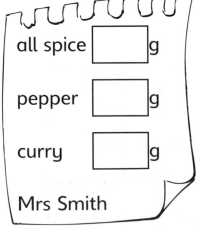

all spice [ ] g

pepper [ ] g

curry [ ] g

Mrs Smith

List 2: Total weight [ ]

List 4

curry [ ] g

ginger [ ] g

pepper [ ] g

Mr Patel

List 4: Total weight [ ]

Name

Symmetrical patterns

| R = red | B = blue | Y = yellow | G = green |

Complete these symmetrical patterns.

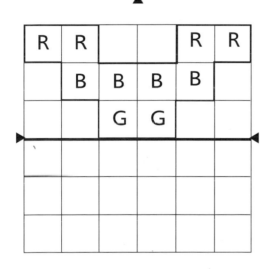

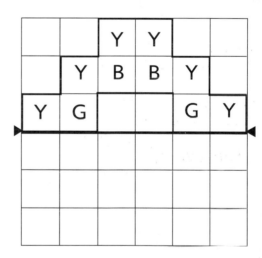

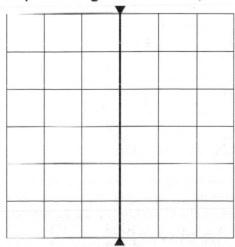

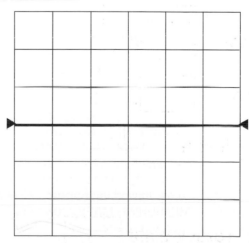

Make up two symmetrical patterns of your own.

UNIT 7: Assess & Review

Choose from the following activities over the two lessons. During the group activities, some children can complete assessment worksheets 5a and 5b which assess their skill with number sequences and describing position, direction and movement. Add a number to the last sequence on 5a before copying to focus on odd or even numbers, above or below 100. To complete sheet 5b, each child will also need an individual 0–99 Number square each. The specific criteria for the assessment sheets can be found at the bottom of each sheet.

RESOURCES

Individual 0–99 Number squares (photocopiable page 13), small cubes, sets of numeral cards 10–30 and even numbers 2–20, three different-coloured plastic hoops, sets of dominoes, 1–6 'spotty' dice, coins, 100g weights, balances, objects to weigh (ranging from 100–500/1000g), pencils and paper, copies of Assessment worksheets 5a and 5b, and photocopiable pages 28 and 138 for each child. Counting apparatus should be available.

PREPARATION

Make copies of the worksheets required. Put the resources for each activity on one table.

ORAL AND MENTAL STARTER

ASSESSMENT

● Can the children: Describe and extend simple number sequences: count in tens from any two-digit number? Use knowledge that addition can be done in any order to do mental calculations more efficiently?
● Do the children: Know by heart: multiplication facts for 2 and 10 times tables?

ADDITION: Repeat 'All change' game with two hoops with numeral cards 10–30. Extend to playing the game with three hoops.
TWOS AND TENS: Count round the circle, as far as possible, in tens and then in twos. Challenge individuals to multiply by 2 or by 10 the numbers on cards you hold up. Then repeat 'Double and half' (see Lesson 4, Unit 8, on page 191) with numeral cards 2–20.

GROUP ACTIVITIES

ASSESSMENT

● Can the children: Understand that subtraction is the inverse of addition; state the subtraction corresponding to a given addition and vice versa? Use knowledge that addition can be done in any order to do mental calculations more efficiently? Choose and use appropriate operations and efficient calculations to solve problems, explaining how the problem was solved? Estimate, measure and compare mass, using standard units?

SUBTRACTION AS THE INVERSE OF ADDITION: Repeat 'Corresponding additions and subtractions' with dominoes (see Lesson 3, Unit 2, on page 162). Check the children write four number sentences for each domino, e.g.: 4 + 2 = 6; 2 + 4 = 6; 6 – 2 = 4; 6 – 4 = 2. Do they count the domino spots, write 'workings', ask for cubes, or work mentally?
ADDITION: Repeat 'Finding the totals of spots on three dominoes'. (See Lesson 2, Unit 2 on page 161.) Check whether children record the numbers in the easiest order to carry out the calculation. Note whether they count the domino spots, write workings or work mentally
USING APPROPRIATE OPERATIONS AND CALCULATIONS TO SOLVE PROBLEMS: Repeat 'Shopping for sweets' using page 138 and 1–6 dice (see Lesson 10, Unit 3, page 109 and Lesson 4, Unit 10 in Term 2, page 136). Note whether children can play according to the rules. In working out the calculations, do they use coins, write workings or work mentally?
MEASURING MASS: Ask the children to weigh each object and record its weight. You may wish to provide a list of the names of the objects to help with spelling, or make a recording chart for the children to complete. Alternatively, ask them to repeat the group activity in Lesson 6, Unit 6 on page 178, where the children balance a number of objects with 100g.

Assessment sheet 5a

Continue and complete.

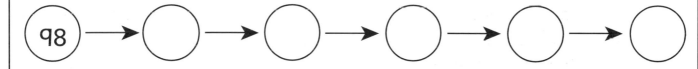

Finish these two-way counts.

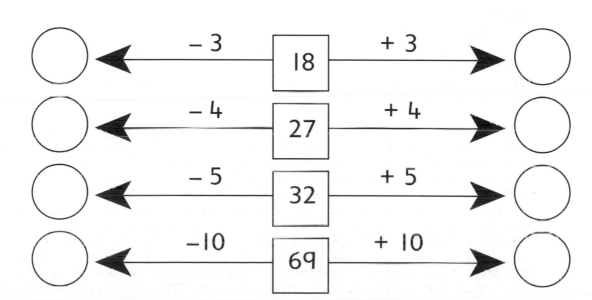

- Describe and extend simple number sequences.
- Recognise odd and even numbers.

Assessment sheet 5b

Draw in arrows to show the amount of turn.

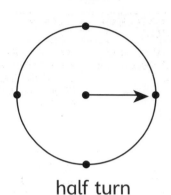
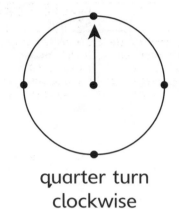
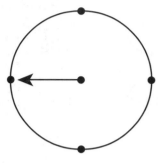

half turn

quarter turn clockwise

quarter turn anti-clockwise

Draw lines on these circles to make right angles.

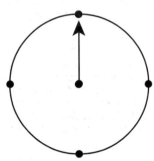
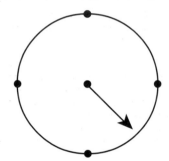
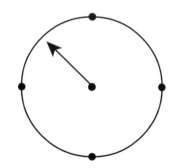

Use a 0–99 number square.

Follow these directions to find the missing number.

24 [↓ 3] [→3] [ ]   17 [↓ 4] [→4] [ ]

76 [↑ 5] [← 1] [ ]   83 [↑ 8] [← 3] [ ]

Write a route for these numbers.

32 → 77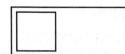

94 → 61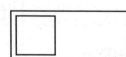

● Use mathematical vocabulary to describe position, direction and movement.

UNIT 8

ORGANISATION (5 LESSONS)

LEARNING OUTCOMES	ORAL AND MENTAL STARTER	MAIN TEACHING ACTIVITY	PLENARY
LESSON 1 +2 +3 ● **Describe and extend simple number sequences:** count on in steps of 3, 4 or 5 to at least 30, from and back to zero, then from and back to any given small number.	COUNTING: Counting back in twos, fives, tens and 100s. Reciting the 2 and 10 times tables.	COUNT ON AND COUNT BACK 3, 4 OR 5.	MY NUMBER/ YOUR NUMBER. COUNT ON AND COUNT BACK 3, 4 OR 5.
LESSON 4 ● Derive quickly: doubles of multiples of 5 to 50 (e.g. 20 × 2 or 35 × 2); halves of multiples of 10 to 100 (e.g. half of 70).	DOUBLE AND HALF: Playing a game with even-numbered cards 2–20.	COUNTING PATTERNS: Finding doubles of multiples of 5 and halves of multiples of 10.	DOUBLES OF MULTIPLES OF 5: Playing a game with cards 5–50 in fives
LESSON 5 ● **Describe and extend simple number sequences:** count on in steps of 3, 4 or 5 to at least 30, from and back to zero, then from and back to any given small number.	HALVES OF MULTIPLES OF 2 AND 10: Playing a game with cards 2–20 and 10–100.	NUMBER SEQUENCES.	Reviewing work from the Main teaching activity.

ORAL AND MENTAL SKILLS **Describe and extend number sequences:** count in hundreds from and back to zero; count on in twos from and back to zero or any small number; count on in steps of 5 to at least 30, from and back to zero, then from and back to any given small number. Begin to recognise two-digit multiples of 2, 5, or 10. **Know by heart: multiplication facts for the 2 and 10 times tables;** doubles of all numbers to 10 and the corresponding halves. Derive quickly: doubles of multiples of 5 to 50 (e.g. 20 × 2 or 35 × 2); halves of multiples of 10 to 100 (e.g. half of 70).

Lessons 1 is given in full – Lessons 2 and 3 extend its content to further number sequences. Lesson 4 is again given in full, while Lesson 5 rounds up the preceding sequences work.

RESOURCES

Photocopiable pages 13 (0–99 number square) and 69 (Two-way counts); flip chart and two different-coloured water-based markers; small cubes; paper and pencils, crayons or felt-tipped pens; 0–49 Number rectangles (see Preparation below).

PREPARATION

Make at least three copies of pages 13 (0–99 number square) and 69 (Two-way counts) for each child. Enlarge and laminate one copy of photocopiable page 13 as a teaching chart. Make a master 0–49 rectangle by cutting the required rows from a 0–99 Number square and pasting them on to another sheet of paper. Copy three for each less able child.

LEARNING OUTCOMES

ORAL AND MENTAL STARTER STARTER
● **Describe and extend simple number sequences:** count in hundreds from and back to zero; count on in twos from and back to zero or any small number.
● Begin to recognise two-digit multiples of 2, 5, or 10.

MAIN TEACHING ACTIVITY
● **Describe and extend simple number sequences:** count on in steps of 3, 4 or 5 to at least 30, from and back to zero, then from and back to any given small number.

VOCABULARY

Numbers to 100; count on three; count back three; number sequence; continue; predict; pattern; rule; multiples; multiples of; describe the pattern; describe the rule; arrow; write in figures.

ORAL AND MENTAL STARTER

COUNTING: Practise counting back in tens from 100; in 100s from 1000; in fives from 100 and in twos from 50. Try to maintain a brisk pace to encourage rapid recall.

MAIN TEACHING ACTIVITY

COUNT ON AND COUNT BACK 3: Sit the children facing the enlarged 0–99 Number square and the flip chart. Tell them they are going to carry out an activity where they count on and count back 3. Remind them how to count on and back by pointing to a few numbers on the chart and choosing individuals to say the 'count on 3' number. Repeat with 'count back 3'.

Next tell the children they will be using a number square sheet and a coloured crayon or felt-tipped pen to colour the pattern of 'count on 3' starting from 4 and writing the number sequence on a separate sheet. Demonstrate this on the Number square teaching chart by colouring the '4' on the square and asking children which number should be coloured next. Scribe the number sequence on the flip chart up to 13, for example: 4 → 7→ 10 → 13.

Then tell the children to use another colour for the pattern of 'count back 3' from 99, again writing the number sequence underneath. Demonstrate this on the chart in the same way as 'count on 3', with numbers down to 90, for example: 99→ 96→ 93→ 90 and so on.

Tell the children to start by copying the 'count on 3' pattern and number sequence from the chart, then to continue colouring and writing the number sequence as far as possible. When they finish this they can start the 'count back 3', copying the pattern and sequence from the chart again, and continuing as far as possible.

DIFFERENTIATION

More able: provide each child with a copy of photocopiable page 28 (Two-way counts), an individual number square and a cube to play a number square and cube game with the rule 'count on/count back 3'.
Less able: provide 0–49 Number rectangles. Ask the children to count back in 3s from 49.

PLENARY

Reinforce the threes pattern by playing 'My number/your number' with 'count on/count back 3'. Use numbers between 3 and 30. (See Lesson 3, Unit 1, Term 2 on page 99.)

LESSONS 2 AND 3

Repeat Lesson 1, but in the **Oral and mental starter** practise reciting the 2 and 10 times table. Then count in fives to 100 together, then round the circle. Choose a different child to start the count each time. Encourage a fast pace to develop rapid recall.

In the **Main teaching activity** carry out the work as in Lesson 1, but in Lesson 2 children should use the number square to colour and count on in fours from 3 as far as possible, then back in fours from 99. In Lesson 3 they should count in fives from 3, then back in fives from 99.

Again in the **Differentiation** and the **Plenary** session substitute 4 and 5 for 3. In the 'Count on/count back' game, ask the children to use 4–40, and 5–50, respectively.

RESOURCES

Shuffled sets of even-numbered cards 2–20 and shuffled sets of cards showing multiples of 5 to 50 (one of each card for each child); paper and pencils; sets of dominoes; Cuisenaire rods.

LEARNING OUTCOMES

ORAL AND MENTAL STARTER

● **Know by heart:** doubles of all numbers to 10 and the corresponding halves.

MAIN TEACHING ACTIVITY

● Derive quickly: doubles of multiples of 5 to 50 (e.g. 20 × 2 or 35 × 2); halves of multiples of 10 to 100 (e.g. half of 70).

VOCABULARY

Numbers to 50; multiples of 5 and 10; odd and even numbers; double; half; divide; share; pattern; rule; sequence; predict; continue; describe the pattern; describe the rule; arrow; write in figures.

ORAL AND MENTAL STARTER

DOUBLE AND HALF: Play this with even-numbered cards 2–20. Hold up a card each time and choose a child to double the number on the card. Then change the rule to halving the number. Play the game at a fast pace to encourage rapid recall.

MAIN TEACHING ACTIVITY

COUNTING PATTERNS: Finding doubles of multiples of 5 and halves of multiples of 10. Demonstrate the task on the board, asking the children to help you build the number sequence of multiples of 5 to 50. Write the sequence on the board: 5 → 10 → 15 →, and so on; then write the number 5 on the board and ask a child to say its 'double number': 5 → 10. Next write 10 on the board for children to say the double number: 10 → 20. Tell them they are to start by writing on their sheet the number sequence of 'count on in fives' to 50. They should then write each number in the sequence followed by its double number. Repeat the demonstration with the number sequence of multiples of 10 to 100, first writing 10 on the board, followed by half the number 10 → 5; then writing 20 on the board and so on. Tell the children that when they finish doubling 'five' numbers they will repeat the activity halving 'tens' numbers on their sheet. Check that they know what they have to do before they return to their tables to carry out the activity.

DIFFERENTIATION

More able: encourage these children to carry out a halving activity with dominoes. Give the group a box of dominoes and each child a fresh sheet of paper. The group should sort out all the dominoes that have an even number of spots and discard the rest, putting them back in the box. They then spread the even-numbered dominoes, face up, on the table. Each child then selects and draws around a domino, marks in the spots and then writes a statement for half the number of spots, for example:

Half of 6 = 3

Less able: provide Cuisenaire rods for children who may require additional support.

PLENARY

DOUBLES OF MULTIPLES OF 5: Play a game with cards 5–50 in multiples of 5. Hold up a card each time and choose a child to say the double number.

LESSON 5

RESOURCES	A set of shuffled cards combining even-numbered cards 2–20, and cards showing multiples of 10 to 100 (one card for each child); a copy of photocopiable page 192 (More number sequences) for each child; pencils; Cuisenaire rods.
LEARNING OUTCOMES	**ORAL AND MENTAL STARTER** ● Derive quickly: halves of multiples of 10 to 100 (e.g. half of 70). **MAIN TEACHING ACTIVITY** ● **Describe and extend simple number sequences:** count on in steps of 3, 4 or 5 to at least 30, from and back to zero, then from and back to any given small number.
ORAL AND MENTAL STARTER	HALVES OF MULTIPLES OF 2 AND 10: Shuffle the even-numbered cards 2–20 and cards showing multiples of 10 to 100. Hold up one card each time. Choose a child to say the 'half' number
MAIN TEACHING ACTIVITY	NUMBER SEQUENCES: Give each child a copy of page 192. Ask them to look at and describe each number sequence on the sheet in turn . Check they know how to complete the sheet before they return to their tables.
DIFFERENTIATION	More able: encourage the children to work mentally where they can, but tell them they can write their 'workings' on the sheets if they are unsure. Less able: provide Cuisenaire rods as support.
PLENARY	Review the work done in the **Main teaching activity** by scribing the examples from the sheet on the board. Invite different children to give their responses and explain their methods.

More number sequences

Continue these number sequences.

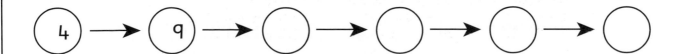

UNIT 9

ORGANISATION (5 LESSONS)

	LEARNING OUTCOMES	ORAL AND MENTAL STARTER	MAIN TEACHING ACTIVITY	PLENARY
LESSON 1	• **Know by heart:** all pairs of multiples of 10 with a total of 100. • **Understand that subtraction is the inverse of addition** (subtraction reverses addition). • Use patterns of similar calculations.	QUICK-FIRE DOUBLES AND HALVES.	ADDITION AND SUBTRACTION PATTERNS: 10; 100; 1000.	QUICK-FIRE DOUBLES AND HALVES.
LESSON 2	• Use known number facts and place value to subtract mentally.	ADD BY GROUPING TENS AND UNITS: Playing a game with cards 10–50.	SUBTRACTION WITH DOMINOES.	Reviewing work from the Main teaching activity.
LESSON 3	• Use known number facts and place value to subtract mentally. • Use patterns of similar calculations.	ALL CHANGE: Playing the game with three hoops and cards 10–30.	SUBTRACTING TWO-DIGIT NUMBERS.	Reviewing work from the Main teaching activity. ALL CHANGE.
LESSON 4	• Recognise all coins and begin to use £.p notation for money (for example, know that £4.65 indicates £4 and 65p). • Find totals, give change, and work out which coins to pay. • Choose and use appropriate operations and efficient calculation strategies to solve problems.	MY NUMBER/YOUR NUMBER: Adding and subtracting 11.	SPEND AND CHANGE FROM £5.00.	Reviewing work from the Main teaching activity. MY NUMBER/ YOUR NUMBER: Adding and subtracting 21.
LESSON 5	• Use the +, – and = signs to record mental additions and subtractions in a number sentence, and recognise the use of a symbol such as □ or △ to stand for an unknown number.	TAKE TWO-DIGITS: Subtraction game with cards 1–30.	ADDITION AND SUBTRACTION PROBLEMS.	Reviewing work from the Main teaching activity.

ORAL AND MENTAL SKILLS   Derive quickly: doubles of multiples of 5 to 50; halves of multiples of 10 to 100. Partition additions into tens and units, then recombine. Begin to add three numbers mentally. Use known number facts and place value to subtract mentally. Add/subtract 11 or 21.

Lessons 1–3 are given in full and develop subtraction skills. Lessons 4 and 5, both in grid form, provide follow-up practice in these skills.

RESOURCES

Paper and pencils; individual number squares, small cubes, a three minute timer.

PREPARATION

Write the following number statements on the board:

1 + 9 = 10	10 + 90 = 100	100 + 900 = 1000
2 + ? = 10	20 + ? = 100	200 + ? = 1000
10 – 1 = 9	100 – 10 = 90	1000 – 100 = 900
10 – 2 = ?	100 – 20 = ?	1000 – 200 = ?

LEARNING OUTCOMES

ORAL AND MENTAL STARTER

● Derive quickly: doubles of multiples of 5 to 50; halves of multiples of 10 to 100.

MAIN TEACHING ACTIVITY

● **Know by heart:** all pairs of multiples of 10 with a total of 100.
● **Understand that subtraction is the inverse of addition** (subtraction reverses addition).
● Use patterns of similar calculations.

VOCABULARY

Numbers to
100, numbers
in hundreds to
1000; equals;
multiples;
predict;
pattern;
continue;
calculate;
mental; add;
addition;
subtract;
subtraction;
number
sentence(s);
rule; number
pairs; number
bonds.

ORAL AND MENTAL STARTER

QUICK-FIRE DOUBLES AND HALVES: Ask for doubles of multiples of 5 (to 50) and halves of multiples of 10 (to 100), for example: *What is double 25? What is half of 80?* Encourage recall, but discuss strategies for figuring out those that the children do not know.

MAIN TEACHING ACTIVITY

ADDITION AND SUBTRACTION PATTERNS: Tell the children to read the number sentences on the board. Choose individuals to try to say some of the missing numbers. Then tell the children to copy the number statements from the board and continue to write the patterns on their sheets as far as possible. Tell them to build the patterns across the page, working with 10, 100 and 1000 each time, rather than building each column separately. Tell them to write down all the additions before starting on the subtraction patterns.

DIFFERENTIATION

More able: give each child an 0–99 number square, a cube and a sheet of paper. They are going to play a number square and cube game with four to six players. The rule is 'add 29'. Everyone starts when a three-minute timer is turned over. The child who completes the most correct 'add 29' statements in three minutes wins. Then they can try 'subtract 29'. Less able: tell children to copy and complete all the addition and subtraction facts for 10, then for 100 and then for 1000. Have Cuisenaire rods and Base 10 apparatus available.

PLENARY

Repeat the 'Quick-fire doubles and halves' game.

RESOURCES

Set of shuffled numeral cards 10–50 (one card for each child); flip chart and pen; paper and pencils; a set of dominoes for each group; Cuisenaire rods and/or 0–99 number squares.

PREPARATION

Place a box of dominoes, sheets of paper and pencils on each table.

LEARNING OUTCOMES

ORAL AND MENTAL STARTER
● Partition additions into tens and units, then recombine.

VOCABULARY

Numbers
0–100; add;
addition;
grouping;
subtract;
subtraction;
take away;
difference;
leaves; count
on; count
back; tens
and units;
equals;
leaves.

MAIN TEACHING ACTIVITY
● Use known number facts and place value to subtract mentally.

ORAL AND MENTAL STARTER

ADD BY GROUPING TENS AND UNITS: Sit the children in a semicircle and give each child a 10–50 numeral card. Ask two children to stand facing the group to show and say the number on their cards. Choose a seated child to say the total each time.

MAIN TEACHING ACTIVITY

SUBTRACTION WITH DOMINOES: Sit the children facing the flip chart. Tell them they are going to carry out a subtraction activity with pairs of dominoes. They should select and draw round two dominoes, mark in the spots, then write the two-digit numbers denoted by the spots underneath both dominoes. They then write a subtraction statement by placing the larger number first and using the easiest method to carry out the subtraction. Explain, and demonstrate with a few examples on the flip chart, that the children should always count a blank as 0 units and not 0 tens and that they can carry out the subtractions using different methods. For example:

20 – 10 (Subtracting the smaller number from the larger number.)

25 – 21 (Counting on from the smaller to the larger number to find the difference.)

41 – 23 (Starting with the larger number, subtracting the tens, and then the units of the smaller number.)

Tell the children that they can choose which method to use each time. Encourage them to work the subtractions out mentally, but invite them to record workings where they are unsure. Tell them to start by spreading the dominoes out face down on their table and to replace the pairs of dominoes back in the box after each pair is used.

DIFFERENTIATION

More able: can spread the dominoes out again to repeat the activity. Ask them to check their answers by adding the smaller number to their answer. Is the total the larger number? Less able: provide Cuisenaire rods and/or 0–99 number squares as additional support.

PLENARY

Review the work done in the **Main teaching activity** on the flip chart by asking children to give examples of subtractions and describe their methods.

RESOURCES

A set of shuffled numeral cards 1–30; three different coloured sorting hoops; flip chart and pen; paper and pencils; 0–99 number squares.

PREPARATION

Write the following subtraction patterns on the board, each from a 30s to a 70s number:

36 – 23 =	37 – 24 =	38 – 25 =	39 – 26 =
46 – 23 =...	47 – 24 =...	48 – 25 =...	49 – 26 =...
...76 – 23 =	...77 – 24 =	...78 – 25 =	...79 – 26 =

LEARNING OUTCOMES

ORAL AND MENTAL STARTER
● Begin to add three numbers mentally.

MAIN TEACHING ACTIVITY
● Use known number facts and place value to subtract mentally.
● Use patterns of similar calculations.

ORAL AND MENTAL STARTER

ALL CHANGE: Play this game with three hoops and cards 10–30 (as on page 30).

MAIN TEACHING ACTIVITY

SUBTRACTING TWO-DIGIT NUMBERS: Sit the children facing the flip chart. Tell them they are to complete the subtraction patterns on the board by subtracting the tens, followed by the units. Explain and demonstrate the method on the flip chart with an example.

Then use a few more examples asking children to contribute the methods, such as:

$35 - 22 \rightarrow 35 - 20 = 15 - 2 = 13$

$45 - 22 \rightarrow 45 - 20 = 25 - 2 = 23$

Encourage the children to work the answers out mentally where they can, but tell them to write down their workings where they are unsure.

DIFFERENTIATION

More able: can these children continue each subtraction pattern through a 90s number?
Less able: provide 0–99 number squares for children who require additional support.

PLENARY

Review the **Main teaching activity** by inviting children to give responses to each subtraction sentence while you scribe answers on the board. Continue each pattern to a 90s number. Can the children say what the number pattern is in each set of answers?

RESOURCES	A copy of photocopiable page 70 (Spend and change from £5.00) for each child; sets of three money dice: marked 2p, 5p, 10p, 20p, 50p, £1.00 and one marked £2.00, £2.00, £1.00, £1.00, 50p, 50p; sets of coins to £2.00.
LEARNING OUTCOMES	**ORAL AND MENTAL STARTER** ● Add/subtract 11; Begin to add/subtract 21. **MAIN TEACHING ACTIVITY** ● Recognise all coins and begin to use £.p notation for money (for example, know that £4.65 indicates £4 and 65p). ● Find totals, give change, and work out which coins to pay. ● Choose and use appropriate operations and efficient calculation strategies to solve problems.
ORAL AND MENTAL STARTER	MY NUMBER/YOUR NUMBER: Adding and subtracting 11.
MAIN TEACHING ACTIVITY	SPEND AND CHANGE FROM £5.00: Use sets of three money dice (see Resources) and coins. Carry out the activity in the same way as 'Spend and change from 50p' in Lesson 5, Unit 9, Term 1 on page 68.
DIFFERENTIATION	More able: repeat the game on a fresh copy of the sheet. Less able: have sets of coin available.
PLENARY	Review both the **Main teaching activity** and the oral work. Highlight the importance of using the decimal point (the 'full stop') in the correct place in £.p notation. Play 'My number/your number', adding and subtracting 21. Draw comparisons with the method of adding 11.

RESOURCES	A set of cards 1–30 (one for each child); a copy of photocopiable page 197 (More addition and subtraction problems) for each child; pencils; 0–99 number squares and/or Cuisenaire rods.
LEARNING OUTCOMES	**ORAL AND MENTAL STARTER** ● Use known number facts and place value to subtract mentally. **MAIN TEACHING ACTIVITY** ● Use the +, – and = signs to record mental additions and subtractions in a number sentence, and recognise the use of a symbol such as □ or △ to stand for an unknown number.
ORAL AND MENTAL STARTER	TAKE TWO-DIGITS: Give each child sitting in the semicircle one of a shuffled set of cards 1–30. Choose two children to stand facing the group and show and say the numbers on their cards. Choose a seated child to say a subtraction sentence (by putting the larger number first) and the answer.
MAIN TEACHING ACTIVITY	ADDITION AND SUBTRACTION PROBLEMS: Give each child a copy of photocopiable page 197. Read through each question on the sheet with the children.
DIFFERENTIATION	More able: encourage the children to work mentally whenever possible, but let them to write workings where appropriate. Less able: provide 0–99 number squares and/or Cuisenaire rods.
PLENARY	Review the **Main teaching activity**. Scribe the questions from the sheet on the board. Invite individuals to give responses and explain their methods.

Name

More addition and subtraction problems

Work mentally to complete:

32 + 5 = ☐	32 + ☐ = 37	☐ + 5 = 37
86 − 4 = ☐	86 − ☐ = 82	☐ − 4 = 82
30 + 4 = ☐	30 + ☐ = 34	☐ + 4 = 34
80 + 7 = ☐	80 + ☐ = 87	☐ + 7 = 87
80 − 4 = ☐	80 − ☐ = 76	☐ − 4 = 76
60 − 7 = ☐	60 − ☐ = 53	☐ − 7 = 53
40 + 24 = ☐	40 + ☐ = 64	☐ + 24 = 64
20 + 56 = ☐	20 + ☐ = 76	☐ + 56 = 76
45 + 11 = ☐	58 + ☐ = 70	☐ + 13 = 43
37 − 12 = ☐	29 − ☐ = 18	☐ − 21 = 21
52 + 30 = ☐	26 + ☐ = 66	49 + ☐ = 99
76 − 40 = ☐	83 − ☐ = 23	95 − ☐ = 45
200 + 400 = ☐	300 + ☐ = 600	700 + 3000 = ☐
700 − 300 = ☐	800 − ☐ = 400	1000 − 600 = ☐

UNITS 10-11

ORGANISATION (10 LESSONS)

LEARNING OUTCOMES	ORAL AND MENTAL STARTER	MAIN TEACHING ACTIVITY	PLENARY
LESSON 1 ● Begin to know: multiplication facts for the 5 times table. ● Use the × and = signs to record mental calculations in a number sentence.	COUNTING IN 5S: Reciting counting in fives to 100 and back to zero. Counting around the circle in fives.	THE 5 TIMES TABLE: Colouring the pattern of fives on a number square and writing the 5 times table.	Reciting the 5 times table to 50. Asking oral questions.
LESSON 2 ● Derive quickly: doubles of multiples of 5 to 50; halves of multiples of 10 to 100.	Reciting the 5 times table to 50. Asking oral questions.	DOUBLES OF MULTIPLES, HALVES OF MULTIPLES: Doubling multiples of 5 and halving multiples of 10 using numeral cards.	Doubling multiples of 5 and halving multiples of 10. Asking oral questions.
LESSON 3 ● **Know and use halving as the inverse of doubling.**	DOUBLES OF MULTIPLES: Doubling multiples of 5 with cards 5–50.	DOUBLE AND HALF TWO-WAYS: Playing with even-numbered cards 20–50.	HALVES OF MULTIPLES: Halving multiples of 10 with cards 10–100.
LESSON 4 ● Use known number facts and place value to add mentally. ● Use known number facts and place value to carry out mentally simple multiplications. ● Use the +, × and = signs to record mental calculations in a number sentence.	Reciting the 2, 5 and 10 times tables. Asking oral questions.	DOMINO MULTIPLICATION AND ADDITION.	DOMINO TIMES.
LESSON 5 ● Recognise all coins and begin to use £.p notation for money (for example, know that £4.65 indicates £4 and 65p). ● Find totals, give change, and work out which coins to pay.	IN MY PURSE: Asking oral questions with three types of coins.	HALF PRICE SALE.	Reviewing work from the Main teaching activity.
LESSON 6 ● Use the ×, ÷ and = signs to record mental calculations in a number sentence. ● **Know and use halving as the inverse of doubling.**	DOUBLE AND HALF: Playing a game with even-numbered cards 2–20.	MULTIPLICATION AND DIVISION BY 2: Multiplying and dividing by 2 with even-numbered cards 10–50.	HOW MANY?
LESSON 7 ● **Know by heart: multiplication facts for the 10 times table.** ● Derive quickly: division facts corresponding to the 10 times table. ● Use the ×, ÷ and = signs to record mental calculations in a number sentence.	DOUBLE AND HALF: Playing with cards 10–50 in multiples of 10.	Multiplying and dividing by 10 with cards in multiples of 10 to 100.	HOW MANY? Playing with cards 10–100.
LESSON 8 ● Use the +, − , ×, ÷ and = signs to record mental calculations in a number sentence, and recognise the use of a symbol such as □ or △ to stand for an unknown number. ● **Explain how a problem was solved.**	MULTIPLE BUYING:	MULTIPLICATION	Reviewing work from the Main teaching activity.

LEARNING OUTCOMES	ORAL AND MENTAL STARTER	MAIN TEACHING ACTIVITY	PLENARY
LESSON 9 ● Begin to recognise and find one quarter of shapes and small numbers of objects. ● Begin to recognise that four quarters make one whole and that two quarters and one half are equivalent.	Asking oral questions. DOMINO TIMES 2 AND 10.	AND DIVISION. DIVIDING SHAPES INTO QUARTERS: Finding halves and quarters of small numbers of objects.	DOMINO TIMES 2 AND 10.
LESSON 10 ● Begin to recognise and find one quarter of shapes. ● Solve mathematical problems or puzzles. Suggest extensions by asking 'What if …?' or 'What could I try next?'	DOUBLES: Playing with cards 5–50.	FRACTIONS OF SHAPES: Finding ways to colour one quarter of a 4×4 square grid.	Reviewing work from the Main teaching activity.

ORAL AND MENTAL STARTER Describe and extend simple number sequences: count on in steps of 5 to at least 30, from and back to zero. Begin to know: multiplication facts for the 5 times table. **Know by heart: multiplication facts for the 2 and 10 times tables;** doubles of all numbers to 10 and the corresponding halves. **Know and use halving as the inverse of doubling.** Derive quickly: division facts corresponding to the 2 and 10 times tables; doubles of multiples of 5 to 50; halves of multiples of 10 to 100. Use known number facts and place value to carry out mentally simple multiplications and divisions. Use simple multiplication and division to solve simple word problems involving money.

In Unit 10, Lessons 1, 2 and 4 are laid out in full, with Lessons 3 and 5 in grid form.
In Unit 11, Lessons 6, 7 and 9 are provided in full with Lessons 8 and 10 given as grids.

RESOURCES

Photocopiable page 13 (0–99 Number square), A4 copies and an enlarged and laminated teaching chart; a flip chart and coloured water-based markers; pencils, crayons or felt-tipped pens.

PREPARATION

Make a copy of photocopiable page 13 for each child.

LEARNING OUTCOMES

ORAL AND MENTAL STARTER
● **Describe and extend simple number sequences:** count on in steps of 5 to at least 30, from and back to zero.

MAIN TEACHING ACTIVITY
● Begin to know: multiplication facts for the 5 times table.
● Use the × and = signs to record mental calculations in a number sentence.

ORAL AND MENTAL STARTER

COUNTING IN 5s: Sit the children in a circle and recite counting in fives to 100, and back to zero. Then count around the circle in fives to 50. Choose a different child to start the count each time. Play the game at a fast pace to encourage rapid recall.

MAIN TEACHING ACTIVITY

BUILDING THE 5 TIMES TABLE: Sit the children facing the teaching chart and the flip chart. Tell them they are to colour the pattern of fives on a number square and write the 5 times table on a separate sheet as far as possible. Demonstrate how they will start to colour the pattern of fives to 10 on the teaching chart and explain that multiplication statements can be written with the numbers in either order. Tell the children that when they write the 5 times table they should write both versions. Demonstrate this on the flip chart:

$$0 \times 5 = 0 \qquad 5 \times 0 = 0$$
$$1 \times 5 = 5 \qquad 5 \times 1 = 5$$
$$2 \times 5 = 10 \qquad 5 \times 2 = 10$$

VOCABULARY

Multiply; times table; equals; lots of; groups of; times; multiply by; multiples; pattern; rule; predict; calculate; sign; describe the pattern; describe the rule.

Tell the children to copy the pattern on the chart on to their number square and copy the multiplication statements to a sheet of paper. They should then continue colouring the pattern and writing the multiplication statements as far as they can.

DIFFERENTIATION

More able: encourage these children to build the pattern and table to 100, then see if they can continue beyond 100.
Less able: encourage children to use the Number square to count on five squares each time.

PLENARY

Recite the 5 times table to $5 \times 10 = 50$. Then ask quick-fire times tables questions, such as: *What are two 5s? …six 5s?* etc. Ask about the rule for numbers in the 5 times table: *What do the numbers always end in?* (5 or 0).

RESOURCES

For each group: a set of cards in multiples of five to 50; paper and pencils; flip chart and pen; Cuisenaire rods.

PREPARATION

Place a shuffled set of multiple cards, paper and pencils on each table.

LEARNING OUTCOMES

ORAL AND MENTAL STARTER
● Begin to know: multiplication facts for the 5 times table.

MAIN TEACHING ACTIVITY
● Derive quickly: doubles of multiples of 5 to 50; halves of multiples of 10 to 100.

ORAL AND MENTAL STARTER

Practise reciting the 5 times table again as in the **Plenary** session of Lesson 1 above.

MAIN TEACHING ACTIVITY

DOUBLES OF MULTIPLES, HALVES OF MULTIPLES: Sit the children facing the flip chart. Tell them they are going to carry out a doubling and halving activity at their tables with multiples of 5 and 10. Explain the word 'multiple' here as: *all the numbers in the 5 and 10 times tables* or *all the numbers in the 'count on 5' and 'count on 10' number sequences when the count starts from zero.* Tell the children that on the tables they will find a set of number cards ending in a 5 or 0. Write up a multiple of 5 ending in a 5 and a multiple of 10. Show how, if they are given a number that ends in 5, they should double it and write, for example: Double 25 = 50. If the number ends in 0, they should halve it and write, for example: Half of 40 = 20. Organise the children into threes, fours or sixes (in a group of five, they will always be dealt the same cards), then tell them how to carry out the activity:
● One child deals out a card to everyone in the group including himself.
● Decide whether you have to double or halve the number you have been given and then write the number sentence down on your sheet of paper.
● Remember that the activity is not a race. Every group member must write down his or her answer and wait for the others in the group to finish before all the cards are handed back together to the dealer each time.
● When the cards have been returned, the dealer puts them on the bottom of the pack and passes the pack to the next child, who becomes the dealer.
● If you are given a card you have already used, return the card to the dealer (who puts it at the bottom of the pack) and ask for another card.
● Stop when everyone has written ten different 'double' or 'half' number sentences.

VOCABULARY

Lots of; groups of; multiply; multiplied by; multiple of; twice; times; equals; double; half; halves; divide; share; group; equal shares; describe the rule.

DIFFERENTIATION

More able: give these children a 0–49 number rectangle and a cube. They should throw the cube on to any square and double any odd number and halve any even number it lands on.
Less able: lay out the cards in two lines of five, separating the cards into numbers ending in 0 and 5, like this: 10; 20; 30; 40; 50
5; 15; 25; 35; 45
Tell the children to double all the numbers using Cuisenaire rods to help them.

PLENARY

Ask oral questions using doubles of multiples of 5 and halves of multiples of 10, for example: *What is double 15? What is half of 60?* Pitch the questions to the abilities of individual children.

RESOURCES	A set of numeral cards in multiples of five to 50; a set of numeral cards in multiples of ten 10 to 100; a set of even-numbered cards 20–50 for each group. A copies of photocopiable page 28 (Two-way counts); pencils.
LEARNING OUTCOMES	**ORAL AND MENTAL STARTER** ● Derive quickly: doubles of multiples of 5 to 50; halves of multiples of 10 to 100. **MAIN TEACHING ACTIVITY** ● **Know and use halving as the inverse of doubling.**
ORAL AND MENTAL STARTER	DOUBLES OF MULTIPLES: Sit the children in a circle. Give each child one of a shuffled set of multiples of 5 cards (5–50). Ask them to take turns round the circle to double the number on their card. Collect in the cards, shuffle them and repeat the game. Play at a fast pace to encourage rapid recall.
MAIN TEACHING ACTIVITY	DOUBLE AND HALF TWO WAYS: Playing with even-numbered cards 20–50. Explain to the children that they will be using a 'Two-way counts' sheet (photocopiable page 28), with the rule 'double and half'. Shuffle the cards and spread them out face up on each table. The children look at the cards and choose a number to write in the centre box on the sheet. They then write the 'half' number in the left-hand box and the 'double' number in the right-hand box. They then select other numbers until they have completed the sheet. Ask the children to tell you what they have to do before they return to their tables to carry out the activity.
DIFFERENTIATION	More able: give these children a fresh copy of the sheet to repeat the activity, choosing different or new numbers each time. Less able: carry out the activity with a set of even-numbered cards 2–20.
PLENARY	HALVES OF MULTIPLES: Sit the children in a circle and give each child one of a shuffled set of multiples of ten cards (10–100). Ask the children to take turns around the circle to halve the number on their card. Collect in the cards, shuffle and give them out again to repeat the game.

RESOURCES

Flip chart and pen; a box of dominoes for each group; paper and pencils; Cuisenaire rods.

PREPARATION

Place a box of dominoes, paper and pencils on each table.

LEARNING OUTCOMES

ORAL AND MENTAL STARTER
● **Know by heart: multiplication facts for the 2 and 10 times tables.**
● Begin to know: multiplication facts for the 5 times table.

MAIN TEACHING ACTIVITY
● Use known number facts and place value to add mentally.
● Use known number facts and place value to carry out mentally simple multiplications.
● Use the +, × and = signs to record mental calculations in a number sentence.

VOCABULARY

Lots of;
groups of;
multiply;
multiply by;
times;
repeated
addition; add;
makes; show
how you...;
give me an
example of...;
equals.

ORAL AND MENTAL STARTER

Recite the 2, 5 and 10 times tables. Ask oral questions, such as: *What are 5 twos? 3 fives? 7 tens?* and so on.

MAIN TEACHING ACTIVITY

DOMINO MULTIPLICATION AND ADDITION: Sit the children facing the flip chart and tell them they are going to carry out a multiplication activity with dominoes. Demonstrate the activity on the flip chart and tell the children what to do.

● Tip the box of dominoes on to the table and spread them out face down.
● Select a domino, draw around it, mark in the spots on your sheet, then replace the domino in the box.
● Write a multiplication statement for the domino, repeat the multiplication in a different order, then check with the equivalent addition calculations, as in the example below:

$$2 \times 3 = 6$$
$$3 \times 2 = 6$$
$$2 + 2 + 2 = 6$$
$$3 + 3 = 6$$

● Complete ten examples with different dominoes.
Repeat with a few more examples, inviting children to say the number statements while you scribe them on the board. Ask the children to tell you what they have to do before they return to their tables to carry out the activity.

DIFFERENTIATION

More able: challenge the children to complete 20 examples with different dominoes.
Less able: provide Cuisenaire rods for children who may require additional support.

PLENARY

DOMINO TIMES: Give each child a domino and ask them to take turns around the circle to multiply the spots on each side of the domino and give the answer, for example: 'Two times three equals six'.

RESOURCES	A copy of photocopiable page 207 for each child; pencils; sets of coins.
LEARNING OUTCOMES	**ORAL AND MENTAL STARTER** and **MAIN TEACHING ACTIVITY** ● Recognise all coins and begin to use £.p notation for money (for example, know that £4.65 indicates £4 and 65p). ● Find totals, give change, and work out which coins to pay.
ORAL AND MENTAL STARTER	IN MY PURSE: Ask oral questions involving three types of coins, for example: *In my purse I have four £1.00 coins, three 10p coins and one 5p coin. How much money is in my purse altogether?* Ask the children to explain their methods.
MAIN TEACHING ACTIVITY	HALF PRICE SALE: Start by talking about half price sales and ask some oral questions, for example: *If a book costs 60p what would it cost in a half price sale?* Give each child a copy of page 207 and read through it with them. Check they know what they have to do before they return to their tables to carry out the activity.
DIFFERENTIATION	More able: encourage the children to work mentally where they can, but tell them they can write workings on the sheets if they are unsure. Less able: provide sets of coins for children who may require additional support.
PLENARY	Review the work done in the **Main teaching activity** by scribing the examples from the sheet on the board and inviting different children to give their responses and explain their methods.

RESOURCES

A shuffled set of even-numbered cards 2–20; flip chart and pen; photocopiable page 28 (Two-way counts); paper and pencils; a shuffled set of even-numbered cards 20–50 for each group; a set of even-numbered cards 10–30; Cuisenaire rods.

PREPARATION

Copy of page 28 for each child. Spread out a set of cards 20–50 face down in the middle of each table. Also place the copies of page 28, paper and pencils on each table.

LEARNING OUTCOMES

ORAL AND MENTAL STARTER
● **Know by heart:** multiplication facts for the 2 times table.
● Derive quickly: division facts corresponding to the 2 times table.

MAIN TEACHING ACTIVITY
● Use the ×, ÷ and − signs to record mental calculations in a number sentence.
● **Know and use halving as the inverse of doubling.**

VOCABULARY

Lots of; groups of two; multiply; multiply by; times; divide; divided by; divided into; share; halve; double; share equally; equals; makes; describe the pattern; describe the rule.

ORAL AND MENTAL STARTER

DOUBLE AND HALF: Hold up one of a shuffled set of even-numbered cards 2–20 each time and ask, for example: *What is double 6?* Alternate between asking children to halve or double numbers on the cards. Play at a fast pace to encourage rapid recall.

MAIN TEACHING ACTIVITY

MULTIPLICATION AND DIVISION BY 2: Sit the children facing the flip chart. Tell them they are going to start by building the multiplication and division patterns of 2 and then use a 'Two-way counts' sheet to multiply and divide numbers by 2. Use the flip chart to show the children how to start building the multiplication and division patterns up to 6, asking them to give the answers each time and say what comes next:

$2 \times 2 = 4$ $2 \div 2 = 1$
$4 \times 2 = 8$ $4 \div 2 = 2$
$...6 \times 2 = 12$ $...6 \div 2 = 3$

(Note: this activity uses only even numbers so that there are no remainders.)

Tell the children to copy the patterns on the chart on to a sheet of paper, then try to continue writing them up to $25 \times 2 = 50$ (or as far as possible). When they have finished, they should take a 'Two-way counts' sheet (page 28) and write 'Multiply and divide by 2' in the rule box. Then they should:
● Pick one of the cards on their table and write the number in the middle box on the sheet.
● Write the number '÷ 2' in the left-hand box and '× 2' in the right-hand box.
● Then replace the card face down on the table and take another, continuing the activity until the sheet is completed.

Check the children know what they have to do before they return to their tables.

DIFFERENTIATION

More able: consider using the full range of odd and even numbers (0–30). Develop pattern building, introducing remainders. For example:

$2 \times 2 = 4$ $2 \div 2 = 1$
$3 \times 2 = 6$ $3 \div 2 = 1\ r1$
$4 \times 2 = 8$ $4 \div 2 = 2$
$5 \times 2 = 10$ $5 \div 2 = 2\ r1$

Less able: use a set of cards 10–30 for the 'Two-way counts' activity. Cuisenaire rods may be of help to children who require additional support.

PLENARY

HOW MANY? Use a shuffled set of even-numbered cards 20–50. Hold up a card. Choose a child to multiply or divide the number by 2, alternating between dividing and multiplying.

RESOURCES

A shuffled set of cards numbered in multiples of ten 10–50; flip chart and pen; photocopiable page 28 (Two-way counts); paper and pencils; for each group: a shuffled set of cards numbered in multiples of ten 10–100.

PREPARATION

Place the prepared copies of photocopiable page 28, paper and pencils on each table. Spread the set of 10–100 cards out face down in the middle of each table.

LEARNING OUTCOMES

ORAL AND MENTAL STARTER

● Derive quickly: doubles of multiples of 5 to 50; halves of multiples of 10 to 100.
● **Know and use halving as the inverse of doubling.**

MAIN TEACHING ACTIVITY

● **Know by heart: multiplication facts for the 10 times table.**
● Derive quickly: division facts corresponding to the 10 times table.
● Use the ×, ÷ and = signs to record mental calculations in a number sentence.

VOCABULARY

Lots of; groups of ten; multiply; multiply by; times; divide; divided by ten; divided into tens; share; halve; double; equals; multiples of; pattern; continue; predict; rule; calculate; mental calculation; left; left over; r, remainder.

ORAL AND MENTAL STARTER

DOUBLE AND HALF: Play with a shuffled set of cards 10–50, holding up a card each time and asking, for example: *What is double 20?* Alternate between asking children to halve or double numbers on the cards. Play at a fast pace to encourage rapid recall.

MAIN TEACHING ACTIVITY

MULTIPLICATION AND DIVISION BY 10: Sit the children facing the flip chart. Tell them they are going to start by building the multiplication and division patterns of 10 and then use a 'Two-way counts' sheet to multiply and divide numbers by 10. Explain that in this activity they will be working with multiples of 10 and with numbers in hundreds to 1000.

Use the flip chart to show the children how to build the multiplication and division patterns up to 30. Ask them to give the answer each time and say what comes next.

$$10 \times 10 = 100 \qquad 10 \div 10 = 1$$
$$20 \times 10 = 200 \qquad 20 \div 10 = 2$$
$$30 \times 10 = 300 \qquad 30 \div 10 = 3$$

Tell the children to copy the patterns on the chart on to their sheets and continue writing the patterns up to 100, or as far as possible.

When they have finished they should take a 'Two-way counts' sheet (page 28) and write 'Multiply and divide by 10' in the rule box on the sheet. Then they:

● Pick up one of the cards on the table and write the number in the middle box on the sheet.

● Write the number divided by 10 in the left-hand box and the number multiplied by 10 in the right-hand box.

● Replace the card face down on the table and take another card, continuing the activity until the sheet is filled.

Check that the children understand what they have to do before they return to their tables to carry out the activity.

DIFFERENTIATION

More able: ask the children to try another Number square and cube game, 'Divide by 10', where the number thrown is represented with the remainder – for example, 46 ÷ 10 = 4 r6. Less able: in the 'Two-way counts' activity: tell the children to look at their multiplication and division patterns sheet if they need help.

PLENARY

HOW MANY? Play with a shuffled set of cards 10–100. Hold up a card and choose a child to multiply or divide the number by 10. Alternate between multiplying and dividing numbers.

RESOURCES	A copy of photocopiable page 208 (Multiplication and division problems) for each child; pencils; sets of Cuisenaire rods.
LEARNING OUTCOMES	**ORAL AND MENTAL STARTER** ● Use known number facts and place value to carry out mentally simple multiplications and divisions. ● Use simple multiplication and division to solve simple word problems involving money. **MAIN TEACHING ACTIVITY** ● Use the +, –, ×, ÷ and = signs to record mental calculations in a number sentence and recognise the use of a symbol such as ☐ or △ to stand for an unknown number. ● Explain how the problem was solved.
ORAL AND MENTAL STARTER	MULTIPLE BUYING: Ask oral questions, for example: *If one packet of sweets cost 10p, how much will five cost? Two ice creams cost 60p, how much does one cost?*
MAIN TEACHING ACTIVITY	MULTIPLICATION AND DIVISION PROBLEMS: Give each child a copy of photocopiable page 208. Read through it with the children and check that they know what to do in each section before they return to their tables to carry out the activity.
DIFFERENTIATION	More able: encourage these children to work mentally where they can but tell them they can write workings on the sheet if they are unsure. Less able: provide Cuisenaire rods for children who require additional support.
PLENARY	Review the work done in the Main teaching activity by going through each question from the sheet on the board, asking the children to give answers and explain methods.

RESOURCES

Dominoes (one for each child); flip chart and pen; a marker pen; for each group: gummed paper squares, 2-D circles and squares, scissors; for each child: 24 interlocking cubes, a paper plate, paper and pencils.

PREPARATION

With a marker pen draw lines down the centre and across each plate to 'cut' it into quarters. Place the materials for each group on tables.

LEARNING OUTCOMES

ORAL AND MENTAL STARTER
● **Know by heart : multiplication facts for the 2 and 10 times tables.**
● Use known number facts and place value to carry out mentally simple multiplications.

MAIN TEACHING ACTIVITY
● Begin to recognise and find one quarter of shapes and small numbers of objects.
● Begin to recognise that four quarters make one whole and that two quarters and one half are equivalent.

ORAL AND MENTAL STARTER

DOMINO TIMES 2 AND 10: Sit the children in a circle and give each child a domino. Tell them they are each to take a turn around the circle to multiply the total number of spots on their domino by two saying, for example: 'Seven times two equals fourteen'.
When each child has taken a turn, tell them that they now have to multiply the total number of spots on their domino by ten. Choose a different child to start.

MAIN TEACHING ACTIVITY

DIVIDING SHAPES INTO QUARTERS: Sit the children facing the flip chart and tell them they are going to cut shapes into quarters and find quarters of numbers. Demonstrate how to divide shapes into quarters (four equal parts) by drawing three circles on the flip chart, then drawing lines to cut one circle into halves and one into quarters.

VOCABULARY

Quarter; one quarter; two quarters; three quarters; one half; two halves; one whole; equal parts; fractions; circles; squares.

Label the circles 2/2 (two halves); 4/4 (four quarters) and 1 whole.

Do the same with three squares. Ask: *How many halves in one whole circle or square? How many quarters in one half/one whole circle or square?* Next, show the children how to draw round and cut out three circles from a gummed paper square, fold and cut one into two halves and one into four quarters by folding the shape in half, then in half again, Do the same with a square. Tell them to stick the shapes on their sheets and label them like the ones on the flip chart. Tell the children that when they have finished cutting and sticking their shapes, they are to take a paper plate and 24 interlocking cubes and put equal numbers of cubes in each quarter of the plate. Demonstrate this, starting with four, then eight, cubes. Demonstrate the method of recording on the flip chart, for example:

¼ of 4 = 1
¼ of 8 = 2 etc

Check the children know what they have to do before they return to their tables to carry out the activity.

DIFFERENTIATION

More able: ask the children to continue writing the quarter statements beyond 24. Can they do these mentally by predicting what will come next?
Less able: tell children to work with a partner to carry out the activity but each child carries out their own recording.

PLENARY

Repeat 'Domino times 2 and 10' from Lesson 4 of Unit 10 on page 202. Remind children to find the total number of spots on their domino before they multiply the number by 2 or 10.

RESOURCES	Shuffled set of cards in multiples of 5 (5–50); a copy of photocopiable page 139 (Shape puzzle) for each child and one enlarged as a teaching chart; flip chart and pen; coloured pens; pencils, crayons or felt-tipped pens.
LEARNING OUTCOMES	**ORAL AND MENTAL STARTER** ● Derive quickly: doubles of multiples of 5 to 50. **MAIN TEACHING ACTIVITY** ● Begin to recognise and find one half and one quarter of shapes. ● Solve mathematical problems or puzzles. Suggest extensions by asking 'What if …?' or 'What could I try next?
ORAL AND MENTAL STARTER	DOUBLES: Hold up one of a shuffled set of cards in multiples of five 5–50 and choose a child to say the double number each time. Play the game at a fast pace to encourage rapid recall.
MAIN TEACHING ACTIVITY	FRACTIONS OF SHAPES: Sit the children facing the teaching chart and tell them they are going to carry out a shape 'puzzle' (or investigation) by finding different ways to colour one quarter of 16 squares. First ask: *What is one quarter of 16?* Then demonstrate the activity on the teaching chart by inviting two children to colour one quarter of the squares (4) in two of the grids in a different way with a coloured pen. Show the children a copy of the photocopiable sheet. Tell them to find different ways to colour one quarter of the squares in each grid.
DIFFERENTIATION	More able: suggest that these children include using three whole squares and two cut diagonally in half in their arrangements. Less able: encourage children to find different ways to colour four different squares on the grid each time. Explain to them that each time they colour four squares they are colouring one quarter of a whole shape as there are 16 squares altogether.
PLENARY	Review the work done in the **Main teaching activity** on the teaching chart. Invite individual children to colour one quarter of each grid, using a different configuration each time.

Name

 **Half price sale**

Item		Half price	Full price
book		60p	
felt-tipped pens		90p	
CD			£4.00
watch		£6.00	
game			50p
notepad		30p	
camera		£12.00	
comic		50p	
trainers			£40.00
personal stereo		£30.00	

Multiplication and division problems

Work mentally to complete.

Double 8 =	Half of 18 =
Double 35 =	Half of 70 =
Double 14 =	Half of 30 =

Twice 6 =	8 + 8 =
Twice 50 =	8 × 2 =
Twice 15 =	8 ÷ 2 =

$\frac{1}{2}$ of 12 =

$\frac{1}{2}$ of 40 =

$\frac{1}{2}$ of 50 =

7   + ☐ = 14

14   ÷ ☐ = 7

☐ ÷   7 = 7

40   ×   2   = ☐

☐ ×   2   =   60

50   × ☐ =   100

30   ÷   2 = ☐

☐ ÷   2 =   10

16   ÷ ☐ =   8

Work across the page.

2 + 2 = ☐   2 – 2 = ☐   2 × 2 = ☐   2 ÷ 2 = ☐

4 + 2 = ☐   4 – 2 = ☐   4 × 2 = ☐   4 ÷ 2 = ☐

6 + 2 = ☐   6 – 2 = ☐   6 × 2 = ☐   6 ÷ 2 = ☐

8 + 2 = ☐   8 – 2 = ☐   8 × 2 = ☐   8 ÷ 2 = ☐

10 + 2 = ☐   10 – 2 = ☐   10 × 2 = ☐   10 ÷ 2 = ☐

UNITS 12-13

ORGANISATION (10 LESSONS)

	LEARNING OUTCOMES	ORAL AND MENTAL STARTER	MAIN TEACHING ACTIVITY	PLENARY
LESSON 1	● Use units of time and know the relationships between them. ● Solve simple word problems.	2 HOURS LATER AND EARLIER: Working with times to the half hour.	Relationships between units of time.	Reviewing oral work from the Main teaching activity.
LESSON 2	● Read the time to the hour, half hour or quarter hour on an analogue clock.	2 HOURS LATER AND EARLIER: Working with times to the quarter hour.	ALL SORTS OF TIMES: Recording time. TWO CLOCKS.	2 HOURS LATER AND EARLIER: Times to the quarter hour.
LESSON 3	● Solve a given problem by sorting, classifying and organising information in simple ways. ● Discuss and explain results.	Reciting the 2, 5 and 10 times tables. Counting round the circle in twos, tens and fives.	Making a graph with the whole class.	Reviewing work from the Main teaching activity.
LESSON 4	● Read the time to the hour, half hour or quarter hour on an analogue and a 12-hour digital clock, and understand the notation 7:30.	Reciting the 5 times table, then counting round the circle in fives forward and back to 100 from 0.	Reading and writing times (hour, half hour and quarter hour) in analogue and digital form.	Reviewing work from the Main teaching activity.
LESSON 5	● Solve a given problem by sorting, classifying and organising information in simple ways. ● Discuss and explain results.	Counting in 100s to 1000. MY NUMBER/ YOUR NUMBER. ADD/TAKE 100.	WEATHER GAME: Making a graph.	Reviewing work from the Main teaching activity.
LESSON 6	● Use units of time and know the relationships between them. ● Use mental addition and subtraction to solve simple word problems.	2 MONTHS LATER AND EARLIER.	DAYS IN EACH MONTH: Solving addition problems involving days in months.	Reviewing work from the Main teaching activity.
LESSON 7	● Read the time to the hour, half hour or quarter hour on an analogue clock and a 12-hour digital clock, and understand the notation 7:30	DOMINO TIMES.	Record time (hour, half hour and quarter hour) in analogue and digital form.	DOMINO TIMES.
LESSON 8	● **Estimate, measure and compare capacities using standard units.**	DOUBLES OF MULTIPLES OF 5.	FILLING CONTAINERS WITH A 5ml SPOON.	Reviewing work from the Main teaching activity.
LESSON 9	● Use and begin to read the vocabulary related to time. ● Suggest suitable units to estimate or measure time. ● **Read a simple scale to the nearest labelled division.**	ADDITION BY GROUPING TENS AND UNITS.	TIMING COMPETITION: Timing games with minute timers.	Reviewing work from the Main teaching activity.
LESSON 10	● **Read a simple scale to the nearest labelled division, including using a ruler to draw and measure lines to the nearest centimetre.**	DOUBLES OF MULTIPLES OF 5.	SHOVE 10P.	Reviewing work from the Main teaching activity.

ORAL AND MENTAL SKILLS   Describe and extend simple number sequences: count in hundreds from and back to zero; count on in steps of 5 to at least 30, from and back to zero. **Know by heart: multiplication facts for the 2 and 10 times tables.** Begin to know: multiplication facts for the 5 times table. Derive quickly: doubles of multiples of 5 to 50. Partition additions into tens and units, then recombine. Use mental addition and subtraction to solve simple word problems.

Lessons 1, 3, 5, 6 and 8–10 are provided in full, with Lessons 2, 4 and Lesson 7 as grids.

RESOURCES
Large teaching clock; flip chart and pen; pencils and paper; Cuisenaire rods.

PREPARATION
Make a teaching chart by copying the following time facts on to the flip chart:

60 seconds = 1 minute
60 minutes = 1 hour
24 hours = 1 day
7 days = 1 week
4 weeks = 1 month
12 months = 1 year

LEARNING OUTCOMES

ORAL AND MENTAL STARTER
● Use mental addition and subtraction to solve simple word problems.

MAIN TEACHING ACTIVITY
● Use units of time and know the relationships between them.
● Solve simple word problems.

ORAL AND MENTAL STARTER
TWO HOURS LATER AND EARLIER: Sit the children in a semicircle facing the teaching clock. Set the hands on the clock to different times to the half hour. Choose a child to say the time two hours later each time. Then change the rule to 'two hours earlier'.

MAIN TEACHING ACTIVITY
Sit the children in a semicircle facing the teaching chart. Ask them to read the facts aloud together while you point to each one in turn. Ask questions about different facts, for example: *How many days in a week? How many days in two weeks?* Next tell the children to return to their tables to copy the chart on to a sheet of paper. While they are doing so, write some 'How many?' questions on the board for the children to answer when they finish, for example:

How many...
days in two weeks?
days in four weeks?
weeks in two months?
weeks in five months?
weeks in ten months?
months in two years?
minutes in half an hour?
seconds in half a minute?

DIFFERENTIATION
More able: invite these children to make up and answer some more questions of their own.
Less able: provide Cuisenaire rods for children who may require additional support.

PLENARY
Review the work done in the **Main teaching activity**. Start by asking the children to recall facts from the chart, then go through each of the questions on the board, asking different children to give answers. Invite children who have made up questions of their own to say the question and give the answer. Scribe any additional questions on the board.

VOCABULARY

Names of units of time, from second to year; fortnight; weekend; bedtime; dinnertime; playtime; yesterday; today; tomorrow; old; older; oldest; times to the hour, to the half hour and quarter hour; quarter past; quarter to; analogue clock, watch; hands; digital clock.

RESOURCES	Large teaching clock; a copy of photocopiable page 16 (Clocks), a cardboard clock, paper and pencil for each child; a shuffled set of cards marked with different times to the hour, half hour and quarter hour for each group.
LEARNING OUTCOMES	**ORAL AND MENTAL STARTER** ● Use mental addition and subtraction to solve simple word problems. **MAIN TEACHING ACTIVITY** ● Read the time to the hour, half hour or quarter hour on an analogue clock.
ORAL AND MENTAL STARTER	2 HOURS LATER AND EARLIER: Working with times to the quarter hour. Set the clock to different times to the quarter hour each time. (See Lesson 1, page 210.)
MAIN TEACHING ACTIVITY	ALL SORTS OF TIMES: Ask the children to record times to the hour, half hour, and quarter hour using photocopiable page 16 and time cards.

DIFFERENTIATION	More able: play the 'two clocks' game with a partner. Each child sets the hands on a cardboard clock to show a time to the hour. Both children write the two times on a sheet of paper, e.g. 4 o'clock; 7 o'clock. They then count round the clock **clockwise** between each of the two numbers and record, for example:
	    4 to 7 → 3
	    7 to 4 → 9
	    Total → 12
	The children then reset the clocks. What do they notice about the total each time?
	Less able: use an appropriate set of time cards to revise times children are still unsure about.

PLENARY	Repeat '2 hours later and earlier' with times to the quarter hour.

RESOURCES

Flip chart, and pen; 2cm squared paper; rulers; pencils, crayons or felt-tipped pens.

PREPARATION

Place sheets of 2cm squared paper, rulers, pencils, crayons or felt-tipped pens on each table.

LEARNING OUTCOMES

ORAL AND MENTAL STARTER
● **Know by heart: multiplication facts for the 2 and 10 times tables.**
● Begin to know: multiplication facts for the 5 times table.

MAIN TEACHING ACTIVITY
● Solve a given problem by sorting, classifying and organising information in simple ways.
● Discuss and explain results.

ORAL AND MENTAL STARTER

Recite the 2, 5 and 10 times tables. Then count around the circle in twos, tens and fives. Repeat this a few times, choosing a different child to start the count each time. Play the game at a fast pace to encourage rapid recall.

MAIN TEACHING ACTIVITY

AT WHAT TIME DO CHILDREN GO TO BED?: Discuss bedtimes with the class. Use the flip chart to write down the times children go to bed in order, earliest to latest. Take a count of hands and write the number against each bedtime. Demonstrate on the board how to make a graph on squared paper with a ruler, writing the bedtimes listed on the board along the bottom of the chart and numbers of children down the left hand side. Show the children a sheet of 2cm squared paper. Tell them to use the squared paper on their tables to copy the graph on the board and then colour one square for each child on the graph using the information on the flip chart.

VOCABULARY

Count; tally; sort; vote; graph; block graph; pictogram; represent; group set; list; table; most/least popular; most/least common; most/fewest number; bedtime; earliest; latest; early; late; before; after.

DIFFERENTIATION

More able: ask these children to write some statements about their graph – for example: 'Most children go to bed at...'; 'Fewest children go to bed at...' and so on.

Less able: draw a graph outline for those children who are unable to do so for themselves.

PLENARY

Review the work done in the **Main teaching activity**. Discuss and compare results, for example: *At what time do most/fewest children go to bed? What is the difference between the number of children who go to bed at 7 o'clock and 8 o'clock?*

LESSON 4

RESOURCES	Large teaching clock; flip chart and pen; cardboard clocks; sets of time cards to hour, half hour and quarter hour in digital form such as 3.15, 2.30, 6.45 etc, also sets of cards showing minutes past the hour in five-minute intervals in digital form, such as 2.25; 6.10; 8 50 etc; pencils and paper.
LEARNING OUTCOMES	**ORAL AND MENTAL STARTER** ● **Describe and extend simple number sequences:** count on in steps of 5 to at least 30, from and back to zero. **MAIN TEACHING ACTIVITY** ● Read the time to the hour, half hour or quarter hour on an analogue clock and a 12-hour digital clock, and understand the notation 7:30.
ORAL AND MENTAL STARTER	Recite the 5 times table. Then count around the circle forwards and backwards in fives to 100. Choose a different child to start the count each time. Play the game at a fast pace to encourage rapid recall.
MAIN TEACHING ACTIVITY	Working with a teaching clock and the flip chart, talk about minutes past the hour in five-minute intervals. Demonstrate ways to record digital times, for example: 3.00; 3.15; 3.30; 3.45. Then ask the children to record times to the hour, half hour and quarter hour in digital form with mixed time cards.
DIFFERENTIATION	More able: ask the children to record times from a set of cards showing times in 5-minute intervals. Less able: use time cards to revise times the children are unsure about.
PLENARY	Review the work done in the **Main teaching activity** with the teaching clock. Set the hands to different times and ask the children to say analogue and digital times to the hour, half hour and quarter hour.

LESSON 5

RESOURCES

For each group: photocopiable page 219 (Weather game); crayons or felt-tipped pens; a sheet of 2cm squared paper; for the weather dice (see Preparation below): large cubes or building bricks, scissors, a can of spray adhesive.

PREPARATION

Make an A3 copy of photocopiable page 219 for each group. Cut the strips of weather symbols from each sheet and stick each symbol with spray adhesive to the face of a large cube to make weather dice (one for each group). Draw the following chart on the board for use in the **Plenary** session (amended to your number of groups, if necessary):

Group	sun	rain	cloud	snow	storm	fog
1						
2						
3						
4						
5						
Total						

LEARNING OUTCOMES
ORAL AND MENTAL STARTER
● Count in hundreds from and back to zero.

MAIN TEACHING ACTIVITY
● Solve a given problem by sorting, classifying and organising information in simple ways.
● Discuss and explain results.

ORAL AND MENTAL STARTER

Count in 100s to 1000. Then play 'My number/your number' games with the rule 'Add 100'. For example, you say: *My number is 300. Edward, your number is...?* (400). Change the rule to 'Take 100'. Play the games at a fast pace to encourage rapid recall.

MAIN TEACHING ACTIVITY

WEATHER GAME: Give each group of four to six a weather game sheet. Tell the children to take turns to throw the dice and draw the symbol thrown on the sheet, starting with the first Monday and finishing with the last Sunday. When the game is finished each child uses a sheet of 2cm squared paper to make a graph which shows the number of days for each type of weather, colouring one square above each weather symbol for each day.

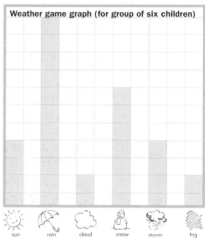

Weather game graph (for group of six children)

sun   rain   cloud   snow   storm   fog

DIFFERENTIATION

More able: ask these children to write some number statements about their results: most/fewest, difference between numbers of types of weather, and so on.
Less able: draw a graph outline on squared paper for any child who finds this difficult.

PLENARY

Review the work done in the **Main teaching activity**. Ask each group to give their results for each type of weather while you scribe the numbers on the chart. Then ask the class to find the total of each column. Discuss the overall results: most/fewest, difference between the number of days with rain and sun, and so on. Ask the groups to look at their charts, decide whether the weather shown would be in the winter or summer and explain why.

RESOURCES

Teaching charts (see Preparation below) and pen; flip chart and two coloured pens; paper and pencils; Cuisenaire rods.

LESSON 6

PREPARATION

Copy the following on to a flip chart or large sheet of card:
   There are thirty days in September, April, June and November,
   All the rest have thirty-one, except in February alone,
   February has twenty-eight days clear and twenty-nine in each leap year.
On the flip chart or large sheet of card draw a table with two columns headed 'Months' and 'Days'. Then write the months of the year from January to December in the first column.

LEARNING OUTCOMES
ORAL AND MENTAL STARTER
● Use mental addition and subtraction to solve simple word problems.

MAIN TEACHING ACTIVITY
● Use units of time and know the relationships between them.
● Use mental addition and subtraction to solve simple word problems.

ORAL AND MENTAL STARTER

2 MONTHS LATER AND EARLIER: Sit the children in a semicircle. Tell them you are going to say the name of a month and they should say the name of 'two months earlier'.

MAIN TEACHING ACTIVITY

DAYS IN EACH MONTH: Sit the children facing the rhyming teaching chart. Point to the words as the children recite the rhyme, then recite the rhyme again. Replace this chart with the second one, then recite the first line of the rhyme again with the children: *There are thirty days in September, April, June and November*. Choose children to say the number of days in each month in the first line of the rhyme (30) and write the number of days beside the names of these months on the chart. Then recite the second line of the rhyme again: *All the rest have thirty-one, except in February alone*. Now choose children to write the number of days (31) beside the names of the other months, apart from February. Recite the last line of the rhyme again: *February has twenty-eight days clear and twenty-nine in each leap year*. Choose a child to say the number of days in February and write the number on the chart (28). Tell the children about leap years – special years which happen every four years when February has an extra day. Write (29) in brackets using another colour on the chart beside the first number.

Next, tell the children they are to choose two different months each time, write the names of the months and then the total number of days on their sheet, for example:

January and June → 31 + 30 = 61 days

Tell them to find the total by grouping and adding the tens together first, followed by the units, for example, 30 + 30 = 60, 60 + 1 = 61.

DIFFERENTIATION

More able: encourage these children to record their answers in the way discussed at the end of the **Main teaching activity**. Invite them to try finding the total of three different months each time.

Less able: encourage them to make each number with Cuisenaire rods, group and count the tens followed by the units, then add them together to find the total.

PLENARY

Review the work done in the **Main teaching activity**. Ask oral questions, such as: *How many days altogether in May and June?*

RESOURCES	A copy of photocopiable page 16 (Clocks) for each child; pencils and paper; sets of dominoes (remove double six dominoes); a flip chart; cardboard clocks.
LEARNING OUTCOMES	**ORAL AND MENTAL STARTER** ● Use known number facts and place value to carry out mentally simple multiplications. **MAIN TEACHING ACTIVITY** ● Read the time to the hour, half hour or quarter hour on an analogue clock and a 12-hour digital clock, and understand the notation 7:30.
ORAL AND MENTAL STARTER	DOMINO TIMES: Sit the children in a circle. Give each child a domino and ask them to multiply the spots on each side of the domino saying, for example: 'Four times three is 12'.
MAIN TEACHING ACTIVITY	REVISION OF TIME IN ANALOGUE AND DIGITAL FORM: Write a set of 12 different times on the board (to the hour, half and quarter hour in analogue and digital form). Read through the times with the children before asking them to use the times on the board to complete photocopiable page 16.
DIFFERENTIATION	More able: these children can be given a fresh copy of page 16 with a set of digital time cards in five minute intervals and asked to complete the sheet (see Resources for Lesson 4 on page 212). Less able: for children who have not yet covered time in digital form write a separate list of 12 different analogue times to the hour, half hour and quarter hour on a flip chart. Provide cardboard clocks for additional support.
PLENARY	Repeat 'Domino times' from the **Oral and mental starter**.

LESSON 8

RESOURCES

Flip chart and pen; teaching chart (see Preparation below) and A4 copies; a shuffled set of cards numbered in fives 5–50 (one card for each child); for each group: a 5 ml spoon, a set of six small containers for each group, such as an eggcup, a small tub, a bottle screw cap or a vitamin pot, a washing up bowl; pencils and paper; waterproof aprons; Cuisenaire rods.

PREPARATION

Make a teaching chart by copying the following on to a flip chart. Make an A4 copy of the chart for each child.

Filling containers with a 5ml spoon			
Container	Estimated number of 5ml spoonfuls	Actual number of 5ml spoonfuls	Total number of millilitres (x5)

Place the equipment on a table for each group. Fill each washing-up bowl with 1 litre of water. Write the following questions on the board:
Which container holds the most spoonfuls?
Which container holds least spoonfuls?
Which child in the group made the nearest estimate? What was the container?
How many millilitres does the largest container hold?
How many millilitres does the smallest container hold?

LEARNING OUTCOMES

ORAL AND MENTAL STARTER
● Derive quickly: doubles of multiples of 5 to 50.

MAIN TEACHING ACTIVITY
● **Estimate, measure and compare capacities, using standard units.**

ORAL AND MENTAL STARTER

DOUBLES OF MULTIPLES OF 5: Sit the children in a circle. Give each child one of the shuffled set of 5s cards. Ask each child, in turn, to double the number on his or her card. Collect in the cards, shuffle them and give them out again. Repeat the game.

MAIN TEACHING ACTIVITY

FILLING CONTAINERS WITH A 5ml SPOON: Sit the children facing the teaching chart and a demonstration table. Use a set of equipment and the teaching chart to demonstrate the activity. Ask two children to choose a container and estimate how many 5ml spoonfuls of water will be needed to fill it. Scribe the number on the chart. Then tell one child to hold the container over the bowl, while the other child collects spoonfuls of water from the bowl to pour into the container, counting the spoonfuls each time. Scribe the results on the chart and ask the group to multiply the number by five to find out how many millilitres the container holds. Scribe the result on the chart, then ask the children to pour the water carefully back into the bowl.

Now tell them to carry out the activity themselves, working in small groups. They should:
● Start by writing down the name of each container in the first column of your sheet, then write down your estimate for each container.
● Take turns, working with a partner, to find out how many spoonfuls one container holds.
● The rest of the group carries out the counting. When the container is full, everyone should record the number of spoonfuls on his or her sheet.
● The next pair then repeats the process with another container, and so on.
● When all containers have been filled and the results recorded, complete the last column in the table by multiplying each number by 5.
● Share your results as a group, then write a group answer to each question on the board.

DIFFERENTIATION

More able: ask these children to predict how many 5ml spoonfuls for two of each container, 3 containers, etc. How many millilitres altogether for two of each container (×5). Less able: provide Cuisenaire rods for children who may require additional support with the multiplying millilitres (×5) problems.

PLENARY

Review the **Main teaching activity**. Invite the children in each group to give their answers to the questions on the board. Discuss results in terms of which container held most/fewest spoonfuls, and the total number of millilitres altogether for each container. How many spoonfuls for two then three of each container? How many millilitres altogether?

RESOURCES

Flip chart and pen; teaching chart (see **Preparation** below) and A4 copies; for each group: a prepared results sheet, a digital stopwatch, pencils and paper; red, blue and green colouring pencils.

PREPARATION

Make a teaching chart by copying the table below on to a flip chart sheet. Make an A4 paper copy for each group. Place the resources for each group on the tables. While the children are completing the timing games, prepare for the **Plenary** session (see below).

Results of timing competition		
	Shoes and socks	
Name	Estimated time in minutes and seconds	Actual time in minutes and seconds

LEARNING OUTCOMES

ORAL AND MENTAL STARTER
● Partition additions into tens and units, then recombine.

MAIN TEACHING ACTIVITY
● Use and begin to read the vocabulary related to time.
● Suggest suitable units to estimate or measure time.
● **Read a simple scale to the nearest labelled division.**

ORAL AND MENTAL STARTER

ADDITION BY GROUPING TENS AND UNITS: Play 'All change' with two hoops and 10–50 cards.

VOCABULARY

Minutes; seconds; shortest/ longest time; quickest; fastest; slowest; closest/ nearest estimate; actual result; stopwatch; second timer.

MAIN TEACHING ACTIVITY

TIMING COMPETITION: Sit the children facing the teaching chart. Explain and demonstrate how to work a stopwatch, reading and recording the time in seconds, or minutes and seconds. Carry out a demonstration of the stopwatch task by inviting a child to remove her shoes and socks, then to be timed putting them back on again with another child working the stopwatch. First ask the child performing the task to estimate the time it will take in minutes and/or secondsto put their socks and shoes back on. Scribe the child's name and estimate on the chart. The other child starts the stopwatch after saying: 'Ready, steady, go', then stops the watch when the task is complete and reads the time taken. Scribe the result on the chart.

Next, divide the class into groups of four or six children and number the groups. Tell the children to choose a partner to work with and ensure that they understand what they have to do before they begin. The task starts with each child in the group writing his or her name and estimated time on the chart. If there is time left when the children have completed the competition, ask them to discuss the results on the chart as a group. Ask them to use a red pencil to colour the box which shows the fastest time taken, then a blue pencil to colour the box showing the slowest time taken. Finally, the box showing the closest estimate to the actual result should be coloured in green.

DIFFERENTIATION

More able: ask these children to make up a timing game of their own and use a stopwatch to time the results – for example, taking shoes and socks off.
Less able: make this a teacher-directed group activity where you support the groups of children in carrying out the game and helping them to time from the stopwatch.

PLENARY

Draw this chart on the board (amended to the number of groups you have, if necessary):

Shoes & socks	Group 1		Group 2		Group 3		Group 4	
Fastest time								
Slowest time								
Closest estimate to actual result	E	A	E	A	E	A	E	A

Review the results of the competition by asking each group to call out their results while you scribe the numbers on the chart. Invite different children to say which group had the highest number, lowest number, and the closest estimate to actual result in the competition. Discuss results in terms of fastest/slowest time. Which part of the task was easiest/quickest – putting shoes or socks on? Do they think that the time would be quicker or slower if the task were to take their shoes *and* socks off? Why?

RESOURCES

A shuffled set of cards numbered in fives 5–50 (one card for each child).
For the demonstration: Shove 10p teaching chart (made from photocopiable page 220 – see Preparation below) and pen; a 10p coin; a Shove 10p game board (photocopiable page 221); water-based marker; a cleaning cloth or sheet of kitchen paper; ruler and pencil.
For each group: a 10p coin; a Shove 10p game board; a water-based marker; a cleaning cloth or paper; rulers and pencils.
For each child: a copy of photocopiable page xx47 (Shove 10p score sheet).

PREPARATION

Make a 'Shove 10p' game board for each group by copying photocopiable page 221 on to sheets of A3 card and laminating. Trim the bottom of each game board to the thick 'starting line'. Make a copy of photocopiable page 220 for each child. Set up a demonstration table and place the resources for each group on a table.

LEARNING OUTCOMES

ORAL AND MENTAL STARTER
● Derive quickly: doubles of multiples of 5 to 50.

MAIN TEACHING ACTIVITY
● **Read a simple scale to the nearest labelled division, including using a ruler to draw and measure lines to the nearest centimetre.**

ORAL AND MENTAL STARTER
DOUBLES OF MULTIPLES OF 5: See Lesson 8 on page 215.

MAIN TEACHING ACTIVITY

SHOVE 10p: Sit the children facing the teaching chart and demonstration table. Tell them they will be working together in small groups, taking turns to see how far they can shove a 10p coin on the playing board. Explain that if the 10p goes off the board then there is no score given. The game board is placed at the edge of a table and the coin is placed half on the edge of the board with the other half protruding. Show the children how to use the palm of their writing hand to push the coin as far as they can up the board. Invite a child to try the game, marking the distance of the farthest edge of the coin with a water-based marker pen on the game board. The child then uses a centimetre ruler to measure the distance between the mark and the starting line to the nearest centimetre. Scribe the child's name and result on the teaching chart. Wipe the playing board clean and repeat with another child.

Next, divide the class into groups of four to six and number the groups. Tell the children to play the game as they have been shown. Explain that each child should record the results of each turn on their score sheet. When every child in the group has had a turn, they complete the statements on the second half of the sheet.

Ask the children to tell you what they have to do before they return to their tables to carry out the activity.

DIFFERENTIATION

Any group that finishes quickly can wipe the game board clean and use a fresh copy of the score sheet to play the game again. They can compare the results of both games to find the longer distance for each child.

More able: add a rule to the game that 5cm is added to a child's measured score if a 10p lands in a space between the lines. 5cm is taken away from the measured score if the 10p lands on a line.
Less able: make the activity teacher-directed with this group, guiding the children to measure distances and record their results on the score sheet correctly.

PLENARY

Copy this chart on to the board (amended to the number of groups you have, if necessary):

	Group 1	Group 2	Group 3	Group 4
Longest distance				
Shortest distance				
Difference				

Invite each group in turn to call out their results for the longest distance while you scribe the numbers, in cm, on the board. Repeat this for the shortest distance. When all the results are written on the chart, ask:
Which group had the child who shoved the 10p the shortest/longest distance?
Did any children shove the 10p the same distance?
What is the difference between the longest and the shortest distance for each group?
Then ask: 'What is the distance between the longest and shortest distance?' for each group. 'What is the longest distances for Groups 1, 2, 3 and 4? Repeat with the shortest distances.

Name

Weather game

	Monday	Tuesday	Wednesday	Thursday	Friday	Saturday	Sunday

Cut out these weather cards.

✂

sun

rain

cloud

snow

storm

fog

Name

Shove 10p score sheet

Name	Distance to nearest cm

The longest distance was ☐ cm.

The shortest distance was ☐ cm.

The difference between the longest
and shortest distances was ☐ cm.

Name two children who shoved the

10p the same distance: _____ and _____

Distance ☐ cm.

Name

Shove 10p game board

Shove 10p

_____

_____

_____

_____

_____

_____

_____

_____

_____

starting line

UNIT 14: Assess & Review

Choose from the following activities over the two lessons. During the group activities, some children can complete assessment worksheets 6a and 6b. These sheets assess children's skills in addition and subtraction and knowledge of 2-D and 3-D shapes and their features. Specific criteria for the assessment sheets can be found at the bottom of each sheet.

RESOURCES

Sets of multiples cards fives to 50; tens to 100; three different-coloured plastic hoops with numeral cards 10–30; sets of three money dice (two marked 2p, 5p, 10, 20p, 50p, £1.00 and marked £2.00, £2.00, £1.00, £1.00, 50p, 50p); sets of all coins to £2.00, centimetre rulers, pencils and paper, 5ml spoons, six small containers, a washing-up bowl of water; copies of Assessment worksheets 6a and 6b, photocopiable pages 70, 220 and 221 and a capacity recording chart (see **Preparation** below) for each child.

PREPARATION

Make copies of the worksheets required and the recording chart in Lesson 8, Unit 12, on page 215, for each child. Put out the resources for each activity on a different table.

ORAL AND MENTAL STARTER

ASSESSMENT
● Can the children: Describe and extend simple number sequences?
● Do the children: Know by heart: multiplication facts for the 2 and 10 times tables? Know and use halving as the inverse of doubling?

DESCRIBING AND EXTENDING NUMBER SEQUENCES: Count in threes, fours and fives together and round the circle from zero. Count on/back 3, 4 or 5 by playing 'My number, your number': *If the rule is 'count on 4' and my number is 11; (Lilly), your number is ?* (15)
ADDITION: Repeat 'All change' game with three hoops with numeral cards 10–30.
MULTIPLICATION AND DIVISION: Recite 2 and 10 times tables. Use quick-fire questions such as: *Six twos? Five tens? How many twos in 14? How many tens in 60?* Use a set of numeral cards 1–10. Give each child in the circle a card. Select children in quick succession to multiply the number on their card by 2, then to multiply the number by 10.
DOUBLING AND HALVING: Play 'Doubles of multiples (of 5), halves of multiples (of 10)' using cards 5–50 and 10–100. See Lesson 2, Units 10–11 on pp 200.

GROUP ACTIVITIES

ASSESSMENT
● Can the children: Understand the operation of multiplication as repeated addition or as describing an array? Know and use halving as the inverse of doubling? Choose and use appropriate operations and efficient calculation strategies to solve problems and explain how the problem was solved? Estimate, compare and measure capacities using standard units? Read a simple scale to the nearest labelled division, including using a ruler to measure lines to the nearest centimetre?
● Do the children know: Addition facts for all numbers to at least 10.
DOUBLING AND HALVING: Use sets of even numbered 20–50 and copies of photocopiable page 28. Repeat 'Double and half' activity in Lesson 3, Units 10–11 on page 201. Check the children's methods; for example, whether they write workings or work mentally.
SOLVING PROBLEMS: Use copies of page 70, money dice and coins. Repeat 'Spend and change from £5.00' in Lesson 4, Unit 9, on page 196. Again note the children's methods.
MEASURES: For length, use pages 220 and 221, centimetre rulers and 10p coins to repeat 'Shove 10p' in Lesson 10, Unit 13 on page 217. Check whether the measurements are reasonably accurate (to the nearest whole or half centimetre). For capacity, repeat the group activity in Lesson 8, Unit 13 on page 215.

Assessment sheet 6a

Work mentally to complete.

$7 + 8 =$ ☐ $7 +$ ☐ $= 15$ ☐ $+ 8 = 15$

$17 - 9 =$ ☐ $17 -$ ☐ $= 8$ ☐ $- 9 = 8$

$15 + 8 =$ ☐ $15 +$ ☐ $= 23$ ☐ $+ 8 = 23$

$23 - 6 =$ ☐ $23 -$ ☐ $= 17$ ☐ $- 6 = 17$

$33 + 12 =$ ☐ $69 +$ ☐ $= 80$ $39 -$ ☐ $= 28$

☐ $+ 16 = 56$ $58 - 13 =$ ☐   ☐ $- 15 = 15$

$22 - 17 =$ ☐ $19 +$ ☐ $= 23$

$93 - 88 =$ ☐ $45 +$ ☐ $= 51$

$64 - 59 =$ ☐ $67 +$ ☐ $= 74$

$68 - 14 =$ ☐ $54 - 15 =$ ☐

$39 - 15 =$ ☐ $72 - 14 =$ ☐

$88 - 12 =$ ☐ $96 - 18 =$ ☐

$74 - 11 =$ ☐ $45 - 17 =$ ☐

● Understand that subtraction is the inverse of addition; state the subtraction corresponding to a given addition, and vice versa.
● Use knowledge that addition can be done in any order to do mental calculations more efficiently.

UNIT 14

Assessment sheet 6b

Draw lines of symmetry on these shapes.

 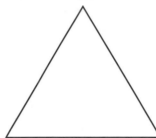 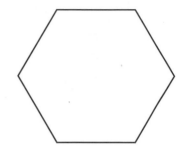

Draw lines of symmetry on these letters.
Draw a ring around letters that are not symmetrical.

A B R Z G X

Name these shapes.

  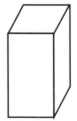 

_____ _____ _____ _____

Draw and name these shapes.

A shape with   A shape with   A shape with
3 sides.   6 equal sides.   4 equal sides.

● Use the mathematical names for common 3-D and 2-D shapes.
● Sort shapes and describe some of their features.